Social Change in Rural Australia

Social Change in Rural Australia

Edited by

Geoffrey Lawrence
Kristen Lyons
Salim Momtaz

Rural Social and Economic Research Centre
Central Queensland University

First published 1996
Reprinted 1997
Rural Social and Economic Research Centre
Central Queensland University, Rockhampton, Queensland, 4702
Contact telephone number: (079) 306 401
Contact fax number: (079) 306 402

Printed and bound by University Publishing, Central Queensland University

Publication data:

National Library of Australia cataloguing in publication data

Social Change in Rural Australia

Includes index

ISBN 1 875902 36 8

1   Rural communities - Australia
2   Agriculture - Social aspects - Australia
I   Lawrence, Geoffrey
II   Lyons, Kristen
III   Momtaz, Salim

Set in Times New Roman

Contents

Part three
Problematising change in rural Australia

Notes on contributors

Margaret Alston is a Senior Lecturer in Social Work and an Associate Director of the Rural Social Research Centre at Charles Sturt University, Wagga Wagga. Margaret was the organiser and coordinator of the first National Rural Women's Forum at Parliament House, in 1995. She is a member of the NSW Anti-Discrimination Board Reference Group and is assisting DPIE's Rural Policy Unit. Her current research includes studies of domestic violence, gender bias in sports reporting, and women and leadership in rural Australia.

Eve Cuskelly is Research and Development Coordinator for the Division of Distance and Continuing Education at Central Queensland University, where she has been involved in studies, including student attitudes toward distance education. Research interests include the use of educational technology by students, factors in adoption of educational technology, and other issues relating to open and distance learning. Eve is co-author of *Student Experiences of Distance Education at Central Queensland University* (1995).

Roger Epps is a Senior Lecturer in the Department of Geography and Planning at the University of New England, where he lectures on rural social issues, and rural planning and resource management. He came to the Department with extensive practical and professional experience in many aspects of agriculture. He co-edited the book *Prospects and Policies for Rural Australia* with Tony Sorensen and has made major contributions to the *Global Interactions* high school geography texts.

Scott Glyde is a PhD student with Charles Sturt University, Wagga Wagga, and is funded by the Cooperative Research Centre for Viticulture. He has an agricultural science degree and postgraduate qualifications in adult education from UNE. His background is in agricultural research, post secondary teaching, and the family farm. His interest in rural sociology stems from an awareness of the often inappropriate nature of agricultural technology development and its 'extension' within farming systems in Australia.

Ian Gray is Senior Lecturer in Sociology, and Acting Director of the Centre for Rural Social Research at Charles Sturt University, Wagga Wagga. He is the author of *Politics in Place: Social Power Relations in an Australian Country Town* (CUP, 1991) and is co-author of 'Predictors of Stress among Australian Farmers' (*Australian Journal of Social Issues*, 1996), 'Farming Practice as Temporally and Spatially Situated Intersections of Biography, Culture and Social Structure' (*Australian Geographer*, 1995) and *Coping with Change: Australian Farmers in the 1990s* (Centre for Rural Social Research, 1993).

Edward Green has been concerned with issues relating to rural youth suicide and presented his provocative analysis - for the first time to a sociological audience - at the TASA '95 Conference. He recently left Australia for Britain to undertake further studies. Prior to his departure he was Senior Education Officer, Flexible Programs Support, at the Open Training and Education Network in Strathfield, NSW.

Darren Halpin is a PhD candidate in the School of Agriculture and Rural Development at the University of Western Sydney (Hawkesbury). He has particular interests in farmer representative organisations and their role in the modern agricultural policy process, and in the role of ideology in guiding collective action. He has previously published in the area of systems theory methodology.

Richard Hindmarsh is an eco-social scientist, and recipient of an Australian Research Council Post-Doctoral Research Fellowship. Based at Griffith University's Faculty of Environmental Sciences, Brisbane, he is researching the historical and politico-philosophical dynamics of genetic engineering, as well as exploring the parameters of holistic technology assessment.

Linda Hungerford is a Lecturer in Sociology at Central Queensland University's Bundaberg campus, where she has just completed a term as Head of Campus and Faculty of Arts Coordinator. She holds a Masters' degree in history and is currently completing a doctorate in sociology on agricultural restructuring within the Australian sugar industry.

Roy Jones is Associate Professor of Geography and Head of the School of Social Sciences and Asian Languages at Curtin University of Technology, Western Australia. His recent work relates to population change within Western Australian country towns, rural restructuring, and social sustainability.

Geoffrey Lawrence is Foundation Professor of Sociology and Director of the Rural Social and Economic Research Centre at Central Queensland University. He has written widely about rural social issues in Australia and has conducted many national research projects. Books include: *Capitalism and the Countryside* (1987), *Rural Health and Welfare in Australia* (1990), *Agriculture, Environment and Society* (1992), *The Environmental Imperative* (1995), and *Globalisation and Agri-food Restructuring* (1996).

Ruth Liepins was awarded her doctoral degree for a thesis on women in rural Victoria and has taken up the position of Lecturer in Geography at the University of Otago, Dunedin. Ruth has been actively involved in the formation of women's groups in farming. Her research interests include feminist approaches to the study of agriculture, women's representation in rural administrative and political organisation, and changes in rural communities.

Stewart Lockie recently completed his doctorate, from Charles Sturt University, Wagga Wagga, on Landcare in Australia. He is currently Lecturer in Sociology at Central Queensland University, Rockhampton, where he teaches in the areas of rural sociology, social theory and Australian society. His research interests include gender, rural representation, and Landcare and the environment. He has assisted in numerous studies for government departments and grower bodies on issues of agriculture and the environment.

Kristen Lyons is a doctoral student attached to the Rural Social and Economic Research Centre at Central Queensland University, Rockhampton. She had previously completed a Bachelor of Science degree with Honours at Griffith University, Brisbane. Her research interests include organic farming practices, the role of transnational corporations in the organics sector, and the environmental and social implications of agribusiness.

Jim McAllister is Lecturer in Sociology at Central Queensland University where he teaches units in research methods and computing applications. Jim's doctoral work was on social change in rural Rwanda, but he is currently investigating paid labour in farming systems both within Australia and South Asia. He has conducted research on the sugar industry, and has investigated petty bourgeois mining in the Emerald region of Central Queensland.

Peter Martin lectures in rural and environmental management at the University of Western Sydney (Hawkesbury) where he is responsible for coordination of the Honours program. He holds a doctorate in the area of rural environmental management and has interests in rural ideology, the sociology of the environment, and governmentality.

Luciano Mesiti, a graduate from the University of Western Sydney (Hawkesbury), is a doctoral student with the Centre for Rural Social Research at Charles Sturt University, Wagga Wagga. He is attached to the Cooperative Research Centre for Viticulture and is conducting research into the socio-economic and socio-cultural aspects of adoption of sustainable practices in the viticulture industry.

Leigh Miller is a Lecturer in Geography in the Department of Physical Sciences in the University of Tasmania in Launceston. He was formerly a Lecturer in Geographical Education in Hobart, and has published in both education and agricultural geography, including a number of articles on contract farming relating, particularly, to the vegetables industries in Tasmania. He is an active participant in the Rural Studies section of the Institute of Australian Geographers and in the Agri-Food Research Network.

Salim Momtaz is a Lecturer in Geography at CQU where he teaches Environmental Management, Environmental and Social Impact Assessment and Geographic Information Systems. His doctoral research was on regional planning in South Asia. His research interests include impact assessment, development studies and applications of GIS. He is the author *of Rural Development in Bangladesh* (University of Dhaka, 1996). He has written many articles on rural social and environmental issues in Bangladesh.

Patrick Morrisey completed a degree in Systems Agriculture at the University of Western Sydney (Hawkesbury) in 1990. After consultancies with government and private bodies he worked as a Regional Landcare Facilitator with the DPI, Queensland. He has undertaken postgraduate studies in sociology at CQU and has recently joined Southern Cross University as a doctoral student. He has a major interest in rainforest restoration.

Janet Norton is currently completing her doctorate in sociology at Central Queensland University, where she is attached to the Rural Social and Economic Research Centre. Her research interests include biotechnologies in agriculture, consumer attitudes to the genetic engineering of foods, and the role of science in society. Janet is the co-author of numerous articles on the sociology of food biotechnologies in Australia.

Rae Passfield works as a tutor in sociology at the Mackay campus of Central Queensland University and is currently completing a research Masters' degree on the impact of restructuring on a cane growing community in the Mackay district. As a qualified social worker who has spent many years in Mackay, Rae's interests relate to impacts on the community of changes to cane production.

Emily Phillips is a PhD student attached to the Centre for Rural Social Research at Charles Sturt University, Wagga Wagga. She is the author of several articles and papers on rural culture and masculine identity, and is currently writing up her ethnographic research on the social and cultural construction of farming practice.

Ken Purnell is a Senior Lecturer in Education at Central Queensland University, teaching in studies of society and environment, classroom management, and assessment. Professional interests and research areas include the use of educational technologies in teaching and learning, environmental education, senior secondary schooling and assessment, classroom management, and open and distance learning and teaching. He is co-author of *Student Experiences of Distance Education at Central Queensland University* (1995).

Peter Smailes is a Senior Lecturer in Geography at the University of Adelaide, where his special research and teaching field is the social and economic geography of rural areas in western nations. He has also taught at the Universities of New England, Flinders, and Oslo (Norway) where he spent eight years. He was the foundation convenor of the Institute of Australian Geographers' Rural Study Group.

Tony Sorensen is the Head of the Department of Geography and Planning at UNE, where he lectures on regional development policy and urban land development. He has recently researched leadership, and the economic initiatives of local government. He has published extensively, and is co-author of the texts *Contemporary Australia,* and *Prospects and Policies for Rural Australia.* He plays an active role in the Regional Science Association, and convenes the Rural Studies Group of the Institute of Australian Geographers.

Dani Stehlik is Senior Lecturer in Sociology at CQU and Coordinator of the Community Development Program in the Rural Social and Economic Research Centre. Current research interests include older parents who provide home care to their intellectually-disabled children, and an investigation of the needs of older persons in regional communities. Recent publications include: *Untying the Knot* (1993), *Feminist Excavations: a Collection of Essays on Women, the Family and Ideology* (1994), and *Futures for Central Queensland* (1996).

Matthew Tonts is a doctoral candidate in the School of Social Sciences and Asian Languages at Curtin University of Technology, Western Australia. He has a major interest in social changes affecting agriculture and has published several articles relating to community adaptation to rural restructuring, and social policy issues.

Frank Vanclay is a Senior Lecturer in Sociology at Charles Sturt University, Wagga Wagga. He is a Key Researcher with the Centre for Rural Social Research and a Project Leader with the Cooperative Research Centre in Viticulture. Apart from rural and environmental sociology, he has interests in research methods, social impact assessment, and in health policy. His recent books include: *With a Rural Focus* (1995), *The Environmental Imperative* (1995) and *Environmental and Social Impact Assessment* (1995).

Malcolm Voyce grew up on a dairy farm in New Zealand, studied law at Auckland University and completed his doctorate at the University of London. He now teaches Law at Macquarie University, Sydney. He has written numerous articles on property in agriculture, including issues of succession, gender and patriarchy. His recent interest is in applying the work of Foucault to understand discourses of dominance in property relations.

Andrea Witcomb recently completed her doctoral work at CQU on contemporary museum practices and now lectures in this field at Western Australia's Curtin University. She was previously a Senior Research Officer with the Rural Social and Economic Research Centre at CQU where she was involved in a number of Centre projects. Recent journal articles have appeared in *Public History Review* (1993), *Culture and Policy* (1993), and *Social Semiotics* (1994).

Preface

Mention 'rural' and many a colleague will yawn, or pretend not to hear you. The more polite usually find an excuse to move away. For many social scientists the rural is not 'glamorous'. In contrast, there *is* something glamorous - even exciting - about exploring the world of deviant subcultures, in skiing the slopes of postmodernity, or in embracing social theories of the body. Farmers, and culture in Barcaldine, tend to come a poor second.

This book is about farmers, and culture in Barcaldine. Of course, we hope, it is more than that. It concerns the future of rural Australia. It is about the regional in the context of the global: it is what is 'happening' in the world economy as demonstrated in the specific context of the lives of people and communities in the regions.

In bringing together papers from the rural sections of the most recent national conferences of the The Australian Sociological Association (TASA) and the Institute of Australian Geographers (IAG), both held in Newcastle, NSW, in 1995, as well as the work of writers whose commentaries have been presented in other fora, this book seeks to provide readers with some of the most up-to-date and theoretically-informed analyses of Australian agriculture and rural society yet to be undertaken by Australian-based social researchers. Importantly, the contributions are from academics and post-graduate students from throughout the nation, all of whom are interested in describing and explaining the changes taking place in their study areas. Given the continued importance of rural Australia (and the desirability of studying the impacts of change on its inhabitants and environment) it is surprising to many of us that more research - of the sort detailed here - is not occurring. Our hopes are that this book will go some way to inspiring our coy and doubting colleagues to look more closely at what 'the rural' can show us in terms of an analysis of social change in contemporary Australia.

We believe this book helps to capture the dynamics of growth and decline in rural regions. It introduces several innovative methodological and theoretical approaches which are beginning to have some influence in the analysis of Australian rural social formations. It points to new directions for research and - in dealing with issues of rural restructuring, new technologies, the changing role of women, resource management, and other trends and tendencies - provides a good example of the impacts of global forces on spatially-defined regions within Australia. It will be of interest to Australian-based students of social change, as well as to an overseas audience which wants to understand comparative (global) aspects of new developments in agriculture and rural communities.

A number of people are to be thanked for their assistance in the preparation of this book. Dimity Lawrence took our edited drafts, puzzled as to why we should call ourselves editors, and then set about reorganising the materials for grammar, style, consistency and referencing. Dimity also produced a camera-ready version of the final document. For these, and a thousand other reasons, we are forever indebted. Eve Prickett from the Division of Distance and Continuing Education at Central Queensland University (CQU) checked all Figures and ensured that the manuscript was ready for printing. Natalie Wyer, Secretary of the Rural Social and Economic Research Centre, contacted the contributors, helped to assemble the drafts, and assisted in the organisation of printing and distribution. Academic members of the Centre including Dani Stehlik, Denis Cryle, and Stewart Lockie provided valuable comments throughout the process of book compilation. Collegial support also came - much further afield, and in quite different ways - from David Burch, Fred Buttel, Hugh Campbell, Ian Gray, Ruth Liepins, Phil McMichael, and Roy Rickson. Members of Chancellery, and Wally Woods, Dean of the Faculty of Arts, and Alice Michaels, Dean of the Faculty of Health Science at CQU, are thanked for their continued financial, as well as more general, support of the Centre.

Finally, we thank David Rowe, John Germov and John Collins from the University of Newcastle. David was instrumental in encouraging a large contingent from CQU to attend - and to provide papers at - the TASA '95 Conference. John Germov was on the organising committee for TASA '95, while John Collins convened the rural section of the Conference. All were most enthusiastic about the prospect of the publication of a book, and gave their blessing to the project. We hope the outcome lives up to the expectations of all who have been part of the process of compiling what we believe will be an important - even exciting! - contribution to Australian rural social research.

Geoffrey Lawrence
Kristen Lyons
Salim Momtaz

Introduction

Geoffrey Lawrence, Kristen Lyons and Salim Momtaz

Australian rural society is undergoing rapid structural transformation, the contours of which are now being 'mapped' by social scientists. Wider structural changes - including terms of trade decline in agriculture, the policies of Transnational Corporations (TNCs) involved in agri-food production, decisions by the state to limit expenditure in Australia's rural regions, and the influences of global regulatory (and other) bodies - are having direct and indirect impacts upon farming systems and rural communities. Some of these changes are contributing to the decline of certain forms of agricultural production, the undermining of farming traditions, and the demise of rural towns. Others, in contrast, are providing new options in farming, encouraging the broadening of the meaning of 'rural' in modern-day Australia, and are giving minority and otherwise disadvantaged groups opportunities to participate in rural community development.

This book is an attempt to examine change in contemporary Australian rural society, drawing largely from the theoretical concerns and methodological approaches from the (sub)disciplines of human geography and rural sociology. It brings together the latest work from social science trained academic staff and postgraduate students who are concerned with rural and regional issues. In doing so, it represents a comprehensive appraisal of the latest findings from social research and demonstrates, convincingly we feel, that social change is pervasive, 'disruptive' and, for many rural Australians, producing - alongside new opportunities - social and economic inequality. Although the book is not explicitly about rural policy, the implications of the sorts of changes being described by the contributors should be readily apparent to policy makers and to those involved in social action. It is possible, from a broad review of the book's contents, to recognise that the forces of change are operating to redefine what it means to be 'rural', and that such changes are impacting in ways not well understood, and not necessarily embraced, by people living in the regions.

Part one
What is happening down on the farm?

In this part of the book, the authors are concerned largely with change at the farm level. The first chapter, by Halpin and Martin, deals with the issue of farmer ideology. They argue that farmers hold tightly to a view of farming as the 'best' lifestyle, even if many now recognise that agricultural policy is progressively favouring corporate entities. The authors argue that if producers continue to be disillusioned with policy there may be an eventual challenge to the hegemonic position of pro-agribusiness organisations such as the NSW Farmers' Association.

In Chapter 2, Lockie provides some comment upon the point, above, relating to corporate agribusiness. He suggests that Australian farmers knowingly link to the wider structures of the corporate sector (in input purchase and produce sale) as a strategy to ensure survival in the face of severe financial difficulties in agriculture. As such, these farmers are indirectly 'subsumed' within capitalist relations of production. Evidence from his research points to the continuing intensification of farming (including the use of agri-chemicals) as something which continues unhindered alongside Landcare. It is for this reason that Lockie is not prepared unambiguously to endorse Landcare as the key to new and more environmentally-friendly options in farming.

In Chapter 3 Glyde and Vanclay, and in Chapter 4 Mesiti and Vanclay, apply the approach of 'farming styles' research (previously developed in The Netherlands) in an attempt to understand the different styles of production in the viticulture industry. In Chapter 3 the authors claim that by understanding the diversity of management approaches of farmers new strategies for extension can be developed. Eight different styles were detected among growers, largely underpinned by four dimensions - professionalism, resource availability, 'wisdom' and efficiency. In the second study, by Mesiti and Vanclay, six styles were identified among grape growers in the Sunraysia district. This, again, supports the view that it is desirable to recognise the heterogeneity among producers rather than to assume that farmers in particular industries have the same views, attitudes, and approaches to farming practice. There is a world of difference between the management styles of 'Traditional' grape growers compared to those described as 'Lifestylers', for example. Use of technology, information networks, and attitudes to production all vary across the grape growing industry - with obvious implications for state assistance (including any provision of extension services). Farming styles research is a new development in Australian sociology and is being reported for the first time, in book form, in this volume. It is hoped that other researchers might embrace this approach as one which, although in need of theoretical development (see Vanclay and Lawrence, 1995; Buttel, 1996), has the potential to provide new insights into farmer attitudes and behaviour.

Changes which have occurred in Tasmanian hop farming as global corporate agribusiness has penetrated the industry is the subject of Chapter 5. Miller suggests that, like it or not, the Tasmanian producers are incorporated into the world market (via foreign control of Australian Hop Marketers by the John I Haas company) and that they are at one and the same time advantaged by the company's market strength and R&D activities, but disadvantaged by policies of global sourcing and a vulnerable world market. From over 110 producers in 1968 the number has fallen to ten today - ample demonstration of the concentration and centralisation of capital in agriculture brought about by the incorporation of hop production into the activities of the world brewing companies.

Alston, in Chapter 6, begins with a comment on the overall decline in the numbers of viable farm producers and the demise of rural community and suggests that, in tandem, they have helped to mobilise rural women into action designed to counter these trends. Women have experienced much of the burden of the recent restructuring of rural regions, and have begun to search for ways to become involved in decision-making processes. The first National Rural Women's Forum held in Canberra in December 1994 produced consensus about what might constitute a way forward. Included in the recommendations were the need to improve: the visibility and general recognition of women's role; access to wider decision-making, and to education and training needs; social justice - including health and child care. It was viewed as essential for women to have equal representation with men on primary industry decision-making bodies. Alston's paper is a sober reminder of the struggle rural women continue to face as they seek to assert their role as equals in decision making.

In Chapter 7 Green deals with an issue which has occupied the minds of many policy-makers and health officials in governmental agencies since the onset, a decade ago, of the crisis in agriculture - that of rural youth suicide. He advances the argument - one not yet fully explored by social researchers in Australia - that in an homophobic rural culture, the marginalisation/exclusion of gay men (and in particular gay youth) is a significant factor in suicide. For Green, the damage to self esteem and the distancing from peer and family groups which results directly from the disclosure (and in many cases the non-disclosure) of gay attitudes and behaviour by some young men, becomes unbearable. Unable to alter society's views and incapable of 'escaping' to the cities, many take their lives. The attitudes of rural society must be changed, Green argues, to accept homosexuality as one important dimension of human sexuality.

Voyce, in Chapter 8, argues that gender has played a highly significant role in rural property relations throughout Australia's history. His insights relating to property in agriculture - including inheritance, the meanings ascribed to land, and liberalist ideologies - allow us to understand how laws have acted firmly to marginalise women in agriculture. He identifies constructions of masculinity (as in the heroic 'bushman' image and the 'mastery' of nature) as helping to discredit claims by women for equal treatment in property law, and by others for a different understanding of the meaning of land ownership. Property as 'a reward for male labour', continues despite women's increased participation in, and contribution to, Australian farming practice.

Part two
Rural restructuring: Socio-economic change and its community impacts

Part Two of the book moves beyond the farm gate to assess restructuring in wider rural society. In Chapter 9 Epps discusses change in communications in remote areas of Australia. While some innovations - such as the telephone and electrical appliances - have improved life in quite obvious ways, some of the more recent technologies - high frequency radios and satellite dishes, for example - appear to have reduced both work-related, and general social, interaction. This 'cost of progress' assessment is also one provided by Smailes in Chapter 10. Smailes shows that the reduction in travel time for rural people who want to access South Australia's capital city, Adelaide, has - in conjunction with rural population decline - led to a growing imbalance between retail activity in the periphery and the core of the South Australian economy. Tonts and Jones, in Chapter 11, employ some of the insights of regulation theory to examine change in the wheat belt of Western Australia. They report that many of the towns in the region they have surveyed are in steady decline. Importantly, their research confirms that the most disadvantaged sections of the rural population are those most affected by rural restructuring. Changes wrought by restructuring are causing uneven development throughout the wheatbelt. While the authors argue governments must look 'holistically' at future options, the apparent demise of the 'regional project' under current government policy, will mean the continuation of pressures for rural decline in areas such as the wheatbelt.

In Chapter 12 Epps and Sorensen report findings from their study of leadership in four towns in central western Queensland. While recognising that inland rural Australians do not have the same employment, social and educational opportunities as those closer to the seaboard, they stress the important role rural leaders play in identifying new options, and creating new strategies, for economic development. They conclude that private and public leadership was low in the towns studied and that 'corporate' leadership (which would bring business development to the town) was all but absent. The region's lagging economic development was seen to be a direct result of business decisions to locate investments in the coastal zones. Local leadership was seen by the authors to be one factor which might help to bring new investment dollars to inland regions. The authors lament that leadership training is not something readily available to rural people.

Chapters 13, 14, and 15 are located firmly within the current rural restructuring literature, seeking as they do to identify how the forces of change at the structural (macro or global) level are impacting at the local level. In Chapter 13 Lyons studies changes in the poultry meat industry. She concludes that processes of agri-industrialisation - represented, especially, in terms of appropriationism and substitutionism (see Goodman, Sorj and Wilkinson, 1987) - continue to be the principle determinants of agricultural organisation in poultry meat production. Rather than questioning, as some writers have recently done (see Watts and Goodman, 1994; Buttel, 1996; Lawrence, 1996), the benefits of applying Fordist/post-Fordist labels to agricultural production, Lyons argues that the poultry industry is quintessentially Fordist. That is, despite purported trends toward 'flexible specialisation' and 'niche marketing' in the wider industrial economy, poultry production exhibits the main characteristics of Fordism - mass production of a standardised commodity (chicken meat) for a mass market.

The commodity systems approach - developed in the US by sociologist Bill Friedland - is applied, in Chapter 14, by Hungerford in relation to the sugar industry. It is argued that by studying production practices, the manner in which growers are organised and represented, labour as a factor of production, scientific production and application, and marketing and distribution networks, it will be possible to understand the ways changes occurring at the global level are impacting upon the sugar industry in Bundaberg, Queensland. While this represents 'work in progress', it nevertheless introduces and discusses - for the first time in Australian rural sociology - the commodity systems approach, one which, Friedland argues, provides the researcher an important means of linking all stages in the growing and marketing of a product (something often ignored in ethnographic and case study approaches at the local level).

Chapter 15 provides an overview of sociological research being conducted in the Mackay region of Queensland - one of the main sugar growing regions of the State. Cost-price pressures are forcing millers and growers to seek measures which will increase industry efficiency. Several years ago mills introduced 'continuous crushing' during the harvesting season, the impact of which was felt directly by growers and small rural settlements in the Pioneer Valley. Now, there are suggestions that growers may be asked to harvest in a more-or-less 'around the clock' fashion. Such an option is not one which is being readily embraced by growers or by rural communities. Some communities, with new residents who have chosen (largely for reasons of lifestyle) to live in the rural hinterland beyond Mackay are beginning to impose their own views of what constitutes acceptable farming practice - in the face of the pressures on sugar producers to intensify production. Producers are finding it increasingly difficult to increase their efficiency in a manner which does not raise the community's wrath. The study provides evidence of the negative local effects of changes which are occurring in the sugar industry at the global level.

Chapter 16 the authors discuss the findings of a major study conducted among distance education students from Central Queensland University. Distance learning is often the only means by which rural people can take advantage of a university education and the research aimed to establish what concerns, difficulties and problems were faced by those seeking a degree through the distance mode. The authors found that among the student body there was a desire to have more personal contact with lecturers, to have more flexibility in delivery, and to be provided with distance education materials which allowed students to achieve the full range of grades. For reasons of cost and inconvenience, the students preferred not to have compulsory residential schools (even though this might bring them 'closer' to their lecturers). Importantly, students felt that much could be done to improve the existing system of providing print materials. One 'simple' option for improving lecturer visibility was to provide cassette and/or video tapes with the materials mailed to students. Distance education students are a major component of many regionally-based universities: Purnell and Cuskelly provide an argument for giving such students a better deal.

Part three
Problematising change in rural Australia

In Part Three of the book the issues of on-farm change and rural restructuring are placed in broader perspective. Here, authors seek to theorise both the processes which are at the root of change in Australian rural communities, and the 'meaning' of recent developments such as Landcare (and other participatory approaches to resource management), biotechnological applications in farming, and drought support.

In Chapter 17, Martin provides a lengthy, detailed, analysis of community participation in an organisation which sought to address the problem of dryland salinity in the Hunter Valley, NSW. He shows that while insufficient state funding may act to limit participatory approaches to catchment management (particularly within a framework of neo-liberalist policies), mobilisation can nevertheless occur - particularly in circumstances in which a problem is well-defined, environmentally-sensitive, and is taken up by the media. In exploring the political character of sustainable agriculture, Martin is able to point to opportunities for the more democratic means of 'governance' of the rural environment.

Morrisey in Chapter 18 reports on his field research in three communities in South East Queensland. He asks the question - is the Landcare model suitable for application to wider rural community development? and suggests a method (one located within the action research paradigm) for assessing the answer. He believes the flexible nature of the action research process - which allows community members to determine the processes which they will employ, the style of meetings, the 'level' at which they want to participate, and the concerns they are prepared to address - is highly valuable in ensuring both organisational flexibility and community commitment. This project, although in its early stages, appears to be involving community participants in different ways - ways largely determined by such factors as group makeup, regional location and support forthcoming from the state.

In Chapter 19 Liepins argues that rural social research can, and has, made a difference in the development of social policy. She outlines the work of several rural-based social research centres throughout Australia to show the diversity of interests and approaches, and relates the agendas of sociology with those of policy to emphasise the important applied nature of much Australian rural sociological research. She comments, in particular, about the role of research in informing issues of cultural diversity, environmental sustainability, agricultural adjustment and rural identity. The task still remains, Liepins believes, to 'temper, and even challenge, the dominance of physical sciences and economics' in policy formation relating to agriculture and rural society.

Chapter 20 confronts the issue of drought - something which, hitherto, has been the almost-exclusive province of those from the 'dominant' disciplines identified by Liepins, above. Here, the authors' aim is to view drought as a social construction. It is argued that a constructivist approach based upon a combination of research strategies (including prolonged engagement, observation, triangulation, and referential verification) will provide an holistic and culturally-based understanding of drought. Such an approach will, it is argued, encourage those participating in the study to provide accounts which are sociologically 'rich' - containing views relating to perception of drought, the on-farm impacts of drought, and the ways they and their family members have coped. This chapter implicitly demonstrates the advantages of qualitative methodologies in seeking an informed assessment of what is perceived (naively) by many experts to be a climatological, rather than a sociological, problem.

In Chapter 21 Gray and Phillips also express the desirability of developing new, more sociologically-informed, approaches to the study of rural issues. Here, they deal with cultural transmission and posit that what appears to be occurring in rural regions is that social traditions are being perceptibly weakened as the rural economy is being restructured. They argue, from research which contains both qualitative and quantitative dimensions, and conducted in the Riverina region of NSW, that many farmers are beginning to question what have been shown to be non-sustainable farm practices - at the very time their support mechanisms (in the form of tradition) are eroding. Without a strong farming culture upon which to rely, these farmers may not have the support needed to challenge, and eventually to abandon, those practices now viewed as being environmentally harmful.

Chapters 22 and 23 problematise another area affecting modern agriculture - that of biotechnology. Norton and Lawrence in Chapter 22 report the results of a small-scale study of consumers in one of Queensland's main regional cities. When asked questions about food preferences, those in the four focus groups stressed that health issues guided purchase. Not surprisingly they were interested in the nutritional value, taste and freshness of foods. When they considered the products of genetic engineering they (generally) approved of products that would be beneficial in terms of animal health, but were reluctant to consider the purchase of foodstuffs which contained 'foreign' genes. Consumers appeared quite concerned about the genetic alteration of foods, and were suspicious about the claims of scientists that what was being developed in food laboratories would pose few risks to health. Those involved in the study simply did not believe the scientists' claims. They wanted proper labelling as a basis for choice of products on the supermarket shelves. The conclusion - that it is unlikely consumers will endorse those genetically-engineered products which they have to ingest has (if it were to be part of a wider trend) profound implications for the future of food-related biotechnological research in Australia.

In Chapter 23 Hindmarsh is eager to demonstrate that the public's views of biotechnology are 'translated' by the media and by pro-science forces in a manner which provides support for the development of new genetically-engineered products. Hindmarsh draws upon his own experiences in questioning the purported advantages of biotechnology to show how a dominant power bloc effectively closed debate through 'disinformation' and the discrediting of opposition. Given the importance of the likely impacts of genetically-engineered foods and other products in the Australian marketplace, the marginalisation of opposition in the ways described by Hindmarsh is of great concern to those who believe that consumers must be fully informed about choices.

In the final chapter, Lawrence provides an overview of many of the concerns raised by contributors to the book. Global processes are viewed as having a determining influence upon developments at the local level. Rather than viewing such change as unidirectional, however, a 'modern' political economy of rural Australia identifies sites of local resistance, and post-modern forces, as being capable of combining to challenge wider tendencies of incorporation and of providing new options for rural people.

It is hoped that readers of the book will, in considering the many and varied approaches and 'case studies' provided by contributors, not only have an insight into the processes, impacts and challenges to change, but also an understanding of the social science-based theories and methods which can be harnessed to improve our knowledge of, and inform actions in relation to, contemporary rural Australia.

References

Buttel, F. (1996) Theoretical Issues in Global Agri-food Restructuring , in Burch, D., Rickson, R. and Lawrence, G. (eds) *Globalisation and Agri-food Restructuring: Perspectives from the Australasia Region*, London, Avebury.

Goodman, D., Sorj, B. and Wilkinson, J. (1987) *From Farming to Biotechnology*, Oxford, Basil Blackwell.

Lawrence, G. (1996) Contemporary Agri-food Restructuring: Australia and New Zealand, in Burch, D., Rickson, R. and Lawrence, G. (eds) *Globalisation and Agri-food Restructuring: Perspectives from the Australasia Region*, London, Avebury.

Vanclay, F. and Lawrence, G. (1995) *The Environmental Imperative: Eco-social Concerns for Australian Agriculture*, Rockhampton, CQU Press.

Watts, M. and Goodman, D. (1994) Reconfiguring the Rural or Fording the Divide? Capitalist Restructuring and the Global Agro-food System, *Journal of Peasant Studies* 22, 1: 1-49.

Chapter 1

Agrarianism and farmer representation: Ideology in Australian Agriculture

Darren Halpin and Peter Martin

Introduction

Commentators on Australian agricultural policy identify its orientation towards increased efficiency - something which exacerbates the concentration of capital in the hands of fewer farmers, consequent removal of inefficient farmers, and an integration of farm production with agribusiness. These changes in rural and broader economic policy include macro-economic policy changes (such as the deregulation of the currency and capital markets) the withdrawal of state assistance and regulation for the rural sector, and the progressive dismantling of state-sponsored collective marketing institutions. Such changes have been the subject of lively debate between rural sociologists and agricultural economists in Australia.

Policy changes which significantly affect the nature of Australian farming necessitate the compliance of farmer organisations at both the state and national level (Trebeck, 1990), and consequently alter the relationships between these organisations and the state. However, these peak organisations have entered into more corporatist-type relationships with the state and have helped facilitate many of the deregulatory reforms. At the same time, there has been increased farmer disaffection with these organisations, evidenced by falling membership and a flurry of consultancies reviewing organisational direction (Michels Warren Pty Ltd, 1993).

Diverse reasons have been offered to explain the declining support for farmer organisations, including a lack of services offered by such groups, competition from local farm-based groups, communication gaps between farmers and the organisations that attempt to represent them and, in the context of the NSWFA, 'that the association is not truly representative and does not reflect the views of grass root members' (Michels Warren Pty Ltd, 1993). It is this issue of 'representation' which we seek to pursue in this paper. We argue that the initial impetus for peak farmer organisations was the representation of agrarian interests (the National Farmers' Federation), and that the cohesion of these bodies has depended to some extent on a shared commitment to agrarian values. However, the more recent changes in orientation of these bodies, which have included a closer relationship with the state and a commitment to the tenets of economic rationalism, indicate a changing ideological commitment. Have these 'public' commitments, and the deregulatory reforms they have supported, influenced the constitution and/or strength of agrarian values amongst membership and possibly undermined the collective capacity of these organisations?

Claus Offe (1985) provides a link between ideology and organised collective political action. He attributes the successful formation and operation of workers associations to ideological strength:

> no union can function for a day in the absence of some
> rudimentary notions held by the members that being a member is
> of value in itself, that the individual organisation costs must not
> be calculated in a utilitarian manner but have to be accepted as
> necessary sacrifices, and that each member is legitimately
> required to practice solidarity and discipline, and other norms of
> a non-utilitarian kind (Offe, 1985: 183).

As a consequence, a reduction in the power of ideology would have severe effects on the internal cohesion within associations/unions and hence may jeopardise their political power. This relationship between ideology, collective action and political power has a parallel in Australian agriculture. Agrarianism can be said to have been a rallying point for farmers' unions in the late 1800s and early 1900s (Graham, 1966), and again in the late 1970s. Could it be that any weakening in agrarianism may threaten cohesion within peak farmer organisations? Does the dominance of a economic rational (goal rational/strategically rational) public discourse by these organisations represent a fundamental change in the power of ideology in farmer political associations?

This chapter reports preliminary research on a branch of the NSW Farmers' Association and indicates differences in the ideological commitments of membership around some agrarian themes. This differentiation in commitment is explored in terms of its impact on organisations political power, and the capacity of farmer peak organisations to effectively represent members interests.

Background to the study

Agrarianism

In what is generally agreed to be the seminal contemporary work in the area, Flinn and Johnson (1974) provide a comprehensive description of agrarianism. They describe agrarianism as constituting five major elements: farming is the most basic occupation upon which others depend; agricultural life is natural and city life is evil; economic independence is desirable; hard work demonstrates virtue; and, family farms are linked with the maintenance of democracy (see Beus and Dunlap, 1994).

This picture of agrarianism - as the staid belief system of the agriculturalist - has been altered significantly by subsequent studies. Singer and de Sousa (1983) explored the relationship between agrarianism and progressive policy agendas. They concluded agrarianism was a significant determinant of policy orientation and in so doing rejected three of the major theoretical arguments regarding the fate of agrarianism namely: agrarianism as 'false consciousness'; agrarianism as a refuge; and, the 'end of agrarianism'. This result lends weight to the growing argument that agrarianism is a complex system of beliefs that are non-specific in nature and hence malleable. Having established the flexible nature of the belief system Singer and de Sousa attributed the role of 'creating and sustaining' traditional values, and hence agrarianism, to small communities, church and family. These institutions continue regardless of class location and ensure '...no political or economic interest can lay exclusive claim to agrarianism' (Singer and de Sousa, 1983). In acknowledging the limitations of their study the authors propose that 'additional research is needed on...the importance that political organisation has for directing agrarian values toward conservative versus progressive political strategies' (Singer and de Sousa, 1983).

In further work on agrarianism, Dalecki and Coughenour (1992), extending the work of Buttel and Flinn (1975), established that agrarian themes and imagery had currency within American society generally. They document a number of variants of agrarianism which co-exist in contemporary American society. Two major aspects of agrarianism inform these variants, the 'hard' (which is supportive of agribusiness) and the 'soft' (which places emphasis on the independence and self-sufficiency aspects of agricultural life).

The conclusions of Singer and de Sousa (1983) and Dalecki and Coughenour (1992) support a reconsideration of the view that ideology is a defensive and unmalleable cultural artefact. It may be that agrarianism has been moulded to reflect the political 'reality' that the agricultural sector is of decreased economic significance. Conversely, it may be that the 'soft' agrarian ideals have lost currency publicly and hence have been dropped from public discourse.

In the most recent of agrarian studies Beus and Dunlap (1994) further expound the argument that agrarianism has a variety of configurations. Each configuration encapsulates the basic tenets of the value system[1], but varies on the strength of agreement to some of the tenets. They postulate that agrarianism is a concept which only takes on any clear meaning when contextualised. That is, it comprises a core number of beliefs which can be moulded to suit the needs of any number of competing interests since '...it says nothing about what type of agriculture is best for society' (Beus and Dunlap, 1994). Beus and Dunlap believe agrarianism has been used by various, and sometimes competing, agricultural interest groups to justify their positions and advance their goals.

Beus and Dunlap attempt to identify whether 'types' of agrarianism are emerging by comparing the expressed level of agrarianism between alternative and conventional farmers. They conclude, 'the two groups tend toward somewhat different agrarian ideologies' (Beus and Dunlap, 1994). In terms of the hard and soft agrarian framework espoused by Dalecki and Coughenour (1992), the conventional farmer identifies with the 'hard' and alternative with the 'soft'.

The post 1970s work on the topic argues that agrarianism has at its core the belief that agriculture is inherently important and worth defending. However, the structural characteristics of a future agriculture are not clearly defined and hence open to continual redefinition and change. This change is likely to mirror that which takes place in a number of key socio-cultural institutions including, small community identity, church and the family unit. This study will seek to explore peak farmer groups as another institution which has a role in defining the negotiable facets of agrarianism.

Agrarianism and farm policy in Australia

Agrarianism as a subject of empirical study has received little attention in Australia, Craig and Phillips (1983) being the only significant study. This research program, the first part of which is outlined in this paper, was designed to augment the findings of this past study and to discuss its meaning within the context of agricultural policy throughout the mid-1990s.

Australian agriculture has changed significantly from that which confronted the respondents in Craig and Phillips' (1983) study. There has been a significant rationalisation of the farming sector, in particular family farm businesses. Farmers terms of trade have declined 20 points, and there are 50,000 less farm establishments than in 1983 (ABARE, 1994). Partnered with this has been a increased level of agribusiness intrusion into the agricultural chain of production, more specifically in the processing sector (Gerritsen, 1987; Lawrence, 1987). The emergence of economic rationalism as a dominant ideology is reflected in the public debate between the government and farm interest groups. Farmers are being urged, by both government and farm interest groups, to consider their enterprise in purely business terms, which appears to have placed significant pressure on traditional values. Deregulation of the agricultural sector signalled the progressive withdrawal of government from this area of the economy. Farm organisations have slowly reduced references to the fundamentalist style of agrarianism and publicly adopted a more rationalist philosophy (Lawrence, 1987; Trebeck, 1990).

A change in public orientation by farmer representative groups is evidenced by the NSWFA's reduced use of militant agrarian imagery as a policy tool. Its initial slogan in 1985 was, 'Now's the time to show your hand.' The image of a clenched fist reinforcing the slogans militant intent. Its 1994 slogan is 'NSWFA Association for Growth', and as it suggests, focuses on creating a collective vision of a bright future for agriculture with which membership can identify.

The imagery of a farm family looking into a sun-drenched future contains none of the militant overtones that past campaigns included. Likewise the NFF has been focusing on controlling memberships use of militant behaviour and the fundamentalist rhetoric. Further, it has exhibited a matching change in policy direction. At its 1990 annual council meeting, the NFF President and the Federal Treasurer agreed that there was no turning back on protectionism (Cleary, 1990). This represents a change from 1979 when the National/Liberal government was warning the NFF to abandon its handout mentality over export incentives (Boyle, 1979).

The agricultural policy process has also changed quite significantly. The election of the Hawke Labour Government in 1983 and a public rally by farmers in Canberra during 1985 signalled the commencement of a new policy agenda. In its 1986 policy statement a change in approach can be detected. The statement concludes that, in its

> review of economic and rural policies, the government has identified many areas where little progress can be achieved by government alone. We are looking for a full commitment from rural groups generally, and farm organisations in particular to join us in developing specific courses of action in these areas. We have suggested machinery to facilitate this process (Hawke, 1986: 1).

The formation of the Rural and Allied Industries Council (RAIC) was part of the new corporatist 'machinery' which the Federal Labor government instituted to see its reformist agenda successfully implemented. The NFF and its affiliate organisations took up the corporate role, as conceptualised by Hawke. The aggressive policy position of the NFF was accompanied by active participation on, and detailed representations to, various quasi-governmental committees and commissions such as the Industries Assistance Commission (IAC) the Australian Agricultural Council (AAC), and the Economic Planning Advisory Council (EPAC).

The peak farm organisation was duly congratulated by Hawke's successor, Paul Keating, who in addressing the 1995 NFF Annual Conference described the peak body as 'able to look beyond sectional interests', having a 'comprehensive approach to policy' and concluded that there is, 'not much more a government could ask for (in an interest group)'.

The NFF increasingly pursued the rationalisation of the farm sector, that is, the removal of inefficient farmers and the restructuring of the agricultural sector into a competitive export earning sector of the economy. Instead of pursuing further government assistance[2] it has adopted the economic rationalist argument highlighting 'individual inefficiency amongst farmers and wage inflexibility in the wider community as two of the main problems facing agriculture' (Lawrence, 1987). This policy program implicitly argues that the value of agriculture must be assessed on a monetary basis. It has had the additional effect of developing a 'myth' that the solution to the agricultural

13

sector lies at the feet of the individual and that they must increase productivity/efficiency or leave the industry (Lawrence, 1987). This appears to have tapped the broad agrarian sentiments of farmers as the family farmers who are the most at risk have shown little evidence of public resistance.

In the context of these marked changes, it is questionable whether agrarian ideology (member commitment), as documented in many studies over the past few decades, is compatible with the new dominant discourse of economic rationality (change in public commitment). Alternatively, it may have stratified agrarianism into a number of variants, each providing a different answer to the question 'what type of agriculture is best for society'. Further, variations in the definition of agrarianism, and hence the ideological commitment necessary for farmers to associate, may signal a threat to the future of a 'peak' farm organisation as a single voice for rural Australia.

This paper outlines preliminary field work which raises the possibility that variations of agrarianism have emerged. This is further discussed in terms of the change in policy orientation of peak farm groups and the general policy process. These formulations of agrarianism provide different visions of what structural aspects of agriculture are best for the nation. Further, they have differing levels of currency in the recently redefined agricultural policy community.

Methodology

The Research Program

The research program is to comprise a series of case studies on a number of NSWFA branches across a diverse range of commodity groupings and geographical locations. The results in this paper are of the first case study at the Goulburn NSWFA branch.

The National Farmers' Federation has no individual members, but rather member organisations. Therefore, in order to explore agrarianism and its relationship to farm interest group activity a state organisation had to be used. In this research the NSW State organisation, the NSW Farmers' Association, was chosen as the case study.

The data were collected from the Goulburn region of New South Wales. Two parallel surveys were conducted to gather data from members of the NSWFA and primary producers who were not members. A census was attempted of all the voting members of the Goulburn branch of the New South Wales Farmer Association (NSWFA). A mail survey was sent out to 160 members of the branch, 83 of which responded (52 percent). Of these respondents 25 were active members and 58 were non-active members. A second survey, using the same questions, was conducted on a sample of 50 non-members from the same region. Of these 50 mail surveys sent out 15 were returned (30 percent). The components of the survey were designed with the investigation of the two themes, agrarianism and farm policy, in mind.

The non-member survey was originally conducted as a control measure, but has shed surprising light on the impact of farmer representative group membership on agrarian and policy attitudes. This explains the sampling procedure which is heavily skewed in favour of farm representative group members.

Agrarian items

Alongside other research undertaken on agrarian issues, within this study we take the position that Agrarianism can be defined as constituting a number of ideals. Whilst these ideals may not consciously be identified by participants as a belief system, they form the basis of an observable system of ideas which cohere around the common experience of an agricultural life.

This study uses agrarian items derived in part from indices applied in previous works (Flinn and Johnson, 1974; Buttel and Flinn, 1975; Carlson and McLeod, 1978; Craig and Phillips, 1983; Beus and Dunlap, 1994), which makes the results more easily comparable. There are however, some major differences.[3]

The five questions which were selected reflect four major themes. Item A emphasises the values reinforcing the moral virtue of rural as opposed to city life. Item B reflects the attitude that the current economic arrangements were formulated to the advantage of corporate farming as opposed to family farms. Item C asks the respondent to indicate whether they see agriculture as the most important determinate of how the whole Australian economy will go. Item D indicates whether respondents see agriculture as its own reward as opposed to monetary reward. Item E indicates how respondents feel about corporate farming and its social and economic influence.

The recognition of agrarian tenets across American society in general, as identified by Buttel and Flinn (1975) and Singer and de Sousa (1983), places under question the role of an agrarian index as a sole determinant of agrarianism. Recognising this point, Beus and Dunlap (1994) question the adequacy of the agrarian index as conceptualised by Flinn and Johnson (1974), and conclude that the best chance of detecting changes in agrarianism is by approaching the items individually. As a result we present and analyse each one of the items individually. This allows for any incremental and partial changes in the belief systems to be identified.

Agricultural policy items

Questions regarding the respondents position on policy issues have been included in the study in order to ascertain whether the traditional cleavages in member preferences particularly along the line of regulation/deregulation and subsidies/no-subsidies exist. The questions were selected from Beus and Dunlap (1994). Each one was chosen to reflect the dominant issues within the Australian context, and in reference to Beus and Dunlaps' (1994: 482) recommendation regarding future research needed in the policy area.

Results

Fieldwork is presented under the two major themes of agrarianism and agricultural policy. Each theme explores the range of views across active NSWFA members, non-active NSWFA members and non-members.

Agrarianism

Whilst heavily skewed in favour of members of farm organisations, the accumulated results from both surveys provide a sample which can be compared with past studies conducted using a similar index. Table 1 provides a direct comparison of the five agrarian items used in this study with results from past studies undertaken in the US and in Australia.

Table 1
Percentage distribution for agrarian index items over past*

Item	Location	Agree %	Not Sure %	Disagree %
Item A The farm is the ideal place to raise a family.[4]	NSW	**84**	**14**	**2**
	S.Aust.	56	21	23
	Idaho	61	7	32
	Wisc.	57	9	34
Item B If the economic situation for farmers continues like it is now, in a few years the family farms will be replaced by large corporate farms.	NSW	**53**	**26**	**21**
	S.Aust.	30	14	57
	Idaho	64	7	29
	Wisc.	69	3	27
Item C A depression in agriculture is likely to cause a depression in the entire country.	NSW	**59**	**26**	**15**
	S.Aust.	87	7	6
	Idaho	87	1	12
	Wisc.	90	3	7
Item D Farmers ought to appreciate farming as a good way of life and be less concerned about their cash income.	NSW	**6**	**5**	**89**
	S.Aust.	30	8	62
	Idaho	38	8	54
	Wisc.	21	2	77
Item E The replacement of family farms by corporate farms would have undesirable economic and social consequences for the nation.	NSW	**60**	**31**	**9**
	S.Aust.	80	8	12
	Idaho	94	0	6
	Wisc.	82	8	10

Source: Craig and Phillips (1983); Beus and Dunlap (1994).
*These results are condensed to a three-point index. There are some differences in strength of the attitudes over the five-point index.

Item A illustrates an overwhelming conviction by farmers that a rural life is the best environment for a family. The reason for the strength of this response may be that item A was worded differently from that which appears in the other studies. Additionally, the increasing urbanisation of the study area may provide more compelling evidence that urban life is corrupt and lacks positive moral influence. Items B and E as a combination illustrate that respondents are in general agreement that corporate farms will eventually predominate over family farms, and that this will result in a negative economic outcome. There has been a change between this and past surveys, in terms of what effect this corporate intrusion will have in economic and social terms. A large number of respondents in past surveys were unsure as to how this change in the nature of agriculture would effect the social and economic situation in Australia.

Item C illustrates a substantive historical change in the way farmers see their role in the well-being of the nation. Recent results indicate farmers are more willing to accept they are not as important as they were in the early and mid 1900s. Responses to item D illustrate that whilst farming is a good lifestyle most members see economic performance as an important goal. In other words, they farm for a combination of lifestyle and economic reasons. This is a substantial change from levels recorded in a South Australian study conducted in 1983.

If there has been a historical change in the strength and constitution of agrarianism, to what factors can we attribute this change? As Singer and de Sousa assert, factors facilitating such change may well include the church, community ownership and the institution of the family. Additionally farmer representative organisations may in fact paly a role in the definition of what 'type' of agriculture is right for the nation. If the rhetoric of these organisations is reflected in membership, then a suspicion of corporate agriculture and a vision of agriculture as the dominant determinant of the economic and social welfare of the nation will be felt most strongly amongst non-members.

Table 2 represents the responses to the Goulburn survey broken up into active member, non-active member and non-member. 'Active' was defined as any person who attends meetings or has a conscious input into the branch process. The Items of importance are C, D and E. Item C suggests that the further away from direct contact with the policy process the less likely farmers are to have a sober picture of the economic importance of agriculture to the nation. Item D illustrates that some non-members still value their work on a lifestyle basis. This is in stark contrast to the active and non-active member of the NSWFA who have almost unanimously adopted the perspective of farm as a business. Item E illustrates that it is the non-members who are most suspicious of the impact corporate farming will have on the nation. The number of those 'undecided' in the active and non-active membership of the NSWFA in item E suggests that they are becoming more supportive of the 'hard' side of agrarianism. The total sample shows an across the board unwillingness to disagree with Item E which suggests that agrarianism in Australia is never likely to consciously embrace corporate farming but is becoming less-likely to actively oppose it on ideological grounds.

In statistical terms only one significant difference between the different membership samples was evident amongst the agrarian items (See Table 3). This was in item C. The large variance within the non-member sample appears to be due to the skewed sampling process. This may well change as further sampling is conducted amongst the non-members in particular.

Table 2
Agrarian index versus pattern of membership

Agrarian Item	NSWFA Membership	Agree %	Not Sure %	Disagree %
Item A The farm is the ideal place to raise a family.[5]	*Active* Non-Active *Non-Member*	*84* 81 *93*	*16* 16 *7*	*0* 3 *0*
Item B If the economic situation for farmers continues like it is now, in a few years the family farms will be replaced by large corporate farms.	*Active* Non-Active *Non-Member*	*52* 55 *46*	*28* 24 *27*	*20* 21 *27*
Item C A depression in agriculture is likely to cause a depression in the entire country.	*Active* Non-Active *Non-Member*	*40* 60 *86*	*32* 28 *7*	*28* 12 *7*
Item D Farmers ought to appreciate farming as a good way of life and be less concerned about their cash income.	*Active* Non-Active *Non-Member*	*4* 3 *20*	*4* 5 *7*	*92* 92 *73*
Item E The replacement of family farms by corporate farms would have undesirable economic and social consequences for the nation.	*Active* Non-Active *Non-Member*	*56* 57 *80*	*28* 36 *13*	*16* 7 *7*

Note: For the NSWFA member survey there were 83 respondents from 160 mailed surveys. 58 were non-active members and 25 were active members. For the non-member survey there were 15 respondents from 50 mailed surveys.

The same approach taken in Table 2 regarding agrarian items has been adopted in examining policy items in Table 4. Responses have been examined in terms of active member, non-active member and non-member. Respondents were asked to give their attitude on four items of agricultural policy. They were not individual policies, but rather a number of assumptions which would underlie any agricultural policy. Hence, the responses represent these members position on what should be the aims of a new agricultural policy.

In terms of farm policy items, the entire membership sample reflects a indeterminacy in views. It would therefore be expected that other factors, such as commodity grouping may be more important in determining these attitudes. However, the non-active and non-member responses to Item Three suggest that a large proportion of the farming community are supportive of an increase in the number of farmers practicing farming within Australia. Further, the non-member response to Item One suggests that this section of the farming community strongly wish a return to the subsidy era of the pre-1980s. Responses in the affirmative to these two items reflects a completely opposing view to that which pervades the agricultural policy community. These results illustrate the contrasting views prevalent on many issues in regard to agricultural policy.

Table 3
Table of means: agrarian items versus membership pattern

Agrarian Item	Active (mean)	Non-Active (mean)	Non-Member (mean)
Item A The farm is the ideal place to raise a family.	4.68^{ab}	4.55^{ac}	4.87^{bc}
Item B If the economic situation for farmers continues like it is now, in a few years the family farms will be replaced by large corporate farms.	3.64^{ab}	3.69^{ac}	3.40^{bc}
Item C A depression in agriculture is likely to cause a depression in the entire country.	3.24	3.97a	4.60a
Item D Farmers ought to appreciate farming as a good way of life and be less concerned about their cash income.	1.24^{ab}	1.24^{ac}	1.93^{bc}
Item E The replacement of family farms by corporate farms would have undesirable economic and social consequences for the nation.	3.80^{ab}	4.00^{ac}	4.47^{bc}

Means followed by the same character are not significantly different at $p \leq .05$.

The response to Item One (Table 4) by non-members further indicates that non-members seem to espouse the policy and agrarian positions of the early 1980s.

Table 4
Agricultural policy versus pattern of membership

Policy Items	NSWFA Membership	Agree %	Not Sure %	Disagree %
1 Subsidies to agriculture should be phased out.	*Active*	*32*	*28*	*40*
	Non-Active	34	20	46
	Non-Member	7	21	72
2 Stricter regulations on conversion of farmland to non-farm uses.	*Active*	*56*	*8*	*36*
	Non-Active	67	14	19
	Non-Member	60	7	33
3 Farm policy should try to increase number of farmers.	*Active*	*28*	*32*	*40*
	Non-Active	48	21	31
	Non-Member	53	40	7
4 Increasing exports of agricultural should be a major policy goal.	*Active*	*88*	*8*	*4*
	Non-Active	98	0	2
	Non-Member	80	7	13

Note: For the policy items response rate varies. For item A n=56 and items B-D n=58 for non-active members and for all items n=25 for active members. For non-members n=14 for item A and n=15 for items 2-4. The questions in this table were derived from a series produced by Beus and Dunlap (1994).

19

A commitment to protectionism and subsidies were the hallmark of Liberal/National governments in the 1970s and the initial impetus for the public commitment necessary for the formation of the NFF.

Table 5 illustrates the only significant difference amongst membership patterns regarding policy positions occurred in Item D. There was a significant difference (at p≤.05) between the mean responses for non-active NSWFA members and non-members.[6] All other items illustrated a polarisation of opinions and hence no significant level of variation between samples was detected.

Table 5
Table of means: policy items versus membership pattern

Policy Items	Active (mean)	Non-Active (mean)	Non-Member (mean)
1 Subsidies to agriculture should be phased out.	2.84^{ab}	2.75^{ac}	1.71^{bc}
2 Stricter regulations on conversion of farmland to non-farm uses.	3.40^{ab}	3.97^{ac}	3.53^{bc}
3 Farm policy should try to increase number of farmers.	2.76^{ab}	3.35^{ac}	3.93^{bc}
4 Increasing exports of agricultural should be a major policy goal.	4.68^{ab}	4.93^{a}	4.33^{b}

Means followed by the same character are not significantly different at p≤.05.

Conclusions

The historical data needed to establish a change in attitude to agrarian items amongst members of farm organisations do not exist which prevents any statistical assessment regarding change over time. However, the public statements of members views as expressed in journals and magazines provides substantive evidence of a coherence between public ideological commitment and farmer belief systems in the 1970s. It is this coherence which, in the late 1970s, facilitated the formation of peak farm organisations at a national and State level. This study suggests that such coherence no longer exists.

> As bureaucratically structured, complex organisations, unions are drawn into a precarious situation to the degree that they allow themselves to be held responsible for fulfilling general economic functions and stabilisation requirements. If this happens, they must extensively weaken their ideologies, symbols and mobilising perspectives in order to be able to effectively play their role as 'trustworthy', 'responsible' and 'committed' discussion partners in the formation of public policy'(Offe, 1985: 163).

The trend Claus Offe identifies in unions is observable in the practice of Australian farm organisations since the early 1980s. At the same time as farmer representative organisations have taken on more of a integral role in public policy, a significant disparity has emerged in the nature of members' ideological commitment for association and the public statement of policy. That is, the NSWFA's charter to 'serve and defend the needs of our members' (NSWFA, 1995) has only been partially fulfilled as many members' opinions on an acceptable form of agriculture and policy orientations remain unrepresented. Divisions exist within the farm community along the lines of commitment to corporate agriculture, the necessity for subsidies, and the need for an increase in farm numbers. In terms of agrarianism, these divisions are most evident between categories of farm organisation members and non-members, whilst on most policy items divisions appear both within and outside of farm organisations.

It appears from this initial survey that all farmers, regardless of participation in farm organisations, are convinced that the rural life is best and that policy is orientated towards corporate farming. However, those who take an active part in farm organisations have a more sober view of the economic contribution and social importance of agriculture. Results of this case study appear to support the thesis that active members are more accepting of the expansion of corporate farming and are less concerned about the cost to the lifestyle aspects of farming. However, this is by no means clear. What these preliminary findings suggest is that association membership may be as significant as some of the traditional determinants of agrarianism such as age, education and farm size.

The results of this study also reinforce the findings of Dalecki and Coughenour (1992) and Beus and Dunlap (1994) in suggesting that agrarianism is multi dimensional and malleable. That is, whilst it has a broad appeal by suggesting agriculture is a special industry, it does not determine the forms and structures of the organisation of agricultural production. In this survey the items A, B and D seem to be the core of the ideology and are held by all. It is on item C that significant differences appear and it could be that this will also prove to be the case on item E.

No significant difference was detected between the policy items pursued by all categories. This suggests that whilst active members have a pragmatic picture of what can be achieved by their organisation, what policy agenda they would like to see accomplished is still unclear. Again, we suspect that a wider sample may show some significant differences on items One and Three.

If agrarianism is open to change and can continue to support a variety of definitions regarding the structure of agriculture, then what does this mean for interest representation? The substantial divisions of members along policy and agrarian items has significant implications for the practice of farmer representative groups. Agreement to both items B and E in Table 2 could be problematic for an organisation such as the NSWFA. The belief in the importance of agriculture and a mistrust of corporate intrusion into this sector, are assumptions which, it would appear, policy makers do not share. Further, the NSWFA may lose credibility with policy makers should they pursue these values, but conversely risk losing credibility with membership if the values they perceive as important are ignored.

However, what may appear as a comprehensive distrust of corporate agriculture, may not permeate some portions of membership. Those members who are *active* members appear to hold a view on the relative social and economic importance of agriculture which is acceptable to the state, and are more comfortable with corporate agriculture. Since these people presumably have the major input into NSWFA policy, their interests would be expected to prevail in the formation of agricultural policy. What remains uncertain is the action non-active membership and non-members will take as the public position of the NSWFA becomes less representative of their privately held views.

The divergence illustrated in this initial research has not been sufficient to trigger a public challenge to the organisation's representative capacity in recent times. However, the loss of membership and the periodic emergence of a splinter group to challenge the hard agrarianism of the institutionalised farm groups points to the possibility that those favouring the softer aspects will have their interests publicly aired.

Further research

This study has made some preliminary conclusions regarding the importance membership of farm organisations has had on the composition of an individual's agrarian belief system. It has also raised a number of new questions which need further research.

The most urgent focus is to establish whether non-members are significantly different from members in their responses to all the policy and agrarian items. Further survey work will be required adopting a less skewed sampling procedure which includes more non-members. Additionally, key items of policy and agrarianism which distinguish progressive versus traditional and hard versus soft forms of agrarianism will need to be identified.

Clarification of some terms used in the policy items will also need to be made. For instance, the term subsidy may well have been interpreted a number of ways. The NSWFA opposes subsidisation of domestic industry as a form of protection from imports. However, it does not support user-pay strategies for fuel, postage and phone services. It is possible that some members have misinterpreted the use of subsidy which in the literature is referring to protection measures used to shield domestic industry from direct competition with exports.

The question as to whether there is a link between a stratification in agrarianism and material conditions will need to be considered. This involves ascertaining whether farmers who have poorer material conditions favour a particular variation of agrarianism.

Further exploration of the possible relationship between the level of off-farm income and agrarianism must also be made. From the initial data, non-active members tend to make up the bulk of part-time farmers. Offe (1985) suggests that unions rely for their strength on the centrality of the experience of labour to the life interests of their membership. If this experience becomes more peripheral or diverge between members, then the association may lose cohesion as members interests become stratified. In terms of agrarianism, the central concept is a common agricultural experience. It may be that if this agricultural experience is markedly different between farmers, agrarianism will become significantly stratified and hence weaken as a cohesive agent for association.

Notes

1   Both alternative and conventional respondents achieve the same overall score on the agrarian index.
2   Gerritsen (1992;107) identifies that the NFF's philosophy of economic rationalism is intermittently broken by a return to a form of agrarian socialism.
3   There are fewer items (five as opposed to eleven) which leaves it open to being more sensitive. The omission of a number of questions reflects a judgement that they were either repeating elements of other questions or were not reflective of the Australian context. In particular, references to 'lack of authority and lawlessness' seemed to reflect North America's domestic situation more than Australia's. Questions reflecting economic independence were also omitted. Finally, Question '4' on the Craig and Phillips (1983) index has been replaced with that from Beus and Dunlap (1994).These authors found the previous question had a low correlation with agrarianism.
4   This question has replaced 'One reason why we hear so much about crime and corruption today is because our nation is becoming so urbanised' (Craig and Phillips 1983). The new question was based on the report of Beus and Dunlap (1994).
5   As in Table 2 this question has replaced 'One reason why we hear so much about crime and corruption today is because our nation is becoming so urbanised.'(Craig and Phillips 1983). This was based on the report of Beus and Dunlap (1994). Therefore, values from past studies for question four have been used in this table.
6   This was calculated using 1-way ANOVA and then calculating Least Significance Difference between sample means at the appropriate level. This appears consistent with Beus and Dunlap's (1991; 1994) approach.

Acknowledgment

We would like to acknowledge Associate Professor Graeme Newell from the Faculty of Management, UWS-Hawkesbury for his assistance with statistical procedures. Ultimately, we take full responsibility for the results and interpretations.

References

Australian Bureau of Agricultural and Resource Economics (1994) *Commodity Statistical Bulletin 1994*, Canberra, Commonwealth of Australia.

Beus, C. and Dunlap, R. (1994) Endorsement of Agrarian Ideology and Adherence to Agricultural Paradigms, *Rural Sociology* 59: 462-484.

Beus, C. and Dunlap, R. (1991) Measuring Adherence to Alternative vs. Conventional Agricultural Paradigms: A Proposed Scale, *Rural Sociology* 56: 432-460.

Boyle, K. (1979) Farmers Get Warning on Handout Mentality, *The Land* 30 August: 11.

Buttel, F. and Flinn, W. (1975) Sources and Consequences of Agrarian Values in American Society, *Rural Sociology* 40:134-151.

Buttel, F. and Flinn, W. (1976) Sociopolitical Consequences of Agrarianism, *Rural Sociology* 41: 473-483.

Carlson, J. and McLeod, M. (1978) A Comparison of Agrarianism in Washington, Idaho, and Wisconsin, *Rural Sociology* 43: 17-30.

Cleary, P. (1990) Keating Rules out Protection Return, *Sydney Morning Herald*, 21 November: 9.

Craig, R. and Phillips, K. (1983) Agrarian Ideology in Australia and the United States, *Rural Sociology* 48: 409-420.

Dalecki, M. and Coughenour, C. (1992) Agrarianism in American Society, *Rural Sociology* 57: 48-64.

Flinn, W. and Johnson, D. (1974) Agrarianism Among Wisconsin Farmers, *Rural Sociology* 39: 187-204.

Gerritsen, R. (1987) Making Policy Under 'Uncertainty': The Labor Government's Reaction to the 'Rural Crisis', *Discussion Paper No.3. Public Policy Program*, Australia, ANU.

Graham, B. (1966) *The Formation of the Australian Country Parties*, Australia, ANU Press.

Hawke, R. (1986) *Economic and Rural Policy - A Government Policy Statement*, AGPS, Canberra.

Offe, C. (1985) *Disorganised Capitalism*, Polity Press, UK.

Lawrence, G. (1987) *Capitalism and the Countryside*, Pluto Press, Australia.

Michels Warren Pty Ltd. (1993) *What Are We Here For?: A Plan to Address Falling Membership Numbers of the NSW Farmers' Association*. Unpublished Report.

Singer, E. and de Sousa, R. (1983) The Sociopolitical Consequences of Agrarianism Reconsidered, *Rural Sociology*, 48: 291-307.

Trebeck, D. (1990) Farmer Organisations, in D.Williams (ed.) *Agriculture in the Australian Economy*, Sydney University Press, Australia.

Chapter 2

Farming practice, capital and Landcare: Subsumption and control

Stewart Lockie

Introduction

There are a number of features of agriculture in contemporary Australia that few farmers, social scientists, environmentalists, or even economists, would dispute. Farm numbers are dropping, tightening terms of trade necessitate constant productivity gains, and there is an increasing awareness of widespread and massive land degradation. Despite periodic forecasts of improving commodity prices, most farms remain unprofitable (Beare, 1995), and many face severe financial difficulty. Declining rural populations lead further to rationalisation of services in both the public and private sectors, and reduced accessibility to these services for those who remain on the land or in small country towns, often when they are needed the most (Lawrence and Williams, 1990; Stone, 1992).

Amidst all the gloom and doom that surrounds agriculture, the National Landcare Program (NLP) is seen by many as a ray of hope, a good news story that holds genuine promise to deal not only with rural land degradation, but to bring communities together to address a range of related social and economic issues. Landcare was launched as a Commonwealth policy and program in 1989 following a joint proposal for a National Land Management Program by the Australian Conservation Foundation and the National Farmer's Federation (Toyne and Farley, 1989), based in part on State programs under way in Victoria and Western Australia. The emphasis in Landcare is on self-help, the centrepiece of the program being a network of over 2,200 community Landcare groups across Australia (Alexander, 1995) that involve representatives of nearly 30 percent of Australian farms (Mues *et al.*, 1994). These are supposedly autonomous groups of mainly rural people, who come together to do something about land degradation in their area (A. Campbell, 1994). They are eligible to apply for funding from the NLP, and a range of State based programs, most typically for the establishment of trials and demonstration sites, assistance with farm and catchment planning, and the employment of group facilitators and coordinators. With the emphasis on self-help, funding programs are designed to mobilise community resources, and few funds are directed towards remedial works to deal with land degradation.

Although concerns are frequently raised about Landcare funding, the program has in general terms been seen as enormously successful (eg. Collins, 1994; Curtis and De Lacy, 1995). Participation in Landcare is markedly higher than even optimistic early forecasts dared estimate (eg. Campbell, 1990), and it is increasingly common to hear people talk about the need to move now from awareness raising to implementation (see Alexander, 1995). Despite the optimism, however, insights derived from agrarian sociology would lead to a more tempered view. Of particular interest here is concern over the last decade or so to explore the social and environmental effects of the commoditisation of relations of production in agriculture, and further, the shifting locus of control of the on-farm production process. The extent to which control is removed from the hands of farmers has obvious implications for the likely effectiveness of programs based on self-help in developing more sustainable production systems, and could suggest that a focus on local community action is misplaced (Lockie, 1994a).

Methodology

The data presented here was collected during research into sociological aspects of Landcare in one Local Government Area in south west New South Wales. This was a mixed cropping and livestock area containing about 260 commercial farming businesses (ABS, 1991). Ethnographic fieldwork was conducted involving a mix of semi-structured interviewing, participant observation and a sample household survey (n=77). In total, 81 women and 103 men were formally surveyed through this research, along with innumerable casual conversations and activities. In an attempt to locate the data generated in the field within a broader social context, the author has also participated in many regional and national Landcare forums. This has provided insights into the range of discursive practices that help to shape Landcare practices at the local level.

Competing perspectives in agrarian sociology

There are two broad strands of theory within agrarian sociology relevant to the control of the farm production process (see also Buttel, 1994). The more dominant of these is that drawn from the political economy of agriculture, which focuses on the commoditisation of relations of production in agriculture, and the increasing integration of farm businesses into wider circuits of capital. Whether positing the demise or survival of the family farm as a dominant, or even viable, organisational unit within agriculture, writers here have generally argued that control of the on-farm production process has gradually been

26

subsumed by larger scale agribusinesses. Later writers have been very concerned to stress that this is a historically contingent process in which family farmers play no functional role in the interest of capital accumulation (see Le Heron, 1993), but attribute primary control of agricultural restructuring to the agribusiness sector. Farmers are seen to have little power within these structures of accumulation, and assume a role subservient to that of capital.

Proponents of 'farming styles research', on the other hand, argue that the commoditisation of relations of production does not necessarily lead to such a loss of control by farmers (Long, 1986; van der Ploeg, 1986). These writers are concerned with much the same processes of commoditisation, but argue that the ways in which these are resolved in particular locales are mediated through localised cultural frameworks. Farming styles emerge as distinctive socio-cultural patterns of farming practice that express the agency and diversity of farmers and farming communities. They embody both 'strategic and normative ideas about how farming should be done', and specific ways 'of organising the farm enterprise' (van der Ploeg, 1993: 241). Despite the homogenising tendencies believed to be implicit in processes of globalisation, the farming styles perspective suggests that the expression of agency and the affirmation of local cultural patterns has maintained, if not increased, diversity (van der Ploeg, 1993). Markets and technologies do not simply subsume control of the production process as posited by political economy perspectives but, according to van der Ploeg (1993: 248), constitute a 'room for manoeuvre' in which farmers position themselves in relation to processes of commoditisation and exchange. While adopting the farming styles perspective would allow us to be immediately more positive about the likely impact of Landcare, which is ideally based on such socio-cultural networks and practices, there are some problems with this perspective. Of particular concern is its tendency to overstate the discursive rationality of farmers, suggesting that farming styles are 'well-elaborated and explicit strategies that are consciously adopted by individual farmers' (Leeuwis, 1993: 268). Conversely, farming styles research also assumes a level of internal unity and logic to each distinctive style, reminiscent of cultural structuralism, that is incompatible with its emphasis on agency and discursive rationality. I would suggest that, contrary to this, the possibility that relatively distinct and autonomous socio-cultural groupings may be identified is often likely to be problematic, let alone the possibility that farmers then go through a substantially conscious process of choosing the group to which they will belong. Farming styles research has also, in practice, ignored a range of localised social relations that might reasonably be expected to influence farming practice, such as gender relations.

An attempt was made in this research to integrate the key insights of both these perspectives by; firstly, seeking to understand those dimensions of difference between farmers they themselves thought important; and secondly, operationalising the scales of subsumption developed by Whatmore *et al.,* (1987a, 1987b) to examine where differences in levels of commoditisation actually lay, and what processes of change in relation to these dimensions were evident. It was hoped that this would both determine whether relatively distinct socio-cultural groupings could be meaningfully identified, and provide insights into the relationships between farmers, agribusinesses and other relevant actors, such as state agencies, and their effects on the farm production process. Implicit in this is the idea that dichotomies between commoditisation and subsumption on the one hand, and local agency and cultural expression on the other, are unhelpful. Instead, it must be recognised that all social relations, no matter how extended or restricted in time or space, involve symbolic and normative dimensions, as well as the more direct enactment of power. The influence of agribusinesses and state agencies, therefore, should not only be considered in relation to direct control of the on-farm production process, but also in relation to practices that influence either the meaning of farming practice (Lockie, 1995a), or the environment within which that practice is undertaken (see also Martin, 1995).

The construction of homogeneity

Although participants in this study were capable of identifying different groups of farmers, based on their approach to farming, their responses suggested nevertheless that agricultural practice was following an essentially unilinear path of development. Their views resonated with those of Buttel (1994), who questions whether once local diversity is found through farming styles research it is of any theoretical interest. The majority of farmers differentiated themselves according to the rate at which they adopted new farming technologies, with somewhat less emphasis on attitudes and motivation levels towards farming, enterprise mixes and input use intensity. While there were many who admitted that they were seldom among the first to adopt the latest innovation, and despite concern about the sustainability of input intensive farming systems (see also Lockie *et al.*, 1995), there were few who were prepared to deviate significantly from the dominant mode of farming practice. In as much as distinct farming styles could be meaningfully differentiated, these were based on agroecological zones, characterised by differences in climate, soils and typography. Within each of the two zones in the study area farmers tended to be involved in much the same enterprises, have similar ideas about what constituted the 'state of the art' in farming practice, and look with suspicion on those who did not keep up with them.

If we accept the proposition that subsumption by capital leads to the homogenisation of agricultural production, these indications of homogeneity could be seen to offer strong, if indirect, support for subsumption theories. However, it is important to consider a range of processes that contributed to local homogeneity over which agribusinesses had no direct control, and which did not necessarily threaten farmer's autonomy. The most immediately apparent reason for farmers to adhere largely to what other farmers in their area did was to reduce risk. Farmers participated in a range of formal and informal arrangements to collectivise risk. These included working closely with each other (even if for some this meant little more than looking over the fence) in the ongoing development of local farming systems. Further, within each district they tended to look towards the same 'leading' farmers for guidance, who in turn were usually closely involved with both public and private research and extension organisations. Technology adoption was seen in this cultural milieu as an exemplar of good farming practice, a wide range of activities such as field days and seminars were organised to facilitate it, and those who fell behind were subject to a degree of personal and moral judgement. This local disciplinary power, expressed through the social practices associated with farming was, however, subject to contest. Not all 'innovations' were adopted; most that were adopted were changed in the process; and agribusinesses and state extension agencies devoted substantial resources to trying to influence conceptions of good farming practice, with widely varying degrees of success. The result was a trajectory of agricultural development that certainly appeared to conform with the broad interests of agribusiness in encouraging input dependency, but over which no group had sole control.

Subsumption theory and loss of control

Under the influence of political economy, agrarian sociology has provided compelling analyses of the changing environment within which farming is practiced. All too often, however, a simple relationship of domination and control between farmers and capital has been assumed; an assumption shown by the farming styles perspective and this research to be problematic. Although also falling into this trap, the attempt by Whatmore *et al.*, (1987a: 22) to specify the processes of commoditisation at the farm level, and to explore 'the changing pattern of direct and indirect controls over the farm production process and its implications for the environment', make it very pertinent to our considerations of Landcare.

Whatmore *et al.*, (1987a) argue that control over farms is subsumed by capital along two dimensions (see Figure 1), and a typology is developed to examine the relationships between the two dimensions. The first of these dimensions is *direct* subsumption, which refers to commoditisation of relations of production internal to the farm enterprise. The scales they develop to measure direct subsumption (see Whatmore *et al.*, 1987b) basically measure the degree to which the farm enterprise moves from one owned, operated and managed by a single family member, to one which is owned by off-farm capital, and operated and managed by employees and contract workers. *Indirect* subsumption refers to the extension of commoditised relations of production external to the farm enterprise. These include links with finance capital, technological dependence and marketing linkages.

In arguing that their measures of direct subsumption indicate a loss of control of the production process, Whatmore *et al.*, have to assume that a positive relationship exists between direct and indirect subsumption (otherwise it is not clear how a family company can have less control of their enterprise than a sole owner).

Figure 1.
A conceptualisation of 'ideal types' of farm business based on degree of direct and indirect subsumption.

Internal Relations: Degree of direct Subsumption		score A	B	C	D
	D				Subsumed Unit
	C			Integrated Unit	
	B		Transitional Dependent Unit		
	A	Marginal Closed Unit			

Composite Categories

External Relations:
Degree of indirect subsumption

Source: Whatmore *et al.*, (1987a).

This is clearly not the case in Australian broadacre agriculture. All but one of the farms surveyed through this research (n=64) fell into the bottom two categories of direct subsumption. Further, the differences that did exist between them were far more dependent on life cycle stages (eg. businesses trying to establish offspring in farming had more 'owners') and gender relations (sole ownership represented, in most cases, exclusion of women) than on anything to do with commoditisation. In relation to indirect subsumption, however, it was evident that the majority of farm businesses were highly involved with off-farm capitals. Mean owner's equity was 83 percent, which was also the national average for mixed cropping/livestock farms in 1993-94 (Beare, 1995). Input use intensity was variable but growing (see also Knopke and Harris, 1991), as was the practice of forward selling grain, with a mean of 12 percent by value for the 1993-94 harvest (7 - 16 percent, 95 percent confidence interval).

While the extension of commoditised external relations of production did not provide evidence of a simple transference of control, it did have major implications for the management of farm businesses. There were no cases here, for example, of finance capital placing direct conditions on farm management as has been evident elsewhere (eg. H. Campbell, 1994). However, with a burden on cash income of 24 percent, on average nationally for mixed farms, to service interest at 83 percent equity (Beare, 1995), farmers were compelled to place more emphasis on cash flow and risk reduction than on sustainability or capital investment. This encouraged input dependency, but not always at economically optimal levels. Similarly, forward selling grain was used strategically to manage risk following the abolition of statutory marketing boards. The crop attracting the most contracting was Canola, as extreme market volatility led many farmers to think they had no choice but to hedge against losses by taking out contracts progressively through the season. The forward contracts taken out in this context did not involve direct controls over farm management, and farmers were very careful not to over-commit themselves until they had a crop harvested. An appreciable number of farmers preferred this deregulated marketing environment as they felt it rewarded those with better than average farming or marketing skills, but the potential manipulation of markets by large trading houses was an ongoing source of concern. The contracts farmers signed certainly helped them to express their own agency in managing the effects of a volatile and uncertain environment, but it was an environment over which they suspected those issuing the contracts had a great deal of influence, and perhaps a direct interest in maintaining such volatility (see also Lawrence, 1991).

The integration of farmers with agriscience organisations, whether public or private, was not a recent development. Technological sophistication, it will be remembered, was the most frequently mentioned dimension of difference between farmers. If we were to argue that the technological treadmill is something that farmers were forced to ride as they waited for agribusiness to progressively appropriate or substitute stages of the production cycle as natural barriers to industrialisation were overcome (see Goodman *et al.*, 1987), we must also, paradoxically, accept that these are processes in which farmers in this study area have been intimately involved. More than half the farmers asked who had the greatest influence on their farming practice nominated the Department of Agriculture (NSW Agriculture) or their District Agronomist, a NSW Agriculture employee. It must be remembered though that leading farmers were highly involved in the activities of research and extension organisations - as were many of their neighbours to a lesser degree - that not all innovations promoted by these organisations were accepted, and that farmers consequently felt that they had had a major impact on the development of local farming systems. The historical association of good farming practice with keeping up to date, as opposed to doing 'what Dad did', saw enthusiastic, but critical, cooperation with agriscience. The resulting trajectory of agricultural development may have been one about which many farmers had reservations, particularly with regard to sustainability (see Lockie *et al.*, 1995), and which appeared to suit the interests of agribusinesses, but it was also one over which research and extension organisations had a great deal less immediately apparent influence than they would have liked (see Vanclay, 1994; Vanclay and Lawrence, 1995).

One area in which the control of the production process may be less problematically ceded directly to agribusiness lies in the ownership of genetic material. Plant Variety Rights legislation was first passed in Australia in 1987, although this has since been superseded by the Plant Breeder's Rights Act 1994 (PBR). PBR gives the breeder control over the multiplication, sale, marketing, exporting, importing and stocking of genetic material. These property rights can be transferred, and there was a trend evident towards the sale of publicly developed plant varieties to private vendors for marketing and distribution. Farmers could keep seed for their own use with most varieties at the time of this research, but a small number of varieties had to be sold back to the breeder in total at the end of each season. This made growers completely dependent on the breeder to both supply inputs and buy back produce. Knowledge of the extent to which they were affected by PBR was extremely low amongst farmers surveyed through this research, suggesting that, for the time being at least, few restrictions were placed or enforced. Registered seed growers, however, expressed more concern, one in particular arguing that the sale of variety rights to companies without other agricultural interests had led to neglect of grower needs in the pursuance of profit. Restrictions on the availability of different varieties of seed could become of major concern, especially given emphasis in research on the development of genetically modified plants that increase chemical dependency (Hindmarsh, 1992). As a consequence, flexibility in the development of farming systems, particularly low input and organic ones, could potentially be reduced.

Commoditisation, farming practice and Landcare

The relative lack of direct controls exercised by agribusiness over the on-farm production process not only has implications for the likely success of Landcare in addressing obvious environmental problems like soil erosion and salinity, but it also makes Landcare of potentially great importance in defining the future of agricultural practice. A volatile environment and appropriation of certain elements of the production process has not handed control of agriculture over to agribusiness. Rather, in addition to seeking ways of extending direct controls (for example, PBR) and limiting the choices available to farmers, agribusinesses engage in a range of discursive practices with a view to influencing how both farmers and public sector officers understand good farming practice. The role of culture in shaping agricultural practice is certainly not, as implied by the farming styles perspective, an exclusively local phenomenon. Landcare has opened up a new domain in which the meanings associated with farming are contested. It offers a new resource both to agribusinesses, to strengthen their relationships with farmers, legitimise their activities in relation to environmental concerns, and to promote industrialised farming practices.

The discursive domain constituted by Landcare is not, however, a wholly democratic one. In any public discourse, power is likely to accrue in hegemonic blocks around actors with most access to resources that may be deployed in that discourse (van Dijk, 1993; Jessop, 1990). As discussed more fully in Lockie (1995a), the emphases in Landcare discourse on participation and inclusiveness have stifled questioning of corporate identification with Landcare through sponsorships and marketing. The Landcare logo has become a widely recognised and powerful signifier. Licensed use of this logo allows a limited range of companies to identify their products, and associated practices, with environmental and social responsibility without critical analysis of either the use or manufacture of these products. Community Landcare group members may have the opportunity to speak their minds at their local meeting, and perhaps attend regional and national forums on Landcare from time to time, but they and their produce seldom appear in nationally distributed newsletters, media releases and other publicity events associated with Landcare.

Similarly, the discursive association that has been made since the 1980s between chemical use and soil conservation through the 'Conservation Farming' metonym has been strengthened through Landcare. Farmers may have expressed concerns about the safety and sustainability of chemical use - concerns that seem to be validated by rapidly developing herbicide resistance (Baynes *et al.*, 1994) - but Conservation Farming, or chemical tillage, was still seen by the vast majority of farmers as an integral component of the best farming practices available (see also Lockie *et al.*, 1995). Landcare newsletters, and other Landcare related literature, distributed to farmers in this study area devoted considerable space to promoting Conservation Farming (Lockie, 1995a). Landcare then comes to mean not so much a reassessment of farming practices, as a reinforcement of those that have been promoted for some time, along with steps to ameliorate some of their adverse consequences, such as planting riparian (streambank) zones with trees so as reduce fertiliser and chemical contamination of waterways. One company even gave away a tree with every tonne of fertiliser they sold. I do not intend to suggest here that there is anything intrinsically wrong with fertiliser application, nor that fencing and planting out riparian zones is anything but a good idea. The point rather is that Landcare has emphasised and supported the continuing intensification of agriculture, and given it environmental and social credibility. In the study area for this research this was evidenced by the lack of any significant differences between the farming practices of Landcare members and non-members, bar the exception of tree planting (which remained arguably way too low to do anything anyway) and the development of property plans (which seemed to lead to greater use of lime and chemicals). These results contradict somewhat those of other studies which have found evidence Landcare members planted more perennial pasture (which helps reduce dryland salinity and soil erosion) and erected more conservation oriented fencing (Curtis and De Lacy, 1995) than non-members. However, while these certainly represent improvements in current farming systems, they are certainly not indicative of any fundamental re-orientation.

Conclusion

It is perhaps unfortunate that the power relations evident in processes of commoditisation were clearly more complicated than the subsumption of control suggested by Whatmore *et al.,* (1987a). Were they not, it would have been possible to score each farm for subsumption, look at the directions these scores were moving over time, and make conclusions over the degree to which an emphasis on community action was, or was not, misplaced. However, while the extension of private property rights to genetic material offered a good example of agribusinesses taking more direct control of aspects of the on-farm production process, that control was restricted to an extension of influence over the range of choices available to farmers. Any influence they exerted through other processes of commoditisation seemed even more indirect.

Apparent cooperation with the interests of agribusiness in selling agricultural inputs and boosting productivity reflected a combination of factors including; the economic environment within which farming took place, characterised by declining terms of trade, increased market volatility and growing indebtedness; and the long standing integration of farming with agriscience research and extension organisations, along with the cultural association of such cooperation and technology adoption with good farming practice. Whether these factors can be meaningfully described as hegemonic processes depends on an assessment of the degree to which their outcomes do not lie in the best interests of farmers. Nevertheless, at the time of this study it appeared that the Landcare Program was reinforcing the conceptions of good farming practice that had already developed through the discursive practices responsible for this integration of farmers with agriscience agencies, and was helping farmers to make better use of existing practices such as Conservation Farming, rather than offering them any genuine alternatives. Landcare should not be dismissed, however, as an inherently conservative phenomenon. The social and cultural changes reflected in its high membership, cooperative focus and inclusiveness are themselves profound and could have more far reaching consequences. Although it is impossible to say at this stage how these potentialities will be resolved, Landcare's role as a discursive field in which the meaning and practice of farming are contested, cannot be ignored.

Note

This chapter is based upon PhD research undertaken with the Centre for Rural Social Research at Charles Sturt University, Wagga Wagga..

References

Alexander, H. (1995) *A Framework for Change: The State of the Community Landcare Movement in Australia*, Canberra, National Landcare Program.

Australian Bureau of Statistics (CD-ROM). (1991) *Agstats: Results of the 1990 Agricultural Census*. Canberra, Australian Bureau of Statistics.

Baynes, P., Rijt, V. van der. and Lockie, S. (1994) *Chemical Use on Farms: Focus Groups Report*, Wagga Wagga, Centre for Conservation Farming and Centre for Rural Social Research, Charles Sturt University – Riverina.

Beare, S. (1995) Farm Financial Performance: Outlook and Analysis, in *Outlook '95, Vol 2: Agriculture*, Canberra, Australian Bureau of Agricultural and Resource Economics.

Buttel, F. (1994) Agricultural Change, Rural Society and the State in the Late Twentieth Century: Some Theoretical Observations, in Symes, D. and Jansen, A. (eds) *Agricultural Restructuring and Rural Change in Europe*, Wageningen Studies in Sociology, 37.

Campbell, A. (1990) *Landcare: Progress Across the Nation*, Canberra, National Soil Conservation Program.

Campbell, A. (1994) *Landcare: Communities Shaping the Land and the Future. With Case Studies by Greg Seipen*, Sydney, Allen and Unwin.

Campbell, H. (1994) *Regulation and Crisis in New Zealand Agriculture: the Case of Ashburton County, 1984-1992*, Wagga Wagga, PhD Thesis, Charles Sturt University – Riverina.

Collins, B. (1994) Commonwealth Overview, in Defenderfer, D. (ed.) *Landcare in the Balance, Proceedings of the 1994 Australian Landcare Conference, Vol 2*, Hobart, Department of Primary Industries and Fisheries Tasmania.

Curtis, A. and De Lacy, T. (1995) Examining the Assumptions Underlying Landcare, *Rural Society*, 5, 2/3: 44-55.

Dijk, T.A. van (1993) Principles of Critical Discourse Analysis, *Discourse and Society*, 4, 2: 249-283.

Goodman, D., Sorj, B. and Wilkinson, I. (1987) *From Farming to Biotechnology: a Theory of Agro-Industrial Development*, Oxford, Basil Blackwell.

Hindmarsh, R. (1992) Agricultural Biotechnologies: Ecosocial Concerns for a Sustainable Agriculture, in Lawrence, G., Vanclay, F. and Furze, B. (eds) *Agriculture, Environment And Society: Contemporary Issues for Australia*, Melbourne, Macmillan.

Jessop, B. (1990) Regulation Theories in Retrospect And Prospect, *Economy and Society*, 19, 2: 153-216.

Lawrence, G. (1991) Agribusiness and Inequality: Changes in the Bush, in O'Leary, J. and Sharp, R. (eds) *Inequality in Australia: Slicing the Cake*, Melbourne, Heinemann.

Lawrence, G. and Williams, C. (1990) The Dynamics of Decline: Implications for Social Welfare Delivery in Rural Australia, in Cullen, T., Dunn, P. and Lawrence, G. (eds) *Rural Health and Welfare in Australia*, Wagga Wagga, Centre for Rural Welfare Research, Charles Sturt University - Riverina.

Le Heron, R. (1993) *Globalized Agriculture: Political Choice*, Oxford, Permagon Press.

Leeuwis, C. (1993) *Of Computers, Myths and Modelling: the Social Construction of Diversity, Knowledge, Information and Communication Technologies in Dutch Horticulture and Agricultural Extension*, Wageningen Studies in Sociology, 36.

Lockie, S. (1994a) Farmers and the State: Local Knowledge and Self-Help in Rural Environmental Management, *Regional Journal of Social Issues*, 28: 24-36.

Lockie, S. (1994b) Community Landcare Groups: Changing Social Relations at the Local Level, in McSwan, D. and McShane, M. (eds) *Proceedings, Issues Affecting Rural Communities*, Townsville, Rural Education Research and Development Centre, James Cook University.

Lockie, S. (1995a) Beyond a Good Thing: Political Interests and the Meaning of Landcare, *Rural Society*, 5, 2/3: 3-12.

Lockie, S. (1995b) Rural Gender Relations and Landcare, in Vanclay, F. (ed.) *With a Rural Focus: TASA '94 Conference Proceedings*, Wagga Wagga, Centre for Rural Social Research, Charles Sturt University – Riverina.

Lockie, S., Mead, A., Vanclay, F. and Butler, B. (1995) Factors Encouraging the Adoption of More Sustainable Cropping Systems in South-East Australia: Profit, Sustainability, Risk and Stability, *Journal of Sustainable Agriculture*, 6, 1: 61-79.

Long, N. (1986) Commoditization: Thesis and Antithesis, in Long, N., van der Ploeg, J.D., Curtin, C. and Box, L. (eds) *The Commoditisation Debate: Labour Process, Strategy and Social Network*, Wageningen Studies in Sociology, 17.

Martin, P. (1995) The Constitution of Power in Landcare: a Post-Structuralist Perspective With Modernist Undertones, *Rural Society*, 5, 2/3: 30-37.

Mues, C., Roper, H. and Ockerby, J. (1994) *Survey of Landcare and Land Management Practices, 1992-93*, Canberra, Australian Bureau of Agricultural and Resource Economics.

Plant Breeders Rights Act 1994, Canberra, Commonwealth Government Printer.

Ploeg, J.D. van der (1986) The Agricultural Labour Process and Commoditization, in Long, N., van der Ploeg, J.D., Curtin, C. and Box, L. (eds) *The Commoditisation Debate: Labour Process, Strategy and Social Network*, Wageningen Studies in Sociology, 17.

Ploeg, J.D. van der (1993) Rural Sociology and the New Agrarian Question: a Perspective From The Netherlands, *Sociologia Ruralis*, 33, 2: 240-260.

Stone, S. (1992) Land Degradation and Rural Communities in Victoria: Experience and Response, in Lawrence, G., Vanclay, F. and Furze, B. (eds) *Agriculture, Environment and Society: Contemporary Issues for Australia*, Melbourne, Macmillan.

Toyne, P. and Farley, R. (1989) A National Land Management Program, *Australian Journal of Soil and Water Conservation*, 2, 2: 6-9.

Vanclay, F. (1994) A Crisis in Agricultural Extension, *Rural Society*, 4, 1: 10-13.

Vanclay, F. and Lawrence, G. (1995) *The Environmental Imperative: Eco-Social Concerns for Australian Agriculture*, Rockhampton, Central Queensland University Press.

Whatmore, S., Munton, R., Little, J. and Marsden, T. (1987a) Towards a Typology of Farm Businesses in Contemporary British Agriculture, *Sociologia Ruralis*, 27, 1: 21-37.

Whatmore, S., Munton, R., Marsden, T. and Little, J. (1987b) Interpreting a Relational Typology of Farm Businesses in Southern England, *Sociologia Ruralis*, 27, 2/3: 103-122.

Chapter 3

Farming styles and technology transfer: Sociological input in the development of a decision support system for viticulture

Scott Glyde and Frank Vanclay

Introduction

Traditional extension methodology has attempted to explain adoption of agricultural technologies by farmers as based on the social-psychological model of diffusion of innovations, perhaps best represented by Rogers (1983). While this model superficially illustrates the adoption process of some new technologies, it fails to address or explain farmer behaviour, and consequently is viewed as unsatisfactory (see Buttel *et al.*, 1990; Vanclay and Lawrence, 1995). The so called 'failure' of farmers to adopt new technologies or practices (especially conservation-related practices) can be explained by a number of key considerations which, when considered from farmers' perspectives, suggest that non-adoption may be rational (Vanclay and Lawrence, 1995).

It has been argued that agricultural production has evolved into an increasingly complex decision making environment (see Thomas *et al.*, 1990; Travis, 1992); that decision making is an essential component of being a farmer; and that successful farmers can be distinguished from less successful ones because they make 'bad' decisions less often (Wagner, 1993). This paper examines the case of the computer based decision support system (DSS) for viticultural management (AusVit) being developed by the Cooperative Research Centre for Viticulture (CRCV). The paper highlights the importance of understanding the basis of farmer behaviour in technology development activities. It addresses the concept of farming styles, and suggests that it plays an important role in the technology transfer process.

Background to this research

Australian viticulture has seen a period of rapid expansion and intensification in recent times. Largely associated with increased Australian wine exports, the industry is characterised by expanding corporate involvement and large areas of new grapevine plantings. Winegrape production is currently a high value enterprise. Current inflated grape prices are a reflection of the high demand by major wine corporations in order to maintain and boost their export markets. Grape production, however, is a practice highly susceptible to weather conditions. Summer rainfall, inducing warm, moist conditions, inevitably results in outbreaks of fungal pathogens, which, if unchecked, quickly destroy not only that season's crop, but reduce the next season's as well.

The complexity of the decision making environment in which farmers operate has arisen as a consequence of diversity in the sources of information necessary to make those decisions. Viticultural management requires knowledge of issues such as marketing, pest and disease management, irrigation, and chemical use. The situation becomes complex because managers seldom have complete and reliable information at their disposal when management decisions must be made. To assist farmers in this regard, scientists have recently developed a range of knowledge based systems to aid plant protection in Australia (see Penrose *et al.*, 1985; Peak *et al.*, 1986; McIntyre, 1990; Moore and Moore, 1989) and overseas (see Travis *et al.*, 1992; Saunders *et al.*, 1991). The development of a computerised decision support system (DSS) for viticultural management (AusVit) commenced in 1990 with support from the Grape and Wine Research and Development Corporation (GWRDC) and state agricultural departments, and became part of the Cooperative Research Centre for Viticulture (CRCV) following its establishment in 1992. AusVit is to be released for general sale in August 1996.

Adoption of previous DSSs has been mixed, and in some cases disappointingly poor (Harrison 1991). Consideration for social science input into agricultural research has been argued by a number of socially informed researchers in the past (Rhoades and Booth 1982; Röling 1988; Hulme 1990; Saltiel *et al.*, 1994; Vanclay and Lawrence 1994; Vanclay 1994). Many evaluations of DSSs have recommended that social considerations inform their early development (Macadam *et al.*, 1990; Vonk 1990; Leeuwis and Arkesteyn 1991; Dunn 1992; Leeuwis 1993a; Leeuwis 1993b). To this end, rural sociology was part of the initial CRCV proposal, and subsequently a project was developed to consider how the application of a rural sociology perspective might lead to a better understanding of the diversity within Australian viticulture, and how an understanding of this heterogeneity might lead to the better development of AusVit.

The initial (and current) intentions of the AusVit developers were to design a computerised decision support system that would provide vineyard managers with 'better' information and to alleviate much of the complexity associated with decision making in vineyard management. Early research priorities centred on developing, structuring and formulating knowledge databases which, when coupled with necessary data input from users, such as current climate parameters and management history, would generate specific recommendations as well as providing relevant information. Several trial sites for each 'module' of the 'expert system' (the decision-making algorithm component of AusVit) were established at various locations across south eastern Australia from 1992. The development of each module was undertaken by research or extension specialists in each field (known as 'domain experts'), and were largely based on the 'recommended practices' as defined by previous and existing research strategies. With certain required information inputs AusVit can provide recommendations to viticulturists about pest and disease control, irrigation scheduling, chemical selection, and fertiliser application. In addition, AusVit provides a useful means of recording spray applications and other vineyard management activities. To generate recommendations, users need to access relevant computerised local weather data (via a local 'weather station' - that is, a privately owned weather monitoring device capable of downloading computer interactive data), as well as provide AusVit with brief details about the vineyard including vineyard description, disease history, phenology, irrigation type, pest and disease scouting records, and details of sprays applied.

The 'expert' (knowledge) component of AusVit has been designed to maximise the efficiency of vineyard chemical use. This is achieved by recommending reactive spray application (that is, in response to symptoms and/or weather conditions) whenever possible in preference to the usual practice of routine application (that is, preventative, regardless of symptoms). While it is somewhat of a complex issue, research scientists and extension personnel consider that, in some cases, vineyard managers are spraying for pests and disease when it is not essential, or when it is not likely to cause crop loss. In order to assist the development and adoption of AusVit, a case study was undertaken to assess the diversity existing among viticulturists, to evaluate vineyard managers' attitudes to new technologies, and to generate an understanding of industry use of computers and 'reactive' management.

The farming styles approach to understanding diversity in agriculture seemed an appropriate theoretical position since it was the approach employed by Cees Leeuwis in his studies of DSSs in Dutch agriculture. It was combined with Vanclay's (*inter alia*, Vanclay and Lawrence 1995) ideas about farming practice representing embodiment of various subcultures in farming. While the case study serves many purposes, the focus here is on the applicability of the farming styles and farming subcultures concepts and how they, and other social issues, could help inform AusVit.

Methodology

A case study methodology was undertaken using a range of research methods. With an objective to provide input to the development of AusVit, much evaluation of prototype models was undertaken. Although the work is on-going, and the fieldwork continuous as newer versions of AusVit are released, two main stages to the research reported here are obvious.

Stage 1: Initial structured questionnaire and prototype evaluation

Through 1994, a number of meetings were held with groups of between six and ten participants comprising grapegrowers, corporate managers, grower/winemakers, extension agents and corporate technical representatives from the grape growing regions of the Hunter Valley and Riverina in NSW, Clare Valley, McLaren Vale and Barossa Valley in South Australia, Sunraysia and King Valley in Victoria, and the Granite Belt of Southern Queensland. Participants were selected from regional grower lists in consultation with horticultural extension agents and corporate wineries so as to provide a wide industry cross section. While the selection process was not random, care was taken to ensure that the range of participants covered all of the known industry 'levels' for each particular region. There are likely to be no specific biasing features in this selection procedure.

Each potential participant was contacted by telephone and invited to participate in a demonstration seminar. They were informed about the research process, and the fact that they would be surveyed regarding their management practices, and their attitudes to AusVit specifically. A survey questionnaire for this stage was developed to classify viticulturists in terms of their management activities, and how such activities relate to age, industry experience, education, computer use, and other factors. While this stage was predominantly quantitative, several questions were open-ended. Furthermore, following completion of these questionnaires, a general discussion was facilitated, with the discussion recorded and subsequently transcribed. Respondents were asked a range of questions including: access to weather stations; concern for relevant management issues such as chemical residues and environmental impact of chemicals; record-keeping practices; ability to identify specific conditions leading to pest and disease outbreaks; pest and disease scouting styles and frequency; and use of industry services.

The questionnaire also intended to reveal the potential for the use of computerised decision support systems such as AusVit as part of total vineyard management. Consequently respondents were also asked about computer ownership and use, and following a thorough AusVit demonstration, their attitude and opinions of the AusVit program.

From a total of 176 industry representatives invited to these meetings, 160 attended meetings, and 145 completed questionnaires (82 percent, 91 percent response respectively). The composition of the sample included 72 percent grape growers and/or family vineyard managers, 17 percent corporate vineyard managers, 6 percent extension personnel, and 5 percent grape growers/winemakers.

Stage 2: Focus groups

The second stage which comprised of focus groups was conducted throughout 1995 and included many of the earlier participants. Participants were asked firstly to describe, on a single card, how they perceived themselves as a vineyard manager, and then on another card to describe how they consider they differ from other managers. In a third step, participants were then given a number of cards, and asked to write down a name, or label, and brief description of as many different types of managers as they could.

Participants were encouraged to differentiate between types of managers on the basis of management style; not demographic characteristics, although it was not discounted that these factors could contribute to different management styles. These cards were then collected, shuffled and sequentially considered. As each card was revealed, the name or label of that particular type of manager was placed on a whiteboard. Each time a new type of manager was revealed it was added to the list.

On completion of this theme-ing process, participants were asked to: (1) identify differences between manager types; (2) explain why these differences existed; and (3) consider any instance where the same type of manager may have attracted different labels. Finally, participants were asked if they could identify one individual from each manager type. Discussion of this theme-ing process was recorded and later transcribed. In total, seven focus groups were conducted in the Hunter Valley, Barossa Valley, Clare Valley and McLaren Vale grape producing regions, involving a total of 48 participants.

In contrast to Stage 1, where all known industry 'levels' were represented in each meeting, this stage isolated viticulturists into focus groups containing participants of like-industry standing. For example, corporate managers comprised one focus group, while family managers comprised another. There were two main reasons for using this 'differentiating' approach. Firstly, corporate managers and extension personnel clearly dominated discussion over family managers in stage 1, and it was thought that by 'separating' them other viewpoints could be represented better. Secondly, the focus group approach asked participants to 'label' certain types of managers, and, sociologically, it was thought to be interesting to see if the different industry group 'levels' would label or distinguish between styles of management differently.

Barriers to adoption of AusVit
Computer illiteracy or computers as a component of management style?

Much of the early concern associated with the perceived likelihood of adoption of AusVit centred on the belief that the (only or major) likely barrier to adoption would be familiarity with computers. It was also thought that so-called top-end growers and corporate vineyard mangers would be more likely to have computer experience than small holder owner-operator growers. It was also considered that there would be resistance to increasing computerisation because of a perceived educational deficit of many growers. Much of this concern came from a technocratic perspective, although in an earlier work, Vanclay also argued that from farmers' perspectives, there were many reasons why computers and DSS were not likely to be adopted (see Vanclay, 1992b).

However, computer use amongst Stage 1 participants was high, with 52 percent indicating that they used computers either at work or at home. Furthermore, it was no greater for highly educated, middle aged corporate managers, than the older less educated, highly experienced growers. This is supported to some extent by Glyde *et al.*, (1994) who reported that 87 percent of grapegrowers and vineyard managers surveyed at the Eighth Australian Wine Industry Technical Conference in 1992 (n=145) indicated that they were using computers at work or intending to do so. However, despite more than half the sample of this study indicating that they used computers, very few used their computer for vineyard management related activities, and few perceived any value or benefit in doing so. The major perception was that using a computer for vineyard management would mean 'spending more time in the office', which would be 'time (they) haven't got'.

Reactive versus preventative spraying

One of the major aims of AusVit is to encourage the 'reactive' control of diseases and pests replacing preventative calendar or routine control. Very few managers were using a 'reactive' control strategy for disease management and collectively provided four major reasons for why vineyard managers controlled pests and diseases preventively.

1   Some pests and diseases (such as powdery mildew) are almost impossible to control once their symptoms are obvious.
2   Managers of large vineyards cannot spray all of their vineyard after a rain event quickly enough to prevent an outbreak of pests and diseases. This is because their equipment can only travel at a certain speed.
3   If there is a large amount of rain, the vineyard may be too wet to drive through with a spray unit. In irrigation regions, this problem is compounded because managers often have to 'order' their water up to three days in advance. As they are aware of the risks of having 'no cover' for diseases (and to a lesser extent, pests), managers almost always spray preventative 'protectants' before watering, just in case it rains after watering and they are unable to get onto the vineyard.
4   Most managers are willing to risk the unnecessary cost of applying a spray that is not needed, rather than risk the much larger loss of 'not having cover', when a rain period occurs.

For the most part, respondents were quite satisfied with their existing methods of production, and were unable to see the logic of changing their management style toward introducing 'reactive' spray practices with which they had differing levels of understanding.

Scouting strategies

Of particular relevance to this study was the variation in pest and disease scouting style. Scouting, the practice of 'checking' for pest and disease incidence, is a management activity considered essential by researchers and extension agents if a vineyard manager is able to 'accurately' assess the level of 'infection' in the vineyard (and therefore the need for chemical use). Scouting is a necessary component of reactive spraying practice. Respondents were asked to describe their scouting techniques and it was this question that especially exposed variation in management style. Of the 145 responses to this open ended question, no two responses were completely similar indicating that such a practice is highly personalised. Nevertheless, the techniques described could be classified into a number of different categories including:

1   the *'tractor'*, where vine inspection occurs while spraying or other viticultural activities with the manager 'having a look'; thus there is no 'active' scouting taking place;
2   the *'motorbike'*, where vine inspection usually means riding up and down rows, intentional scouting restricted to 'only what is necessary';
3   the *'walk'*, where vine inspection does occur through intentional, 'active' scouting, but is mainly restricted to known vineyard 'hotspots' (known areas of pest and disease outbreaks developed through intimate knowledge and experience of one's own vineyard);
4   the *'view'*, similar to the 'walk', but involves inner canopy inspection, carried out at the individual vine level;
5   the *'study'*, where, as well as inner canopy inspection, various scouting aids such as a magnifying glass are used to identify microscopic spores and pests, and is conducted at the individual leaf level.

The effort, skill and time required to undertake scouting increases as the complexity of the scouting technique increases. Interestingly, scouting was regarded as a specific vineyard 'duty' or 'job' by only 25 percent of the study group, the remainder claiming that they mostly carried out scouting whilst going about their other duties such as watering or spraying. As watering may involve walking or riding a motorbike, and that spraying involves the tractor (as does cultivation), it appears likely that this 75 percent of the sample would be included in the first three categories described above.

Variation in scouting frequency also demonstrated the heterogeneity of the sample with some respondents claiming that they scouted every day, while some scouted less than once per fortnight. Interestingly, those respondents claiming that they scouted using the 'study' approach outlined above, also generally scouted more often than those from other categories. Likewise, respondents who claimed to only have a look while driving the tractor generally scouted less often. All respondents, however, indicated that scouting frequency was inevitably related to weather conditions, and that they scouted more frequently in wet weather. This suggests that viticulturists are very much aware of the relationship between pest and disease *incidence* and prevailing weather conditions. It does not suggest, however, that the respondents understood the life cycles of those pest and diseases affecting them, nor the role their management played in preventing outbreaks, apart from an understanding that if they didn't spray, outbreaks would occur.

There was no indication from any respondents that they considered their current management practices were not ideal for controlling pest and disease outbreaks. Among many roles AusVit is being perceived as playing (by experts at least) is one of enabling viticulturists the ability to 'evaluate' existing weather conditions in terms of the potential for pest and disease outbreaks. Since there would already appear to be an understanding of the relationship between weather events and pest and disease outbreaks, and because there was apparent satisfaction with current scouting and spraying practices, there would appear to be no need by growers for AusVit in this regard.

Farming styles

As AusVit is a computer based DSS, computer use is a key issue in its adoption. But of equal importance are the issues of farmer behaviour, pest and disease scouting style, and style of overall vineyard management. This study has exposed the heterogeneity in viticulture, and in particular, has highlighted the discrepancy which exists between actual vineyard management activity and the 'desirable' or recommended practices as defined by agricultural scientists and extension agencies. It suggests that extension activities are likely to be unsuccessful while they fail to appreciate the social basis of adoption; while they treat the viticulture industry as an homogenous group; while they fail to appreciate the various worldviews of growers; and, while they hold assumptions, implicit in the scientific worldview, that are not shared by farmers.

The notion of farming styles refers to the socio-cultural basis of the management practices of groups of farmers within a region and commodity, and has mainly stemmed from work by Jan Douwe van der Ploeg (1993), expanded on by Cees Leeuwis (1989, 1993a, 1993b), and more recently by Frank Vanclay (see, for an evaluation of the approach, Vanclay and Lawrence, 1995). The perspective argues that the diversity or heterogeneity in farming can be explained, and that farmers can be classified into groupings of similar, but not identical, individuals on the basis of management practices, worldviews, and general orientation towards key issues. In its most reified form, farming style becomes the total explanation for all diversity in agriculture, and supersedes any other categorisation of farmers. There are numerous problems with the concept, the most obvious being the lack of a precise operational definition and consequent practical articulation of the styles in any one region/commodity. Despite these problems, the concept has been shown to be useful (Leeuwis 1993a; van der Ploeg and Long 1994), and provides what we believe is the most useful contemporary theoretical perspective to understand diversity and to inform extension practice.

Farming style as embodiment of technique

The discussion of scouting strategies and the identification of five methods of scouting demonstrates that farming techniques are not unambiguously defined, and that they are not implemented as discrete units delivered by extension. Adaption rather than adoption is what characterises the technology transfer process (Vanclay and Lawrence, 1995). Tied up with the way new technology or farming practices are adapted are the meanings that farmers assign to those innovations, and the way innovations interact with other farm practices and farmer values and priorities. Furthermore, the process of adoption is sub-cultural, with individual assessment in favour of adoption only likely to occur when other farmers in that farming subculture (or style) are also likely to come to the same assessment (Vanclay, 1992a; Vanclay and Lawrence, 1995). Thus differences in the operationalisation of specific farming techniques represents a manifestation of farming styles.

The explanation of why some growers only scout while 'having a look' by 'tractor', while others undertake a 'study' complete with magnifying glass and careful examination of inner canopy, vine, leaf, stem and berry, cannot be due solely to the explanation of practical benefits, since all growers report satisfaction with their own method. While there are practical explanations given, behind the logic of any explanation is a large set of assumptions, premises, beliefs and values. It is these points which suggest that farmers' orientations to an innovation are likely to be generally predictive of their orientation to other innovations. Thus, the pattern of adaption (or adoption) is not technical, but socio-cultural. Variation in the implementation of a specific farm management technique can be seen as the manifestation of farming style. However, since these patterns should occur across a range of farming practices, and because diversity in farming practice represents the embodiment of underlying socio-cultural values and beliefs, the concept of farming style should also serve as an organisational principle of farmers at levels other than that of specific technique.

Farming style as a form of social organisation

Testing the theory elaborated above, seven focus groups were held to explore the issue of differentiation in overall vineyard management. While there were differences in the outcomes of each focus group, a pattern of eight distinct styles did emerge. The main explanation for differences between the focus groups, and the reason why such differences does not represent methodological uncertainty, is that the focus groups were structured to comprise different sections or levels of the viticulture industry. In addition to the eight main distinct styles of management that were identified, several other 'fringe' styles were mentioned, but they lacked the clarity of the eight main styles, and in some ways were considered unimportant or marginal to understanding the nature of managers in Australian viticulture. Nevertheless, such a finding does indicate that the concept of farming style is difficult to implement, and may represent a heuristic device for considering the ideal types of farmers rather than a mutually exclusive categorisation. The eight styles that were identified are:

1 Progressive managers: Progressive managers were commonly identified as being industry leaders. They were considered to be highly motivated and professional in their attitude toward management. Progressive managers were regarded as being at the 'cutting edge' of technology, had considerable experience and/or a high level of viticultural education. The main feature of these types of managers which enables them to remain at the 'cutting edge' of technology is that they have developed and maintained specific information links which keep them informed of current developments and future directions of the industry. What differentiates progressive managers from other managers is not their access to information, but that they are active information 'seekers', and over a period of years, have developed an information network with researchers, extension agents, marketing experts, and similar managers from other regions. From a technology adoption and information transfer viewpoint, progressive managers are constantly looking for alternative production methods and new practices which may give them a competitive edge over other managers. Consequently they not only act as avenues for technology to enter regions, but in some cases *cause* it to happen. It was suggested that progressive managers make up approximately 5 percent of the industry.

2 Innovative managers: Innovative managers are similar to progressive managers except that they are not regarded as information seekers, rather they are information absorbers. Innovative managers frequently adopt new technology, but often only become aware of such technology via the progressive managers. Innovative managers include corporate managers with large investments, highly experienced managers, and managers who are aware of the cost:profit ratio in production. Innovators make up approximately 15 percent of the industry.

3 Modern managers (progressively cautious): This group differs from progressive and innovative managers by virtue of their conservative approach to technology adoption. While open minded about technology development and transfer, this group of managers tend to wait until the technology is tried by others. Generally speaking, this group is innovative, but possesses limited experience potentially resulting in limited confidence, and a reluctance to do things too early. This group comprises approximately 15 percent of the industry.

4 Modern managers (spendthrifts): Spendthrifts are highly capitalised managers, but who have limited experience, and many may be new to the industry. Generally, spendthrifts consider that the only way to succeed in viticulture is to be at the cutting edge of technology. They do not however, have the information networks, experience or the knowledge that progressive managers have, and believe the only way they can be competitive in viticulture is to be willing to spend large amounts of money on new equipment and new techniques of production. This group comprises approximately 10 percent of the industry.

5 Traditional (conservative): This style refers to traditional managers who are conservative in their approach to vineyard management by choice. Traditional refers to the use of practices that have been well established in the industry and may now be regarded by some as being less efficient than more modern practices. This style includes managers near retirement age, managers of small holdings, and managers who are simply satisfied with their current methods and see no reason to change. Generally speaking, these managers control pests and diseases in a routine, preventative fashion, take few risks, and are basically comfortable with the knowledge they are not doing everything as efficiently as possible, but are satisfied with their lifestyle. It was suggested that this style constituted approximately 25 percent of the industry.

6 Traditional (limited resources): As implied by the name, this style of management refers to those managers who believe that they are restricted by their resources to manage in any other way. This group may be reluctant to take risks, or to go into debt, although this style also includes managers with limited equity in their vineyard. While mostly including managers of non-irrigated holdings, it also includes managers in marginal areas (with respect to viticulture), and it was therefore considered that these managers were more at the mercy of weather extremes than other styles, since water especially at certain times is a primary determinant of grape quality and yield. Consequently, much of the management activity in this style relates to water conservation, and in particular, cultivation to control weeds and prevent moisture loss. This style comprises about 15 percent of the industry.

7 Traditional (limited capabilities): This style was regarded as including managers who, for a variety of reasons, practice management strategies (albeit unintentionally) which, it was perceived, may not be in the best interests of the long term sustainability of their vineyard. Potential reasons for this included a lack of practical experience, and limited knowledge related to viticulture. Practical examples of this style that were given included the inappropriate watering of vines (quantity and timing), inappropriate chemical selection and spray rate, inappropriate soil management, poor canopy management, and poor vineyard maintenance generally. It was suggested that this style of management was included approximately 10 percent of the industry.

8   Turkeys and ostriches: The last management style that was articulated by the focus groups comprised growers who were labelled 'turkeys' or 'ostriches'. This group of growers were considered to be undertaking practices regarded as being totally unsuitable for viticulture. It referred to poor management of resources, poor pest and disease control brought about mostly from poor scouting practices, and poor vine management. This style was regarded as being different from the traditional (limited capabilities) style in that those managers were making a conscious effort to grow grapes to the best of their ability. 'Turkeys' and 'ostriches' were regarded as being lazy managers, not willing to provide the commitment and effort needed to produce 'good' grapes. They represent only a small fraction of all growers.

Farming styles as a reflection of the various dimensions of vineyard management

Another topic of the focus groups was what were the reasons for different styles. Analysis of the transcribed discussion on this topic reveals that there were four distinct dimensions that structured the various styles. The eight styles that were identified were largely the interplay of these four dimensions as they were embodied by each grower. These dimensions were professionalism, resource availability, wisdom, and efficiency.

1   Vineyard management as a function of professionalism: Many growers emphasised that the key aspect of all vineyard management was professionalism, with more 'professional' being 'better' across a range of management practices, including: preparation for sudden changes in weather conditions; control over potential pest and disease outbreaks; scouting and monitoring techniques; canopy management practices; irrigation management strategies; varietal selection and existing grapevine resources; and, the likelihood of adoption of new technology. Professionalism, however, could be considered a value judgement in that it was defined only by those managers who determined themselves to be 'professional' or 'better', and was especially pronounced in the focus groups containing corporate managers. The concept of professionalism was also revealed to be strongly related to knowledge, and it was knowledge which largely influenced behaviour and consequently style. However, professionalism as a descriptor for distinguishing between management styles has many flaws. Professionalism has little or no consideration for the reasons which give rise to diversity in vineyard management styles. It does not, for example, account for variation in existing resources such as irrigation or non-irrigation. Professionalism implies that only professional growers have 'got it right' and that their management strategies are the only ones suitable for 'proper' management. Professionalism demands

49

that maximising profit is the most important farming objective. Professionalism attempts to explain viticultural management in terms of capabilities and knowledge, and that the 'best' managers are those who are most capable, and contain the most knowledge for maximising production and profit in any given season.

2   Vineyard management as a function of resource availability: The capacity of any manager to maximise profits in any given season was also revealed to be largely dependent on resource availability. This was emphasised by focus groups containing resource poor family viticulturalists. This concept is deterministic or structural in that it regards managers as being somewhat powerless as represented in the view that managers were 'doing the best they could do in the circumstances'. It suggests that vineyard management is determined by physical factors, with such things as variation in soil type, access to irrigation, variable summer rainfall, and financial resources as being the key issue in determination of management style. Although not necessarily admitted, it could be seen that a range of social resources such as knowledge, education, and social or information networks, could also comprise this dimension. While some diversity can clearly be seen to be due to the structural factors, this factor cannot account, for example, for those managers who manage their vineyard traditionally conservatively by choice, and not because their resources restrict them.

3   Vineyard management as a function of wisdom: The term wisdom in this case, refers to the suggestion that management is a function of experience and knowledge, that the more experienced managers 'have got it right', and that less experienced managers haven't encountered 'all the ups and downs yet'. Wisdom over-rides professionalism, because professional managers may be better managers in a particular season, but they may not be able to cope with unusual seasons. Consequently experience (and therefore knowledge) determines a manager's attitude toward new technologies and overall style of management. Such a view does not account for resource variation, or for example, for those managers of limited experience who 'farm the way their father farmed' because they know no other way.

4   Vineyard management as a function of efficiency: Efficiency differs from professionalism in that it requires that growers be efficient with respect to their goals, but profit is not necessarily the only objective. Thus, growers whose farming goals may include, quality of life, craftship notions about producing quality produce, or autonomy, for example, can still operate in ways to increase their efficiency with respect to these goals.

It is likely that viticulturists identify with these dimensions more easily than they would identify with the overall styles. Thus, individual managers could claim to be more professional or more efficient than other managers, rather than describe themselves as a being a progressive manager. Managers tend to point out 'big picture' issues which impinge, influence and determine their capacity to manage their vineyards, and are not necessarily conscious of the structure of styles in a region. Resource poor managers, for example, claim that resource availability determines their capacity to produce quality fruit, while highly professional managers claim that 'their way' is the right way and all other methods of management are less suitable.

The important point to note from this is that managers do not consciously relate to their particular farming style. They do, however, tend to mix socially with managers of a similar style as themselves, often perhaps without being aware of it. Managers who view grape production as a function of professionalism tend to view themselves as being industry leaders (whether they are or not, and whatever that is), frequently attend field days, work on committees for local organisations, hold conversations about committee plans and extension activities, and subconsciously or otherwise, regard managers who don't, as being less professional and less efficient. On the other hand, managers who are restricted by their resources (by their own definition), tend to mix with similar 'less fortunate' friends and associates, and hold conversations about the same issues, management practices and problems. As a consequence of this interaction, managers are more likely to remain in their group.

Conclusion

Two important points emerge from this case-study. Firstly, technology transfer is not about developing new technology and assuming that it will be automatically beneficial to a receptive, appreciative and homogenous target audience who share a similar worldview to the agricultural scientists and extensionists responsible for developing and promoting it. Technology design criteria must incorporate an objective towards understanding the behaviours and management styles of the perceived beneficiaries before research and development is undertaken. In the context of AusVit, the assumptions held by the scientists appear to be misplaced. AusVit is not likely to be widely adopted - not because farmers are not likely to be owners or users of computers - but because they are unlikely to be convinced that a DSS will provide information that they ought to consider above their own experiences. Further, recommendations within AusVit require a high level of scouting, but our research has shown that there is a wide range scouting styles, with most growers not undertaking scouting to the standard recommended by AusVit, and they are not convinced of the need to do other than their current strategies. While it was originally considered that social research would inform the development of AusVit, with potentially different versions being produced for different styles, it transpires that some viticultural styles are unlikely to regard AusVit as helpful in any form. The assumptions of AusVit development - that growers need more complete information, that growers need help to make decisions, that growers would favour 'reactive management' of pests and diseases, and that growers would subordinate all other sources of information, including their own experience to the decisions of the AusVit - are untenable.

Secondly, the notion of farming styles is a worthwhile analytical tool for classifying farmers. While it would appear to be a concept that individual farmers may themselves not appreciate, and may not consciously identify with a particular style, the concept and the classification system that emerges in this research did have reliability and validity, and did appear to be useful in understanding the diversity that exists in Australian viticulture. Furthermore, the styles appeared to be consistent across each of the viticultural regions studied. However, the focus of this research was on wine grape producers, and it is possible that there are style differences relating to dried fruit or table grape producers.

Finally, within the CRCV there remains conflict between the technocratic top-down science of the so-called 'domain experts' who largely believe that they are doing what is best for growers and the future of the industry, and the socially-informed researchers who appreciate the social basis of the adoption process. Efforts to contribute in a theoretically informed way to the development of AusVit have been thwarted, with technoscience having its way once again. This is understandable given the dominance of technoscientific researchers within the CRCV, their historical role in research and development, and their genuine, albeit misplaced, conviction that they have the interests of the industry at heart. However it is also disappointing, as at this stage in the development process, it appears that adoption of the AusVit system will be restricted and not include most owner-operator, small holder grape-growers. Unfortunately it appears, yet again, that a considerable amount of public funding has been used to facilitate corporate influence in agriculture.

Acknowledgments and caveat

This research was funded by the Cooperative Research Centre for Viticulture (CRCV). However, the views represented in this paper should not be taken to reflect the views of the CRCV. We wish to thank all growers who participated in focus groups and interviews, as well as numerous extension staff in various agencies who are affiliated with the CRCV. Associate Professor Brian Freeman deserves special mention for providing general guidance and supervision of this project from a viticultural perspective.

References

Buttel, F., Larson, O. and Gillespie, G. (1990) *The Sociology of Agriculture*, Westport, Greenwood.

Dunn, A. (1992) Extension Models Assisting the Development of Decision Support Systems, in Ash, G. *et al., Decision Support Systems for Farming in Southern NSW and Northern Victoria, July 1992*, Charles Sturt University, Wagga Wagga: 106-110.

Glyde, S., Vanclay, F. and Freeman, B. (1994) Computers, DSS and Viticulture, *The Australian Grapegrower and Winemaker* 364, 14-15.

Harrison, S. (1991) Validation of Agricultural Expert Systems, *Agricultural Systems*, 35: 265-285.

Hulme, D. (1990) Agricultural Technology Development, Agricultural Extension and Applied Social Research: Past Contributions and Future Roles, *Sociologia Ruralis* 20 (3/4): 323-335.

Leeuwis, C. (1989) *Marginalisation Misunderstood: Different Patterns of Farm Development in the West of Ireland*, Wageningen Studies in Sociology 26, Wageningen Agricultural University.

Leeuwis, C. and Arkesteyn, M. (1991) Planned Technology Development and Local Initiative: Computer Supported Enterprise-comparisons among Dutch Horticulturists, *Sociologia Ruralis* 21, 2/3: 140-161.

Leeuwis, C. (1993a) *Of computers, Myths and Modelling: The Social Construction of Diversity, Knowledge, Information and Communication Technologies in Dutch Horticulture and Agricultural Extension*, PhD thesis, Department of Communication and Innovation Studies, Wageningen Agricultural University.

Leeuwis, C. (1993b) Towards a Sociological Conceptualization of Communication in Extension Science, On Giddens, Habermas and Computer-based Communication Technologies in Dutch Agriculture, *Sociologia Ruralis* 33, 2: 281-305.

Macadam, R., Britton, I., Russell, D. and Potts, W. (1990) The Use of Soft Systems Methodology to Improve the Adoption of Australian Cotton Growers of the Siratac Computer Based Crop Management System, *Agricultural Systems* 34: 1-14.

McIntyre, G. (1990) The Use of Expert System Programs in Agricultural Extension by Q.D.P.I., Workshop Proceedings, *AJCAI*.

Moore, C. and Moore, J. (1989) HERBIGUIDE - a herbicide selection program for field crops, in Proceedings, *Computers in Agriculture*.

Peak, C., Fitzell, R., Hannah, R. and Batten, D. (1986) Development of a Microprocessor-based Data Recording System for Predicting Plant Disease Based on Studies on Mango Anthracnose, *Computers and Electronics in Agriculture* 1: 251-262.

Penrose, L., Heaton, J., Washington, W. and Wicks, T. (1985) Australian Evaluation of an Orchard Based Electronic Device to Predict Primary Apple Scab Infections, *Journal of the Australian Institute of Agricultural Science* 51: 74-78.

Ploeg, J. van der (1993) Rural Sociology and the New Agrarian Question: a Perspective from the Netherlands, *Sociologia Ruralis* 33, 2: 240-260.

Ploeg, J. van der and Long, A. (eds) (1994) *Born From Within: Practice and Perspectives of Endogenous Rural Development*, Assen, Van Gorcum.

Rhoades, R. and Booth, R. (1982) Farmer-back-to-farmer: A Model for Generating Acceptable Agricultural Technology, *Agricultural Administration* 11: 127-137.

Röling, N. (1988) *Extension Science: Information Systems in Agricultural Development*, Cambridge, Cambridge University Press.

Rogers, E. (1983) *Diffusion of Innovations* (3rd edn.), New York, Free Press.

Saltiel, J., Bauder, J. and Palakovich, S. (1994) Adoption of Sustainable Agricultural Practices: Diffusion, Farm Structure, and Profitability, *Rural Sociology* 59, 2: 333-349

Saunders, M., Haeseler, C., Travis, J., Miller, B., Coulson, R., Loh, K. and Stone, N. (1987) GRAPES: An expert system for viticulture in Pennsylvania, *AI Applications* 1: 13-20.

Thomas, J., Ladewig, H. and McIntosh, W. (1990) The Adoption of Integrated Pest Management Practices Among Texas Cotton Growers, *Rural Sociology* 55, 3: 395-410.

Travis, J. (1992) The Penn State Apple Orchard Consultant: The Development and Implementation of an Expert System, in: Ash, G. *et al., Decision Support Systems for Farming in Southern NSW and Northern Victoria, July 1992*: 74-79.

Travis, J. *et al.,* (1992) A Working Description of the Penn State Apple Orchard Consultant, and Expert System, *Plant Disease*, June 1992: 545-554.

Vanclay, F. (1992a) The Social Context of Farmers' Adoption of Environmentally Sound Farming Practices, in Lawrence, G., Vanclay, F. and Furze, B. (eds), *Agriculture, Environment and Society*, Melbourne, Macmillan: 94-121.

Vanclay, F. (1992b) Barriers to adoption: A general overview of the issues, in: Ash, G., Bailey, B., Moore, R. and Robinson, B. (eds) *Decision Support Systems for Farming in Southern NSW and Northern Victoria, July 1992*: 96-99.

Vanclay, F. (1994) *The Sociology of the Australian Agricultural Environment*, PhD Thesis, Agricultural University Wageningen, The Netherlands.

Vanclay, F. and Lawrence, G. (1994) Farmer Rationality and the Adoption of Environmentally Sound Practices: A Critique of the Assumptions of Traditional Agricultural Extension, *European Journal Of Agricultural Education and Extension* 1, 1: 59-90.

Vanclay, F. and Lawrence, G. (1995) *The Environmental Imperative*, Rockhampton, Central Queensland University Press.

Vonk, R. (1990) *Prototyping: The Effective Use of CASE Technology*, London, Prentice-Hall.

Wagner, P. (1993) Techniques of Representing Knowledge in Knowledge-based Systems, *Agricultural Systems* 41: 53-76.

Chapter 4

Farming styles amongst grape growers of the Sunraysia district

Luciano Mesiti and Frank Vanclay

Introduction

Farming is often perceived solely as a technical process in which improvement of agricultural systems means improving and optimising what already exists, for example, plant varieties and machine technology. In terms of understanding diversity within agriculture, what is more important is viewing farming as a social process with environmental, ecological and political components. Farmers' world views, motives, ideas, beliefs and vision determine farm management practices. Appreciation of this is vital to the understanding of the motivations farmers hold in their decision to adopt new technology. This understanding is also essential in attempting to improve extension programs and their relevance.

The concept of farming styles is one of many theoretical perspectives that maybe useful in extension science, and is most relevant in understanding social diversity and determining differences in management as expressed by differences in farming styles amongst farmers (van der Ploeg, 1993; van der Ploeg and Long, 1994; Vanclay and Lawrence, 1995). By developing an appreciation of the types of farmers that exist, an understanding of the possible different management strategies can be determined. One long term benefit of this understanding is the ability better to target extension programs to each farming style. Research to identify these styles was based on focus groups with grape growers in the Sunraysia region of Victoria and NSW.

This research is being conducted as part of the research program of the Cooperative Research Centre for Viticulture (CRCV). In addition to much technical research into plant physiology and biotechnology, and artificial means of enhancing wine flavour, the CRCV is researching and developing strategies for the promotion of sustainable viticulture and effective technology transfer. An issue of major concern to the viticulture industry is the rate of adoption of sustainable practices such as reduced chemical use and Integrated Pest Management (IPM).

This paper discusses the outcomes of a preliminary focus group research phase, which forms part of a wider project examining technology adoption through investigating the ways growers make decisions about grape growing. Apart from identifying farming styles, some consideration is also given in this paper to the usefulness of the concept of farming styles in relation to grape growers, the appropriateness of the methodology, and to whether the styles that emerged through the focus groups are likely to help promote sustainable viticulture and inform extension in the viticulture industry and the activities of the CRCV.

Conceptualising farming styles

The farming styles analysis provides the opportunity to understand diversity and heterogeneity that exists in agriculture. Farming styles is based on the assumption that all farmers have different ways of managing and operating their farms, which is based on a variety of processes and beliefs. These processes and beliefs are not solely based on technical needs, but on a combination of social and cultural factors that are consistent with their world views. It is the linking of these different processes and beliefs that create groupings of farmers into similar farming styles. The expectations of these particular groups formulate the attitudes, ideas, beliefs and certain behaviours and practices of the people within those groups (Vanclay, 1992; Vanclay and Lawrence, 1995). Vanclay (1992) refers to this as farming subculture. It is these attitudes that influence the acceptance of new technology and practices in farming situations, so these new practices must be accepted by the whole farming style or subculture before the majority of farmers will accept them.

The concept of farming styles implies that farmers develop different ways of going about their farming life or production and management in general. 'The essential feature of the concept of farming styles is that different groups of farmers have different notions about the most appropriate way to farm in order to fulfil their objectives' (Vanclay and Lawrence, 1994: 70). 'Farming styles refers to a cultural repertoire, a composite of normative and strategic ideas about how farming should be done . Therefore a style of farming is a concrete form of praxis, a particular unity of thinking and doing, of theory and practice' (van der Ploeg, 1993: 241).

Farming styles also implies that farmers are rational about their farm management decisions, based upon their own knowledge and experience. Farmers are seen as having developed 'their own conceptual basis about how their farm ought to be managed' (Vanclay and Lawrence, 1995: 148).

Methodology

The study involved a number of focus group discussions which forms part of a larger research project examining the promotion of IPM and sustainable viticulture. The second phase of the research will involve quantitative analysis of questionnaire data. The focus group technique was chosen for this phase of the study to assist in developing a picture of the farming styles that exist amongst grape growers of the Sunraysia. Information from the focus groups was augmented by unstructured interviews with selected growers, extension officers, horticulture research scientific staff and rural counsellors.

Focus group sessions were decided as most appropriate to assist in operationalising of farming styles into questions that can be utilised in the questionnaire being developed for this research project. By understanding the types of farming styles that exist, accurate questions can be created that will provide the desired outcome of an understanding of farming style preference. The focus group sessions also provided an opportunity to develop a qualitative research process for exploring farming styles. An adaptation of the methodology used by Cees Leeuwis (1993) was developed.

Three main questions were used to frame each of the focus group meetings. They were:

i) Describe yourself as a grape grower;
ii) How do you differ from other growers in this area;
iii) Identify and describe all the types of growers that exist in this area.

Responses to questions one and two were recorded on a small card and collected before proceeding to the next question. For question three, participants were asked to put each description on a new card. Once the three questions were completed, a theming process was utilised to group and theme the responses of all participants. The overall result was then examined and participants were questioned about: a) whether the final groups were complete; b) whether each participant could identify themselves as belonging to one of the groups; and c) whether each participant could identify the group to which their neighbours and friends belonged.

Grape growers were selected from lists provided by the Australian Dried Fruits Association (ADFA). From this, two groups of growers were selected. Apart from the growers, another focus group was set up with Agriculture Victoria extension staff. It was hoped that this would provide a picture of styles from an extension perspective of those staff who work with growers or who themselves maybe part time growers. A total of 20 participants was involved, from focus group sessions and several unstructured interviews. All focus groups and unstructured interviews were facilitated by Luciano Mesiti and Frank Vanclay.

Styles of farming in Sunraysia viticulture

The focus groups yielded similar but not identical results. By considering the amenity value of the various styles, the researchers combined the various classification schemes. Certain styles were clearly and strongly identified by all groups, and account for most of the grape growers in the district. There were a small number of fringe styles that were mentioned, and there was a small percentage of farmers who would be difficult to classify into one of the main styles. Consequently the styles should be seen as heuristic and not necessarily definitive of all farmers, but does provide a typology covering the substantial majority. In all, six styles were articulated in the final typology.

Traditional growers

The farming style category that was dominant in all focus group session discussions was that of traditional grower. Traditional growers seem to fit into two main types: type one is the ethnic grower, predominantly growers who were born in another country. Type two comprises those growers who have been farming for many years in district and have not changed their crop management strategies very much from what they did ten to twenty years ago.

Traditional growers were also described as being non efficient users of chemicals and water. The focus group outcomes seem to indicate that traditional growers were very concerned about diseases and pests, and so over applied chemicals to vines when it may have been unnecessary to do so.

The picture of a traditional grower includes the following:

- has older vines (twenty to thirty years old or older)
- poorly managed and older trellis systems
- many of the growers are middle aged and older
- rely on hand pruning and harvesting
- use furrow irrigation
- mainly farm on small blocks (two hectares)
- generally don't seek out information, rely on experience
- have no mortgage, will not get into debt

Conventional growers

Conventional growers were described in the focus group discussions as being similar to traditional growers in that they are conservative in their approach to changing farm practices. Yet conventional growers seem to have the ability to plan ahead and are willing to consider alternative management options. However, conventional growers seem to lack the financial support to invest in improvements and so are not likely to take risks at a debt level.

The discussion groups noted that conventional growers have improved production aspects such as new irrigation and trellising systems. Another main difference between these growers and traditional ones is in access to information. Conventional growers rely and expect information from the Department of Agriculture. It was highlighted in the discussions that they seem to use Spray Diaries[1] and access the Hotline[2] service provided by Agriculture Victoria.

A self-description by a 'conventional' grape grower follows:

> having taken over the parents' farm finding it very hard to bring it back into the twentieth century ... lack of capital. Definitely look at all options of extension/advisory advice. Farming on the block is very good as a family life.

Innovative growers/progressive growers

This category of growers was described by growers not in this group as 'spend a fortune'. Innovative growers were characterised as being willing to accept new technology, are technologically advanced and willing to adopt new practices. It was also said they are progressive in their approach in that they seek out information from a wide variety of sources and are up to date with current research and production ideas. Most of these growers are industry leaders - proactive in the industry organisations. They are not afraid to borrow heavily on new technology and take the risks associated with this investment. They were described as 'make or break', 'boom or bust' growers by participants in the focus groups.

Some other areas that create the picture of an innovative/progressive grower are described below:

- Use only the best and latest technology
- Attends all appropriate field days, technical information courses
- Have extensive networks with many other growers
- Are usually characterised as having large land holdings (between twenty five and forty hectares)
- Read new information, such as industry newsletters the moment they arrive.

Two self-descriptive responses from 'innovative' growers are given below:

> I think that in my case, I have used newer technology to increase income, which in turn allows more expensive innovation to be used. Most of my neighbours have still got their early nineteen hundreds model vines and trellis, not applying new methods ... like machinery pruning and machine picking. I seem to be more willing to go out and find new ideas and put them in place.

> Try things (new advances: new technology, equipment, management practices) that others might not. Will try to think if something may work over time rather than dismiss it immediately. Use advice to help management decisions. Understand processes of pest and diseases better than some other growers.

Labour efficient growers

The growers in this category were described as managing their vineyard in such a way so as to minimise the need for external labour thus, increasingly using mechanical technology on farm and utilising modern/advanced trellis systems. The majority of growers in this category predominantly grow wine grapes, compared to dried vine fruit on their properties. This is due to an ability to use mechanical technology in wine grape harvesting, whereas all dried vine fruit must be hand picked. Use of mechanical harvesting and pruning equipment and utilising minimal pruning strategies seem to be the main labour reduction techniques employed.

This group are adopters of new technology in terms of trellis design, harvesting and so on, but rarely innovators and do not take large risks. They usually have a high mortgage. The reasons for adopting this style relate to concern about the availability, reliability and efficiency of labour and that owners/managers have a need to manage their time efficiently in farm activities.

Collins Street growers/corporate growers

The primary identification of this category was related to having a large vineyard with an absentee owner/s with seemingly unlimited capital, although viticulture is seen for its investment potential in the long term. Farms are operated by managers and consequently management styles on these farms are quite different from other farms. They are adopters of new technology but not excessive risk takers. Sometimes vineyards will be mixed with other crops.

Below is a written comment from a grower in relation to corporate growers:

> More diversified, travel to global competitors. Accept challenges better. Adopt new technology. Prepared to experiment on the farm. Able to listen to other ideas. Have capital to develop at will.

Lifestylers (including hobby farmers, part time growers)

The final category of growers was described by participants as those growers who have the vineyard as a second income to some other full time work. Their off farm employment is the main source of income and they have a vineyard because of the lifestyle benefits. In most cases here, farming is a part time activity, performed after work or on weekends. In this category most of the growers are on small blocks, often left to them by family and in some cases these have not been viable as exclusively grape-growing properties.

Focus group participants identified two types of growers in this category: those who were described as 'responsible part time farm managers' and those who were seen as 'careless in their management attitude'. Responsible managers are seen as doing the right thing and have been farming for many years. They don't have the money to implement new strategies. But know what is expected of them by industry and they achieve positive results on farm even though they are not on the farm full time.

The careless growers are seen as those that 'go with the flow', are happy with lifestyle and are seen to lack direction in their management strategies. They tend to neglect their duties on farm, and don't attend to the vine production needs, such as chemical spraying, irrigation monitoring often missing crucial times for spraying and managing the vine crop. Many of these farms are perceived to be run down and non viable. These growers were viewed as generally not able to produce a very good crop and are considered to place neighbouring crops at risk to pests and diseases.

Many of the growers who participated in the focus groups said that lifestyle was an important aspect of the reason why they are grape growers. But in most cases, lifestyle was not the main factor, just an added benefit to the financial security.

Conclusion

The outcomes from the focus groups provide an understanding of the heterogeneity and diversity that exists in this form of agriculture. This paper demonstrates that the farming styles concept is a valid and useful theoretical tool which needs to be utilised in other agricultural commodity/regions. The six grower categories that were identified in the Sunraysia viticultural region provide an understanding of the different management styles that exist and how these management styles and their related sociocultural contexts influence grower decision making. It demonstrates further that farm management is not a technical activity based on rational decision making, but a sociocultural activity that needs to be understood in terms of farming subcultures (Vanclay, 1992; Vanclay and Lawrence, 1995).

Identification of farming styles is important in the understanding of diversity in agriculture, and in understanding farmers' relationships to other farmers, to the state, and to state agencies, such as extension services. It also provides an understanding of how the sociocultural basis of farmer behaviour is actually affected. Any understanding of farmer resistance to change, of farming lifestyles, of farmers' value and attitude systems, of the so-called barriers to adoption, of gender relations in agriculture, and farm management practices, can be interpreted in terms of farming styles. It has the potential to contribute in a significant way to the development of a micro-level understanding of rural sociological processes.

There is a further valuable application of farming style theory. By identifying the styles that exist in a particular commodity/region, extension can be targeted better in terms of how best to provide growers with appropriate information regarding production and sustainability. Identification of farming styles also allows research to be directed more specifically towards farmer needs and could possibly increase farmer participation in research. Instead of research and extension focusing only on those styles that align with the science/extension worldview, potentially, science and extension could address themselves to the individual needs of all styles. This may be of dire importance as environmental issues gain increasing importance (Vanclay and Lawrence, 1995). More specifically, an understanding of farming styles could assist in the development of appropriate education packages for specific farmer groups. In relation to extension, the identification (and utilisation) of farming styles can provide improved knowledge of how farmers use extension services, extension literature and agricultural information, and of the networks they develop with other growers and industry.

Further research in the second phase of this project will involve interviewing a wide range of grape growers. This quantitative survey will utilise the qualitative data collected in the focus groups to formulate questions that can be used to classify survey respondents into various styles. This is being done to research further the operationalisation of the farming styles concept and, in particular, to consider how clearly delineated the styles are, the extent to which they are mutually exclusive, and the extent to which farmers identify with styles, and can be unambiguously defined as being of a specific style. One important question is whether the styles are only heuristic or whether they are real.

Further information about each style will be collected to determine, in particular, how each style accesses and utilises agricultural information, and makes decisions about new technology. This knowledge will help the Cooperative Research Centre for Viticulture implement strategies for effective extension of its research outputs and to tailor its research program to service the needs of all growers. This should assist it the primary aim of the CRCV which is to promote sustainable viticulture in Australia.

Notes

1 Spray Diaries are information guides for growers regarding chemical spraying for their vine crops. They provide details on when a grower needs to spray and the type and amount of chemicals required. Growers are encouraged to record each spraying application and any other relevant production information in their diaries. Most agriculture departments produce a spray diary each year. Most large commercial wineries provide their contract growers with specific spray diaries so that maximum chemical residue levels are regulated.

2 The Hotline is a recorded phone message service provided by Agriculture Victoria at the Sunraysia Horticulture Centre located in Mildura. The service provides growers of the Sunraysia region with information about what they should be doing on farm during that particular vine production period that will help prevent possible disease and pest break out. Data from weather stations based in the region are then used to create a simulation model for several of the main pests and diseases. The Hotline service is available for all growers.

Acknowledgments

The Cooperative Research Centre for Viticulture provided funding for the scholarship held by Luciano Mesiti, and for the majority of field work expenses. Field work expenses of Frank Vanclay were met by Charles Sturt University. The Sunraysia Horticulture Centre provided facilities during the period of the focus group sessions. Other research support was provided by the Centre for Rural Social Research and the Ron Potter Centre for Grape and Wine Research at Charles Sturt University. A number of people contributed ideas or information including Assoc Prof Brian Freeman (CRCV and CSU), Alison MacGregor (Agriculture Victoria, Sunraysia Horticulture Centre), and Scott Glyde (fellow CRCV PhD student CSU). We would also like to thank the growers, extension staff and rural counsellors who participated in interviews and/or focus groups.

References

Leeuwis, C (1993) *Of Computers. Myths and Modelling: The Social Construction of Diversity, Knowledge, Information, and Communication Technologies in Dutch Horticulture and Agricultural Extension*, PhD thesis, Department of Communication and Innovation Studies, Wageningen Agricultural University.

Ploeg, J. van der (1993) Rural Sociology and the New Agrarian Question: A Perspective from the Netherlands, *Sociologia Ruralis* 33(2): 240-260.

Ploeg, J. van der; and Long A (eds) (1994) *Born From Within: Practice and Perspective of Endogenous Rural Development*, Van Gorcum, Assen The Netherlands.

Vanclay, F. (1992) The Social Context of Farmers' Adoption of Environmentally Sound Farming Practices in Lawrence, G., Vanclay, F. and Furze, B. (eds), *Agriculture, Environment and Society*, Melbourne, Macmillan.

Vanclay, F. and Lawrence, G. (1994) Farmer Rationality and the Adoption of Environmentally Sound Practices: A Critique of the Assumptions of Traditional Agricultural Extension, *European Journal of Agricultural Education and Extension* 1(1): 59-90.

Vanclay, F. and Lawrence, G. (1995) *The Environmental Imperative: Eco-Social Concerns for Australian Agriculture*, Rockhampton, Central Queensland University Press.

Chapter 5

From contract farming and dependency to control by transnational capital: A case study in Tasmanian hops and agribusiness power

Leigh Miller

Introduction

The major structural transformation of Tasmania's hop industry from the dominance of petty commodity producers to monopsonistic industrial capital was completed by the late 1970s. In a study at the time (Miller, 1979, 1980), mechanisation, genetically improved hops and local competition were seen to have contributed to the change, but above all was the historical development of dependency between farmers and processors. This relationship suffered one major draw-back not associated with current vertical co-ordination strategies of farmers and processing firms in the Tasmanian vegetable and allied crops enterprises (see Wood, 1978, 1987; Miller, 1995a, 1995b) - a high degree of farmer dependency upon a single agribusiness firm. Hop farmers had few alternative enterprises. Their smallholdings were inadequate for livestock raising other than as a sideline on poorer land, and options for other cash crops were negligible; precisely the reverse of the situation pertaining to the island's specialised contract cropping localities which today are evidencing considerable resilience in the new international trading environment.

In the period from the 1968 crop year to the 1978 crop year - just ten years - in Tasmania the number of family-owned farms which depended either solely or substantially upon hops for their livelihood fell by 80 percent (from 111 to just 22). The severity of the collapse was seen to relate to peculiarities of the enterprise at the time, but a revisit to the hop regions in 1995 revealed that even in the industrially restructured and technologically competitive enterprises the lessons of the past have not been learned and further collapse is all but inevitable. There are now fewer than 10 hop farms in the state, and the major area is owned by just one company. There has been no significant fall in the number of hectares planted to hops in Tasmania since restructuring commenced, new plantings on larger holdings more than making up for losses as smaller farmers quit the industry. As well, massive increases have occurred in yields both from increased alpha-acids content of the newer hop varieties and from the higher absolute productivity of these varieties.

Paradoxically, in 1995, one component is more Fordist than Post-Fordist: beer manufacture today is all but universally dependent on two or three hop varieties whereas in earlier times the uniqueness of different lagers, ales and stouts derived much from multiple hop varieties (now known as 'aromatic' hops) that imparted unique and distinctive flavours. There was also a strong element of local pride in brewing skills and indeed in the nuances of local brews. In the 1990s brewing has moved to standardised ingredients and manufacturing technologies with low labour inputs, and breweries and associated hotel chains are traded amongst the corporate giants of international finance like any other commodity such as tons of coal or shopping centres.

The issues raised by such structural adjustments within rural enterprises have relevance to wider matters such as rural community sustainability (see Smailes, 1995) and are reflected in concerns over such matters as enterprise scale or farm size from elsewhere in the world (see Winson, 1990). It is an underlying theme of this paper that the events embedded in the locational and temporal specificity of this case study may well shed light on the potential for repetition of the phenomenon of rural social collapse across other communities, other enterprises and different time frames.

The demise of family hop farms

For about a century from 1850 when hops had become well established in core localities in southern Tasmania, the industry attained a degree of prosperity and security matched by few other enterprises over such a long period. There were periodic downturns as in the depressions of the 1890s and 1930s when less viable farms failed, and in the earlier years there were failures due to drought and poor locality choice. But the industry as a whole was particularly robust, gaining much of its economic health from the range of markets for the product - for bread yeasts, for home brewed beer (almost ubiquitous) and demand from commercial breweries.

In the late nineteenth century the hop market became confined almost entirely to larger commercial breweries; alternative bread yeasts were developed and home brewing and the number of breweries declined rapidly with improvements in transport which had enabled the emergence of larger breweries and market domination by progressively fewer companies. Because hops represent only a small fraction of the cost of manufacturing beer, their market is subject to price inelasticity of demand - the quantity of the commodity produced is unrelated to (and unresponsive to) price changes, while the latter are much more likely to reflect the available supply. Put simply, unlike the case where substitution of different vegetables might tend to even out price fluctuations for such crops, with hops a slight increase in supply can cause a massive price drop, and a slight shortage will cause a price boom. The inelasticity of demand concept was a crucial element in the demise of the hop industry as a family-farm enterprise (Miller, 1980).

The first substantive study of the Australian hop industry which identified the over-all pattern of price fluctuations in the industry was that by Pearce (1976). As with most agricultural commodities there is a discernible relationship between supply and demand which readily translates into year-to-year price variations, and over time there is a discernible cyclical production pattern. In Tasmania, hop plants require at least two years from planting to attain full production. The enterprise is capital intensive and requires substantial physical input in the system of poles and trellises upon which the crop is grown. It is therefore almost impossible for a hop farmer to respond quickly to a price change either by increasing or reducing the area devoted to the crop. This means that the enterprise has to be founded on the basis that it can withstand periodic declines in price which reflect high yield years, over-production or competition from external sources.

The phenomenon of cyclic over-production and concomitant collapse within a regional hop industry was first identified by Harvey (1963) in the case of the industry in the United Kingdom. Characteristically, in the Tasmanian case as with that of the UK, along with the cyclic declines in the industry there occurred a marked contraction of production localities, so that at the troughs in the production cycles the majority of production was localised within identifiable 'core' regions. In the case of Tasmania there was traditionally only one such locality - the Bushy Park/Glenora region in the middle Derwent Valley. Rising prices would be followed by a noticeable increase in production in more distant localities at the extensive margins where farmers were able to obtain contracts from leading 'processors' (actually known as hop factors). Such farmers usually lacked their own drying kilns and therefore were dependent on the main processors who purchased the freshly harvested crop and dried it in their kilns in the core localities.

Brewers have traditionally required dried hops, so that growers who lacked their own kilns were entirely at the mercy of the hop factors. As the factors also were, in several cases, major growers in their own right, the natural effect of price declines was that the 'peripheral' growers were deprived of their market and went out of production. Despite this, hops were an attractive proposition when times were favourable, and growers who could secure contracts were generally rewarded by returns for their enterprise that were well above those obtainable from any available alternatives. It was possible, for example, to maintain a comfortable middle-class lifestyle with trappings such as private schooling for children on just 2 hectares (5 acres) of hops during extended periods of prosperity within the industry (Milton, 1977).

From Figure 1 it may be seen that prior to about the 1960s declines in the industry seem to have occurred in concert with the general economic health of the nation. This phenomenon is not unexpected as the demand for beer appears to fall during recessionary times. It is evident from the earlier study (Miller,

1980) that the industry was able to self-regulate; the market was almost entirely national and average annual production was more or less geared to this.

Figure 1
Cyclic production patterns in Tasmania's hop industry: 1820-1995

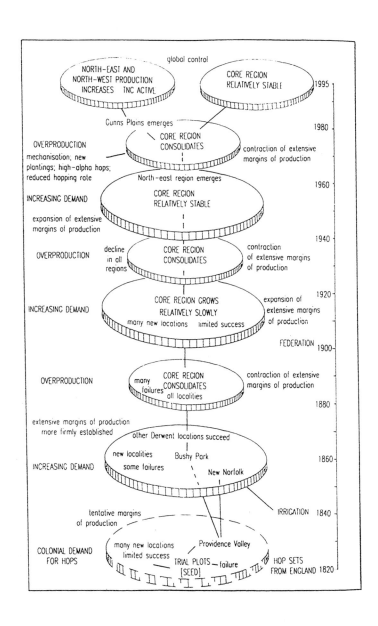

In periods of local shortage the brewing trade imported hops, while in periods of oversupply there was wastage and hops were simply left to rot on the 'bine' (the climbing hop vine together with supporting string).

The first externality to impinge upon Tasmanian hop growers resulted from selective breeding of a new hop variety, the Ringwood Special. This hop had much-improved alpha acids content (the critical bittering and flavouring substance in the plant). The usual average alpha acids content of the wide variety of hops produced in Tasmania ranged from less than 2 percent to perhaps 3.5 percent of the dried weight of the crop. The Ringwood Special had an alpha acids content of around 6 percent - a dramatic improvement by any measure. At this point, the warning lights should have triggered alarm within the hop producing localities. Here after all was a plant which could produce all of Australia's hop requirements on half the land area presently employed.

Instead, the majority of Tasmania's hop farmers followed obediently the instruction from the brewers via the hop factors to pull out all present varieties and replant with the new variety. Almost all the hop farmers went along with this instruction; they lost around two years of harvest in the transfer, and they ended up with a crop averaging over twice the brewing value that derives from essential alpha acids which colour, flavour and preserve the beverage. Had these farmers been alert to what was happening they must surely have demanded a price increase commensurate with the higher value of their product, and been prepared to cut their total area of production. They did neither, and some years later an industry report was to lament this fact and to recommend that those remaining within the industry pay future heed to this suggestion (Makeham, 1970).

There was further agricultural productivism to follow: despite the advantages of its higher alpha acids yield, the Ringwood Special was found to be so susceptible to hop diseases that it was decided that the industry could not risk continued planting of it. By the late-1960s, when the industry was being sustained by externalities such as the prosperous economy, described by Fagan and Webber (1994) as the Long Boom, and unbounded optimism about the future of the 'Lucky Country', a new higher yielding hop variety, the Pride of Ringwood, was demanded by the dominant brewer-come-factor cartel. Some hop growers became disheartened and withdrew from the industry, but by far the majority of small hop farmers again went for at least two seasons without a crop while the replacement variety was established. Depressed income and total production was masked somewhat by a phased replanting. By about 1973, however, the industry was back to former total capacity with the crop now yielding close to 10 percent by dried weight of alpha acids, or almost four times the previous brewing value.

Paralleling the varietal changes, the rising costs of labour were making the newly developed mechanical harvesters attractive. Machines which warranted substantial throughput were purchased by numerous hop farmers in a vain attempt to remain competitive. Meanwhile, payment for the crop continued as before - payment by weight of the crop, with total disregard for its vastly increased brewing value. While it may be argued that farmers were not in a position to demand payment by brewing value, the fact that the leading hop factor was also a grower must make it abundantly clear that there was plenty of awareness at the processor end of the extent to which farmers were being taken down the path of financial uncertainty. Amidst the severe cost-price squeeze, demand for hops was increasing only because of the state of the economy. Inevitably that began to taper by around the end of the 1960s and then fell substantially with the commodities induced economic crises of the early 1970s, (the end of the Long Boom).

One of the contributing elements in the collapse which commenced in the late 1960s was the system of hop factoring. By this time, both production and marketing of the majority of hops was in the hands of a single brewer which also owned the largest hop factor. Most smaller hop growers were linked to this firm by contracts for sale of their 'green' (undried) hops, as were many of the medium-sized farms including some who actually dried their own hops. In return for marketing the hops, the factor sold the farmers their hop-growing requisites such as twine, poles, wire, fertiliser and even groceries on credit against anticipated hop returns, provided advice to them on planting, trellises, cultivating, handling of the crop, and so forth. The leading hop factor in Tasmania also competed directly with other hop growers as it owned a sizeable proportion of the choice middle Derwent hop fields.

A central theme of the earlier study of this industry involved investigation of information flows to farmers from and about their industry. The vast majority of the southern Tasmanian farmers relied upon other hop farmers for their knowledge of externalities. By contrast, a group of well educated and skilled entrepreneurial individuals entered hop production in the late 1950s in a completely new locality, the North-east of Tasmania around Scottsdale and Ringarooma. They had recognised the existence of the dependency relationship that continued to characterise the small farms of Southern Tasmania (Davey, 1977) and initiated a highly mechanised and innovative approach that would eventually capture a substantial proportion of the market for hops within the State.

Recognising the tight degree of control over the domestic market exercised by the existing producer cartel, these growers oriented their production to the export market; they developed new packaging methods and pelletising to reduce bulk and enhance their international competitiveness, and formed a cooperative purchasing and marketing body to centralise processing and packaging. Meanwhile, the smaller growers' continued acceptance of the prevailing price per kilogram of hops, together with the inherent inelasticity of demand for the product almost guaranteed their inability to withstand the inevitable cost-price squeeze arising from vastly improved production economies on the new holdings, and the eventual certainty that the North-eastern growers would market their hops domestically as soon as the export market experienced oversupply.

While there were many interlinked causes of the catastrophic decline in the number of hop farms as the industry chose the path of agricultural productivism from the mid 1960s, there is little doubt that many of the farmers were their own worst enemies. Rivalry and misplaced competitiveness among and between close neighbours was frequently revealed during interviews undertaken immediately following the demise of the industry. Farmers tended to disguise the truth about their annual yields for little reason other than personal pride, but by pretending to the world that they were happy with their performance they were clearly at odds with their own best interests which might have seen a concerted and co-coordinated approach to the new competition and the restructuring policies of the hop factor-brewer conglomerate. For example, growers with holdings of less than 6.0 hectares (approximately 15 acres) should not have contemplated purchasing harvesting machines. Instead, co-operative purchase would have allowed the benefits of mechanisation to be obtained and farms to remain more than competitive with the newly established, more capital intensive enterprises in the North-east of the state.

Farmer interviews revealed however, that rivalry dominated the industry, and talk of co-operative ventures sounded too much like alternative and unacceptable economic theories; socialism or even communism. Ironically, one of the few growers to have survived the collapse of the industry up until about 1980 was an avowed communist, and continued to grow the original varieties of hops for the home brewing market. This individual also had played a major role in reducing the child-labour dependency of the family and company farms up until the 1960s (another reason for increased labour costs). His philosophy was, of course, anathema to the majority of hop farmers. In fairness to smaller hop farmers there was a feeling that with the new single variety of hops the harvesting would be confined to a very short period and co-operatively owned machines would lead to arguments over whose crop was to be harvested at the optimum time and so on. However, the machines for harvesting of hops have fixed locations and the hop bines are brought to them, so there was no good reason why rotation by days or even portions of days could not have been organised on any given harvesting machine.

There were two broad categories of outcomes for the majority of the smaller peripherally located hop farms: first, those farms with less than about two hectares in hops continued to harvest by hand with family labour and the like until the final down-turn in the industry in the mid-1970s; and secondly, farms with from two to ten hectares purchased harvesting machines and attempted to remain competitive. The majority of the latter group rapidly reached a point where they had overheads far higher than returns and many then mortgaged previously debt-free farms - often to the major hop factor or its agents - in an attempt to remain solvent. When the over-production-induced price collapse in the mid-1970s, arrived, these growers often lost their farms and left the industry as paupers.

This point pertaining to enterprise scale is central to the whole efficiency debate within intensive agriculture. Contract vegetable growers in North-west Tasmania, following the tenets of Davis and Goldberg (1957) have been urged to get bigger and become more 'efficient' in order to survive international competition. Yet many farmers who have not taken heed of this advice have continued to prosper in the region (Miller, 1995a).

The process of collapse of the smaller farms in the hop industry also varied spatially according to the level of dependency upon the hop factors, as can be seen from Figure 1. In the case of hop farmers who possessed their own drying kilns there was always the possibility of marketing their crop independently of hop factors, and the smaller breweries were not averse to by-passing traditional suppliers if the price was right. There were hop farmers in the Derwent Valley with quite small holdings of hops who had access to a kiln or actually owned one. By contrast, those growers who had gone into production in the late 1940s through to the late 1950s with the intention of selling their crop 'green' to the hop factor were quickly left out in the cold when an over-supply developed. These growers were located further from the core locality at Bushy Park and generally had smaller acreages in hops than was the case with the former group. The hop factor had actually built a large kiln in the core locality specifically for handling the output of these independent growers. In turn, of course, these growers acquired farming supplies through the factor and became quite dependent upon the mutual relationship being sustained.

The situation with regard to contracts did not make planning much easier for growers committed to a perennial crop either. Year to year switches in crops to be grown are simply not possible in this industry, yet for the smaller producers a contract longer than one year's duration was a rarity. In the case of larger private growers the contract periods were frequently of several years' duration and almost always at least two years in length. In effect, the factors were able to hold a core group of longer term contracted producers to ensure their main market throughput, and at the same time they encouraged the locationally and economically peripheral growers to sign up one year at a time in order to allow themselves the flexibility of adjustment to seasonal yield variations on their own holdings and variable market demand.

Yet many 'smaller' farmers went along with this system, taking all the capital risks to commence and then remain in the business while being especially vulnerable to externally-induced efficiencies brought about by their very own purchasing agents. The subsumption of agriculture by industrial capitals was in top gear in this industry; to transfer wealth from the propertied labourer to the agri-corporation seemed an implicit aim. Davis (1980) expounds the difficulties of demonstrating the Marxist conception of this process taken to its ultimate wherein the former owner of capital is transformed into a proletariat wage labourer, but there were many who walked off their hop farms penniless, and indeed owing money to hop factors or banks. Within two years of the final collapse, the hop factor was setting up its own land with new acreage for planting in Tasmania's North-west. The supreme irony for some of these displaced individuals must have been the appearance of real estate signs on their farms with the selling agent being one and the same company which had managed their crop from farm gate to brewery and on to the hotels and liquor outlets. Subsequently, this company formed part of one of Australia's largest and most respected, publicly listed pastoral houses with major international operations. Ironically, in very recent years it, too, had to face the fact that 'bigger' is not always 'better', as it experienced financial strains brought about by economic events in 1987, the drought of the early 1990s and recession in the wider economy. Sadly, its financial decline has also affected most newer and more highly capitalised hop farms in Tasmania which are now at least tied to marketing through, if not actually owned by, an international conglomerate.

The global Tasmanian hop industry in the 1990s

Today some 80 percent of area planted to hops in Tasmania is owned by Australian Hop Marketers which is in turn, owned by a major hop grower and marketer in the United States, John I. Haas. In turn, John I. Haas has some share holding by the Barth family from Germany, the world's largest hop marketer. The former owners of the Australian Hop Marketers cartel developed their capital base from the Tasmanian agribusiness scene, including hop factoring and marketing, before selling out to the overseas concern to alleviate some of the debts built up in the speculative over-enthusiasm of the 1980s. The local manager of one of the larger plantations owned by this company informed this author that farmers were better off having the security of seasonal work in the hop fields than they would be if they owned their own hop farms (Dudgeon, 1992). In the light of the state of events in 1995, he may well be right.

There is, at the present time, an astonishing similarity to the post structural adjustment period in the Derwent Valley in the early 1970s. At that time, larger farmers were saved from over-production-induced collapse only by the demise of their many smaller competitors, while the dominant hop factor and marketer continued to do reasonably well. Today, ironically, it is the global corporation which dominates the industry in Tasmania that the remaining growers can thank for their prospects of surviving the present world over-supply. Despite the fact that there are now a few new varieties of hops compared with almost two decades of domination by the Pride of Ringwood, these have been selectively bred for yet higher alpha yields to around 14 percent, and because they also yield more weight of hops, true yield increases of around 100 percent over the Pride of Ringwood variety are occurring. The intellectual rights to these varieties are held by Australian Hop Marketers. In terms of the market outlook for hops at the present time, there has been, during the last few years, a significant shift towards lighter beers, a reduction in the amount of alpha acids required through newer post-fermentation additive technology, a total decline in per capita beer consumption in Australia, and an increase in the consumption of imported beer. These events account for much of the push to market the crop overseas.

Prices received for hops by Tasmanian hop growers are now lower, in actual dollar amounts, than prices received in 1957, although of course productivity is far higher today. The minimum cost of production of hops is $4.00 per kg. while prices received are around $4.50 per kg. (Davey, 1995). All capital repayments and depreciation must be met from a mere 50 cents per kg. margin, which allows nothing for seasonal aberrations, pests or diseases and other unavoidable losses. Further, old lessons have not yet been learned; prices are still received by weight of the dried product, not by alpha acids content, although a premium is now being paid for 'high-alpha' hops. This is somewhat akin to all wool producers receiving the same price per kilogram for wool.

Part of the expansionary push within the industry in Tasmania since the late 1960s has been geared towards the global market for hops. There have been continued efforts in this direction from the major corporate entity in the industry: a new world class kiln and packaging facility in the Derwent Valley is entirely premised on the quality of the hops able to be produced in Tasmania. However, globally, the market for hops is grossly oversupplied. China has a rapidly rising beer consumption but is more than capable of matching it with increased hop production in the North-western provinces. The Australian Hop Marketers is building a pelletising plant in Kansu state. Brewing technology, including efficient use of minimalist alpha acids, is being shared with the Chinese in return for joint-venture access to the burgeoning market for beer in that country.

In the USA, any possible global shortfall is now able to be made up rapidly by one to two-year plantings with 80 percent yield in year one. Storage of hops in vacuum sealed bags, developed in Tasmania by the export-oriented North-eastern farmers, has made stockpiling against seasonal shortage a reality for brewers. There are unlikely to be any more sudden peaks in price brought about by poor harvests. In countries of lower latitude such as Mexico and South Africa, formerly less suited to hop production, artificial lighting is used to induce inflorescence in the hop plant and thus eliminate the need for imported hops. Again, the global company which controls the Tasmanian hop industry has interests in these countries and could move to fill any shortage in Australia with hops from elsewhere in the world. The place and importance formerly held by the Tasmanian hop industry is thereby all but eliminated by the globalisation of the enterprise. The last of the very small and medium-sized family farms is ending the activity at the present season, and indications are that the future of the larger family-owned and corporate holdings may depend upon continued competitive strategies and the natural advantages of Tasmania's clean green environment.

As with the situation of decades ago in the Derwent Valley when brewers would sometimes find hop growers to by-pass the normal purchasing channels, in the North-east of Tasmania at least one of the former co-operative members has set about to gear his operation specifically to supply one major brewer. His future is assured only so long as a cheaper alternative does not arise for the brewer. Most of the larger private growers (and there are only a handful of these remaining) now work off-farm for the hop cartel in one capacity or another, or have turned to other off-farm income to survive. Proletarian wage labour within industrial conglomerates in rural areas seems frequently to be peopled by either displaced farmers or present-day part-time 'petty commodity' producers.

Australian Hop Marketers now owns some 80 percent of the hop fields in Tasmania and markets about 90 percent of all hops produced. While this firm promotes a disease-free and low chemical-residue product as part of its strategy of commitment to Tasmania, it is able to fill seasonal shortfalls with imported hops from its parent firm's farms in Washington State or Germany, and to engage in all the other activities of global firms as outlined by Fagan and Webber (1994). For example, it conducts its own research into improved varieties, sets its own quality standards, markets a uniform product and responds quickly to changing consumer tastes such as low alcohol and 'ice beers'. Work in the hop fields is still unavoidably labour-intensive but a great deal of the processing and packaging of hops is undertaken in the most highly automated of plants at Bushy Park with very low labour input. At the same time, fewer than ten individual hop farming families remain in Tasmania and profits from the industry would be largely remitted to the parent company in the USA. In a globally competitive environment, any other strategy would probably have spelled disaster for the remaining hop farmers.

The Australian Hop Marketers strategy of continuing to develop high-alpha hops in the face of declining or stagnant markets is part of its global competitive strategy. The family farms which have survived in the industry to this point in time are largely the ones which have been prepared to change, to innovate, to cooperate with the global market push and to stay cost competitive with other countries. Exports now account for some 75 percent of all hops produced in Tasmania. In terms of offering stability to the farmers, the AHM has forward sold some 82 percent of its 1996 harvest and some 60 percent of its 1997 harvest. Prices are by no means buoyant but the AHM believes this strategy is one of survival whereas the few farmers who continue to rely on the open or 'spot' market will potentially face price collapse at any time.

Conclusion: An industry poised for decline

In a world of declining demand for hops it seems to make little sense to go on increasing the volume of output of that commodity. Yet this is what the 'bigger is better' philosophy has brought about in Tasmania's hop industry - fewer and fewer farms producing greater total output for, at best, a static market. Total collapse, even of the largest company-owned farms, cannot be ruled out. On the hopeful side, continued technological and biological improvements will hold the Tasmanian industry's share of the global market, but it must be questioned whether the current situation is sustainable on economic grounds and some further rationalisation is quite possible. It is quite conceivable that this will come in the form of a decision to import Chinese hops to Australia in return for a licence to sell some more German beer to the Chinese. Hop production in Germany has also undergone massive increases in recent years and also has suffered a rapid decline in the number of their smaller growers; control by cartels is not unique to Australia.

Globalisation is a feature of many areas of intensive horticulture but few of such character and flavour as the hop industry. For farmers who have survived in the Tasmanian hop industry to the present point in time, it is likely that the best chances of continued survival lie in cooperation with the global corporation which will wish to maintain its own investments in Tasmania for a range of reasons, not the least of which is the highly suitable growing conditions and consequent quality of the product. But farmers will need to continue to compete with hop growers in other parts of the world including China, South Africa and Mexico. Should more serious over-supply occur, the remaining hop farms on the island will surely be severely affected.

References

Cowan, T. (1995) General Manager, Australian Hop Marketers, Hobart, pers. comm.

Davey, H. (1977) Hop farmer and processor, Tonganah, Tasmania, pers. comm.

Davey, J. (1995) Hop manager, Tonganah, Tasmania, pers. comm.

Davis, J. (1980) Capitalist Agricultural Development and the Exploitation of the Propertied Labourer, in Buttel, F. and Newby, H. (eds), *The Rural Sociology of the Advanced Societies: Critical Perspectives,* Montclair, Allanheld, 133-152.

Davis, J. and Goldberg, R. (1957) *A Concept of Agribusiness,* Boston, Harvard Business School, Division of Research.

Fagan, R. and Webber, M. (1994) *Global Restructuring: The Australian Experience,* Melbourne, Oxford University Press.

Harvey, D. (1963) Locational Change in the Kentish Hop Industry and the Analysis of Land-Use Patterns, *Transactions of the Institute of British Geographers* 53: 123-143.

Makeham, J. and Associates (1970) *Hop Industry of Australia Survey 1969-70,* Melbourne.

Miller, L. (1979) Structural Adjustment and Regional Relocation in the Tasmanian Hop Industry, *Proceedings 10th NZ Geography Conference and 49th ANZAAS Congress,* Auckland: 180-185.

Miller, L. (1980) *Structural Adjustment and Regional Relocation in the Tasmanian Hop Industry,* unpublished MA thesis, Hobart, University of Tasmania.

Miller, L. (1995a) Enterprise Survival and Cropping 'Diversity' under Contract Farming in North-West Tasmania, *Institute of Australian Geographers Conference Proceedings 1993,* Melbourne, Monash University: 222-232.

Miller, L. (1995b) Agribusiness, Contract Farmers and Land-Use Sustainability in North-West Tasmania, *Australian Geographer* 26, 2: 104-111.

Milton, A. (1977) Former hop grower, Molesworth, Tasmania, pers.comm.

Pearce, H. (1976) *The Hop Industry in Australia,* Melbourne, Melbourne University Press.

Smailes, P. (1995) Sustainable Systems: Introduction to a Theme, *Australian Geographer* 26, 2: 101-103.

Winson, A. (1990) Capitalist Coordination of Agriculture: Food Processing Firms and Farming in Central Canada, *Rural Sociology* 55, 5: 376-394.

Wood, L. (1978) Poppies in Tasmania, *Geography* 63: 213-217.

Wood, L. (1987) The Legal Production of Narcotic Material in Australia, *Australian Geographer* 18, 2: 161-165.

Chapter 6

Backs to the wall: Rural women make formidable activists

Margaret Alston

Introduction

Australian agriculture has been buffeted by unprecedented natural disasters and a period of rapid restructuring. A prolonged and widespread drought has severely reduced livestock numbers and has undercut our cereal grain production at a time when Australian farming families have been struggling to maintain their competitive edge in a world marketplace. Dramatic changes in the structure of agriculture have resulted. Chiefly, the numbers of farm families have declined from 200,000 in the 1950s to the current 120,000. Predictions are that this number may further reduce to 70,000 in the next ten years (Vanclay and Lawrence, 1995:15). The farm labour workforce has been significantly reduced because of the combined effects of farm family poverty and the replacement of capital intensive work practices with labour intensive practices (Alston, 1993). Farm incomes have fluctuated dramatically. For instance, average broad acre farm incomes have been negative for eight of the sixteen years from 1976 to 1992 (Farm Surveys Report, 1992). My own research with farm women in southern New South Wales reveals that one third of the farms in the study produced no income upon which the family could rely to survive (Alston, 1993).

The results of these rapid and wide-ranging changes have been dramatic. Farming families have been left fragmented and demoralised. Rural suicide figures, particularly among young rural males, have risen alarmingly. The largest rise is amongst males from 15 to 19 in towns with fewer than 4,000 people, rising from 3.6 per 100,000 people in the 1960s to 31.6 per 100,000 in 1991 (*The Land*, 11 August 1994). Other social problems are also apparent. For example, there is emerging evidence of increasing rural domestic violence (Alston, 1995a), and rural communities are contracting because of out migration as young people leave searching for work. The current government economic rationalist agenda dictates that, as populations contract, services will decline. Consequently, rural communities are losing essential services such as Post Offices, banks and court houses. Many rural communities can no longer attract a doctor leaving them vulnerable and isolated (*Wagga Daily Advertiser*, 2 December 1995). As young people move out they leave behind a poorly serviced aging population.

Against this background of agricultural and community upheaval and escalating social problems, I have focussed my recent research on the effects of wide ranging social change on the lives of farm women. Much of this work is detailed in my book *Women on the Land: The Hidden Heart of Rural Australia* (Alston, 1995 b). In brief, I have argued that women have borne a great deal of the burden of changes occurring in rural Australia. With no renegotiation of their domestic load, farm women face a triple burden which includes their almost total responsibility for household and child care tasks, an increase in farm work replacing previously hired labour, and an increasing off-farm work load which includes paid work for much needed income and voluntary community work to support and sustain their communities as services contract.

The rise of rural women's political activism

This paper will focus on the political response of rural women to the structural changes outlined above. Firstly, it must be recognised that women's position in rural society has been marginalised and trivialised (James, 1989; Macklin, 1995). Their history, concerns and attitudes have rarely been reflected in the dominant discourse of rural life. However, in the 1990s, faced with an increasing and fragmented workload, farm women have begun to reassess their invisible and secondary position. A rural women's movement, which had its genesis in Victoria, has emerged and is spreading across Australia. The Victorian Labor Government of the 1980s appointed the first women's advisers in the Department of Agriculture. The resulting Victorian Rural Women's Network based in Ballarat has provided the impetus for the mobilisation of rural women's activism. Critical to this effort has been the series of successful 'Women on the Land' gatherings held annually in various locations across rural Victoria. The Victorian Network model has been adopted by NSW Agriculture with the unit established in Orange four years ago. Currently, Queensland, South Australia and Tasmania are all working towards similar network structures. The success of these units is founded on their government funding, and their appointment of key committed women charged with linking up groups of isolated women, providing information and allocating resources for group activities and programs. The annual women's gatherings and the regular newsletters allow Network personnel to communicate regularly with women.

These State initiatives have recently been matched at Federal level with support for rural women coming from several quarters. The need for representation of rural women was first targeted in the *Half Way to Equal* report produced by the House of Representatives Standing Committee on Legal and Constitutional Affairs in April 1992. Recommendation 52 of that report states that to:

> improve recognition for rural women, the Committee recommends
> that a rural women's section be established within the Office of the
> Status of Women to monitor government policy and legislation to

ascertain if it adequately reflects the needs of rural women. The rural women's section should undertake to liaise directly with rural women's organisations and networks and to ensure greater feedback on government policy, research and development to the rural women.

While the Office of the Status of Women has yet to take up this initiative, the former Minister for Primary Industries and Energy, Senator Bob Collins, responded by providing public affirmation for rural women. This has recently been demonstrated by the former Labor government's support for the International Women in Agriculture Conference in August 1994, for the First National Rural Women's Forum in June 1995, and by the establishment of a Rural Women's Policy Unit within the Department of Primary Industries and Energy (DPIE) in July 1995.

Coupled with government support for rural women has been the development and growth of rural women's community organisations such as Australian Women in Agriculture (AWiA) and the Foundation for Australian Agricultural Women (FAAW), groups which have moved away from the traditionalism of the Country Women's Association (CWA). These organisations are leading the push to challenge and expose the problems facing rural women, their families and communities. The coupling of government initiatives and grass roots community activism have been essential to the development of a new radicalism among farm women. I would further add that the contribution of academics to the process of legitimation of the rural women's agenda has been equally important to the continuation of this development.

In 1994 the successful International Women in Agriculture held at the University of Melbourne attracted 850 women from 34 countries. In opening the conference the then Governor General, Bill Hayden, noted that it was the largest agricultural conference ever held in Australia. Rural women had gathered in force and their message was clear. Amongst their recommendations, they demanded recognition of their efforts and access to the decision-making process (Women in Agriculture, 1994).

The announcement by a Federal Labor Government that a women's policy unit was to be established within DPIE was seen as a victory for the organisers of the conference, and heralded women's access to the policy making arena. Women have previously faced many constraints in their attempts to enter the agri-political arena predominantly because the traditional farmer organisations remain patriarchal and hierarchical and because the organisational resistance to women has been overt (Alston, 1993). The announcement of the establishment of the unit was met with excitement and anticipation by women as it would finally allow women's voices to be heard at the policy making level. Initially, however, the very idea of such a unit evoked enormous expectations amongst women including a widespread hope that the constraints they have experienced would be addressed immediately and comprehensively. Submissions were received by government from many sources detailing directions for the unit. Overwhelmed by these expectations, there was some uncertainty after the announcement of the proposed unit as to whether it would actually proceed.

In December 1994 after meeting up with Anna Lottkowitz, Victorian Rural Women's Network, and Ruth Liepins, a researcher from University of Melbourne (now based at the University of Otago), at the Australian Women's Studies Conference, I put a proposal to DPIE that the Centre for Rural Social Research from Charles Sturt University hold a National Rural Women's Forum. This Forum would bring together representatives of rural women's groups from across Australia to draft a National Agenda for Women which could provide consensus and a blueprint for the unit to proceed. This initiative was sanctioned and funded and led to the First National Forum in Parliament House, Canberra on 7 and 8 June, 1995. Invited on to the Steering Committee were:

- Ms Margaret Carroll, Rural Women's Network, NSW Agriculture
- Ms Dorothy Dunn, President, Australian Women in Agriculture
- Mrs Sylvia Laxton, National President, Country Women's Association
- Ms Ruth Liepins, Department of Geography and Environmental Studies, University of Melbourne
- Ms Anna Lottkowitz, Rural Women's Network, Agriculture, Victoria; and
- Ms Mary Salce, President, Foundation for Australian Agricultural Women.

Seventy-seven rural and remote women representing over 40 organisations from across Australia came together for an historic meeting to carve out a National Agenda. After two days it became clear that a united and powerful women's voice had emerged and that consensus had been achieved on a wide variety of issues. The key areas which formed the basis for the twenty-seven recommendations included:

- visibility and recognition of rural women
- access to and participation in the decision-making process
- national networking
- recognition of the importance of women's contribution to agricultural and environmental sustainability
- recognition of women's contribution to viable rural communities and the management of change
- women's education and training needs
- social justice issues (including adequate social security, flexible and accessible child care, adequate and equitable health care, adequate and equitable transport services and a structured and targeted drought policy)
- future directions.

Recommendations framed around these areas directly address gender issues and not only challenge reigning hegemony but also highlight the issues which are of major concern to rural women. It is notable that these recommendations did not prioritise commodity concerns or market strategies, items which tend to dominate the agendas of the traditional farmer organisations. In assembling the recommendations for the Forum, delegates were indirectly exposing the failure of these traditional farmer organisations to centralise social issues or to give prominence to the concerns of women.

Implications of a rural women's movement

The implications of this newly mobilised and politically powerful women's movement are worthy of considerable contemplation. As a sociologist and social worker I have been fascinated to observe these changing dynamics. Firstly, women appear to be shifting the debate from concentration on commodity issues to an incorporation of concern about community decline and an exposure of the impact of an economic rationalist agenda on support services to rural Australia. The final recommendation of the Forum called for the inclusion of a Rural Communities Impact Statement in all policy submissions to Cabinet and that gender impact be a significant part of this appraisal. If this recommendation is acted on it will give centrality to rural issues and spotlight the effects of government policies on rural communities.

Another consequence of the rural women's movement has been their identification with the issues of environmental and ecological sustainability. The Landcare Movement, one of the fastest growing movements in the country, is strongly supported by women. The International Women in Agriculture conference noted the need for clean, green agriculture, a theme that was reinforced by the National Forum. Delegates demanded the Federal Government investigate the problems associated with chemically controlled agriculture and, in particular, they called for assurances that the health of rural families and of the environment was not at risk. Further they demanded the Government support research into alternatives to chemical farming. As Elbert (1988:263) notes, farm women 'have demonstrated a form of feminism that reaches beyond any simple definition of autonomy or individualism - farming women have claimed the right to integrate work and family life with an enduring respect for the earth'. Allowing women's voices to be heard may allow a new way of farming to develop which incorporates women's nurturing and caring capacity and may go some way towards challenging an agribusiness agenda for agricultural production.

A further initiative resulting from the activism of rural women has been the push to have 50 percent representation on agricultural boards and statutory authorities by the year 2000, a move endorsed by Forum delegates. Women have called on state governments, industry bodies and farmer organisations to match the initiative, to support women with leadership training, to set targets for the appointment of suitably qualified women, and to develop child and respite care programs to assist women with their leadership goals.

The movement has mobilised the dormant aspirations of many women and threatens to challenge the gendered hierarchical structure of agricultural production by confronting accepted stereotypes. For example, the Forum report noted the failure to recognise women's contributions and the consequent lack of access to decision making had produced barriers for women including, and I quote:

- a lack of a sense of ownership by women of their industries
- a lack of legal/financial ownership
- a lack of identity (they are viewed as helpers not participants)
- oppressive attitudes founded on traditional stereotypes of women

- a lack of identity (they are viewed as helpers not participants)
- oppressive attitudes founded on traditional stereotypes of women
- a lack of gender equity in grass roots organisations
- the traditional culture of many farmer organisations which leads to a narrow blinkered perception of women's roles and a lack of credibility for women
- the 'old boys' networks which protect the existing culture
- gender discrimination
- a lack of access to positions of power
- inappropriate selection criteria which may render women ineligible while also underestimating and overlooking the skills women have to offer
- intransigent organisational structures and processes
- a lack of women in policy decision-making
- a lack of acknowledgment of women as critical clients/customers
- policies which are not inclusive of women.

Gender backlash

Raising such issues and framing them in language which is hardly conciliatory has produced an inevitable backlash from some male conservative industry leaders and commentators. For example, shortly after the Forum, the editor of *The Land* newspaper warned of the 'risk of gender fragmentation' if women continue with their 'increasing desire to pursue their own agri-political agenda in frustration at what they see as resistance to their ambitions within mainstream farm organisations'. He continued:

> The last thing we need is for, say, Australian Women in Agriculture to become an alternative voice on *mainstream* [my emphasis] issues now properly the province of the National Farmers' Federation and its member State bodies. ... That's not to say Australian Women in Agriculture (or for that matter, the CWA) doesn't have an important role to play in specific areas, but if it allows itself to become a refuge for disgruntled fugitives from the likes of NSW Farmers, and tries to run a parallel agenda, then it won't be doing anyone a service.

What he fails to note is the fact that NSW Farmers' has hardly served the interests of women and that no women form part of the governing executive committee and few have reached delegate status. He concludes his editorial comment by saying:

> What worries me is that the need to stack our boards and committees with women is fast becoming an obsession in some quarters, to the point where sound policy-making will soon be put at risk. ... The day we start to see women being appointed, or press-ganged, into positions to satisfy arbitrary gender quotas, when more suitable males are available, will be a sad day indeed for rationality.

the existing power structure. What is unacknowledged in this piece is the failure of NSW Farmers' and other traditional organisations to allow women access to the decision-making and agenda setting positions where they can raise their concerns. For instance, child care, aged and respite care, lack of health and welfare services, domestic violence and rural suicides are not prominent on the NSW Farmers' agenda. Evidence of the neglect of women and the failure of organisations to consult with women are not hard to find. For example, in 1990 the NSW Farmers' Association made a submission to the Federal Government condoning the assets testing of the Family Allowance, a payment to women, without having consulted any women (Alston, 1993). Traditional organisations have been found wanting and women are turning to their own organisations to raise and address social issues.

Conclusion

The crisis in agriculture and the rapid restructuring taking place in rural Australia has aroused an activism in rural women which has spread nationwide. While this activism has resulted from the rural crisis, it is important to note that government support has allowed the movement to consolidate and grow. The establishment of the Rural Women's policy unit within DPIE and the development of state government supported networks have been important initiatives in legitimising and sanctioning the activism of women. The action by women is challenging the gender stereotyping which has characterised the public face of agriculture and which has ensured women have been invisible players. Yet, without government action and support, this challenge cannot shift the dominant male hegemony endemic to rural society.

Rural women have been successful in raising awareness of social, environmental and community issues which have largely been ignored by farmer organisations. The response from some traditional bodies and rural commentators indicates a gender backlash and suggests that the future of the women's movement remains in the balance and may yet be overturned by deteriorating conditions and/or a change of government. Nevertheless, it is apparent that rural women have a great deal to contribute and have the capacity to change the very nature of rural society and agricultural production should their political activism continue.

References

Alston, M. (1995a) *Domestic Violence in a Rural Context,* Paper in press.

Alston, M. (1995b) *Women on the Land: The Hidden Heart of Rural Australia,* Kensington, University of NSW Press.

Alston, M. (1993) *A Study of Farm Women,* Unpublished PhD thesis, Kensington, University of NSW.

Australian Bureau of Agricultural and Research Economics (1992) *Farm Surveys Report 1992,* Canberra, Commonwealth of Australia.

Elbert, S. (1988) Women and Farming: Changing Structures, Changing Roles, in Haney and Knowles (eds) *Women and Farming: Changing Roles, Changing Structures*, Boulder, Westview Press.

Women in Agriculture (1994) Women in Agriculture: Farming for our Future, Australia, *International Post-Conference Proceedings*.

James, K. (ed.) (1989) *Women in Rural Australia*, St Lucia, University of Queensland Press.

Macklin, M. (1995) Local Media and Gender Relations in a Rural Community, in Share P. (ed.) *Communication and Culture in Rural Areas*, Wagga Wagga, Centre for Rural Social Research.

Vanclay, F. and Lawrence, G. (1995) *The Environmental Imperative*, Rockhampton, Central Queensland University Press.

Chapter 7

Rural youth suicide: The issue of male homosexuality

Edward Green

Introduction

In a book about his travels through gay America in the 1980s Neil Miller recounts:

> Main Street was simply off limits, except for brief visits home for birthdays, weddings and funerals (Miller, 1989: 15).

Some years later in, *On Being Different*, the novelist and editor, Merle Miller, wrote, with only 'slight exaggeration' that he had started packing to leave his birthplace, Marshalltown (Iowa), when he was two years old. For a gay person in a small town there were only two options - 'either they ran you out of town, or you left before they got around to it'.

On 22 January 1994 the interestingly named Dubbo newspaper, the *Daily Liberal* ran a story headlined 'Gays in the Bush'. Contrary to expectations that it might be a story, even a poofter-bashing story, about gay men and lesbians living in the bush, it told, instead:

> the tragic story of Nicholas, a young gay man who failed to come to terms with his sexuality in a country town....
>
> His friends described Nicholas as an outgoing and confident boy who was always charming the girls and popular with boys. 'He played football, perved on the girls, got into fights and acted like a loud-mouthed hoodlum sometimes', his friends said. Nicholas did have a sensitive side which made him popular with both boys and girls because he was a great listener and always ready to give sensible advice.
>
> The irony of it all is that Nicholas had parents who were both counsellors. They didn't think their son was different to anyone else. In his suicide letter, Nicholas ... apologised to his mother for

the grief he knew he would cause her and the utter desolation she would feel. But Nicholas felt trapped and alone.

He explained how he couldn't live up to the role of a 'typical country Catholic boy'. He knew that he would never be accepted for what he really was. 'You're shunned in the Catholic Church if you are a homosexual', a friend said.

Nicholas felt his place in the church, family, school and local community would no longer exist and therefore his life was not worth living because these things were so important to him.

While he never enjoyed an intimate relationship with another male, Nicholas always knew who he really was and that he could never be accepted in his community (O'Sullivan, 1994).

The story goes on to tell of a second young man:

A young Dubbo man spent his high school days playing football, dating girls, drinking with his mates and was always considered one of the 'boys'. None of his friends suspected that he was anything but a robust heterosexual. They did, however, notice a change after he returned from an overseas holiday. The young man moved to Sydney soon after, where friends heard that he openly expressed his homosexuality. He attended gay nightclubs with the trendy gay groups and dabbled in light drugs. 'I think it was all part of the Sydney scene, where it is almost fashionable to be gay', a former close friend said. 'He was the type of guy you wouldn't expect to be gay. I think he finds it socially acceptable in Sydney to express his homosexuality, but he certainly wouldn't come back to Dubbo to live. Dubbo just isn't ready to accept gay people (O'Sullivan, 1994).

The very existence of a visible gay community, and in Australia this might be partly associated with the staging of the Sydney Gay and Lesbian Madi Gras, has had one very important effect - some kids are realising the 'truth' about themselves much sooner.

It is now less possible to procrastinate on what Due (1995: xxii) calls:

the shores of possibility, imagining that what one assumed was a phase at thirteen is still only that at seventeen.

Yet, the sooner we come to realise who we are, the sooner we are exposed to 'the killing fields of stigma' (Due, 1995: xxiii). Almost always, it means we distance ourselves from those who were important in our lives. Adolescence becomes years of loneliness and alienation. As Due (1995: xxii) states in her book, *Joining the Tribe*:

we emerge from high school feeling like cowards (if we've hidden), failures (if we've escaped), or exhausted martyrs (if we've come out).

And that is if we have survived. Too many of us don't. The sooner a kid recognises he or she is gay or lesbian, the more difficult life becomes. This difficulty has little to do with the condition of homosexuality *per se*, but much to do with what Goffman calls a 'spoiled identity' (Due, 1995: xxii). It is difficult to feel confident about one's persona, and yet live in the midst of condemnation and enforced invisibility. It is difficult to maintain an inner sense of being a good and decent person. It is exhausting and soul destroying and yet paradoxically (if we survive), it is ultimately strengthening (Due, 1995: xxiii).

Youth suicide trends in Australia

In Australia, the problem of youth suicide has gradually worsened since 1960. Prior to then, suicide was positively correlated to age. The risk of suicide increased with age. Since 1964, suicide risk has significantly increased in two theatres of life - the young and the old, while at the same time there has been a relative and absolute decline in the rate of suicide among people aged between 35 and 60 years.

Thus, that section of the population which is now parenting the teenagers with a high suicide rate have themselves as a group experienced a remarkable decline in suicide rates over the past 30 years (McKillop, 1992: 2).

An analysis of suicide trends suggests that among 15-19 year old males, the suicide rate has increased from 7.3 per 100,000 in 1968 to 17.0 per 100,000 in 1988. That is a 250 percent increase in 20 years. The rate at which 20-24 year old males killed themselves during the same period rose from 15.3 to 32.0 per 100,000 - again, a greater than 200 percent increase.

For women in the 15-19 year old bracket, the increase in suicide was large - up from 2.4 to 4.7 per 100,000. However, the suicide rate in the 20-24 year old cohort remained stable at about 6.0 persons per 100,000 (McKillop, 1992: 2).

In looking at these figures, one must be careful and aware that the advancing sophistication of data collection may account for some of the increase. But that factor alone is insufficient to account for the trend. We should also keep in mind the latent homophobia often present in the reporting of data such as these. The most recently-published collection of papers to deal with this issue in Australia originated from a conference entitled *Preventing Youth Suicide*, organised by the Australian Institute of Criminology (!) in July 1990 (McKillop, 1992: 2). The index to that collection cites some 18 'causes' of suicide in youth such as family problems, alcohol, unemployment, mental health, availability of means, and so on.

But nowhere is sexuality, let alone homosexuality, mentioned. So while it might be 'fashionable to be gay' from a subcultural perspective, it is not fashionable, let alone acceptable, to ascribe a person's difficulty in coping with their sexual identity as a cause of suicide. Could this mean that to do so is an admission that society itself has failed the gay men and lesbians of our society - an admission wider society is unwilling to make?

In passing, it should be noted that the phenomenon of youth suicide is a world-wide trend. Lester, in a study (1988: 956) cited figures from 29 countries detailing the rate of suicide for 15-19 year olds in 1970 and the percentage change in 1980. Only six countries (Venezuela, Sweden, Chile, West Germany, Guatemala and the Netherlands) showed decreases. It was shown, in a study by Diekstra (1989) that Australia, in the period 1985-86, had - after Hungary - the second highest rate of male suicides in the 15-29 year old age bracket, at 26.1 per 100,000. By 1993, the United Nation's Childrens' Fund Report (Penley, 1993: 1) listed Australia as having the highest rate of suicide in the industrialised world. Sir Gustav Nossal of the Victorian Health Promotion Foundation was quoted in *The Herald Sun* as saying that research showed:

> suicide is now the second most common cause of death among
> Australian males (reported in Penley, 1993: 2).

It appears that Australian society might be nearly ready to accept the fact of (if not the responsibility for) the problem of suicide among its young people. Recent research and media reports point to a (hesitant) change in attitude. But one wonders still at the hesitancy and prevarication. Gail Mason (1990: 13) in *Youth Suicide in Australia: Prevention Strategies* intoned:

> it is essential that before answers (in the form of suicide
> prevention strategies) are brought into place, we possess a sound
> knowledge of the nature of youth suicide.

If we are to tackle the issue of youth suicide, we must put aside notions of niceties, coyness and etiquette. We must be honest and confrontational. We must not dilly-dally any longer. In Mason's study, eleven causal factors and a further eleven 'common risk factors' are mentioned. Some include:

> low self-esteem, lack of a support network, social and emotional
> isolation, poor communication skills and inadequate coping
> mechanisms (Mason, 1990: 44).

Nowhere does she cite issues related to (homo)sexuality nor to the special circumstances of suicide among rural youth. The remainder of this paper will attempt to address both these issues.

Rural youth suicide

In their excellent study of urban/rural suicide trends among NSW youth, Michael Dudley and his colleagues (see Dudley *et al.*, 1992) reveal some alarming statistics. The 10-14 year old age group constituted only 6.1 percent of the total youth (under 19) suicide. Of these, 25 percent were girls and the rate of suicide among this age group of girls, over the period 1966-1989, shows a decline. In boys, aged 10-14 years, the rate of suicide shows an increase from 0.5 to 0.9 per 100,000. This does not sound much, but it is an 80 percent increase!

However, it is the older youth who are more likely to suicide. The rate of suicide among male youth has increased since 1964. In NSW in 1966 it was 7.0 per 100,000 and by 1989 had all but doubled to 13.2 per 100,000. (The average annual rate for NSW females in this age bracket has not increased over the past 25 years).

While these figures, reflecting the national figures quoted earlier, are alarming enough, they pale when we look at the trends in rural NSW.

Over the 25 year period under discussion, Dudley suggests that, in Sydney, the rate of youth suicide, both male and female, has remained fairly stable, being 3.4 per 100,000 in 1966 and 3.8 per 100,000 in 1989. In Newcastle and Wollongong, on smaller figures, the rate also remains stable. But in rural NSW, youth suicide rates have increased consistently over the 25 year period from 1.6 per 100,000 in 1966 to 6.1 per 100,000 in 1989. This is a 400 percent increase! It is double the national average for this population cohort.

Again, though, this is only part of the story. Of the rural youth suicides, 35.9 percent have occurred over the last five years of the period (in 20 percent of the time) and this is largely a phenomenon of the older group, with the largest single increase being in young men aged 17.

The rates per 100,000 for 15-19 year old males in rural cities more than doubled from 5.1 per 100,000 in 1966 to 12.5 per 100,000 in 1986, whereas in rural municipalities and shires, the rates have gone from 3.5 per 100,000 in 1966 to 21.6 per 100,000 in 1986. This is a 600 percent leap in the rate of suicides among small-town youth!

Let us consider these figures further by examining suicide in Western NSW (Fitzsimmons, 1995). Between 1981 and 1993, 263 people in this region completed suicide, of whom 31 were women and 232 were men. That is a ratio of 7.5:1. The average male crude death rate out there is 25/100,000 (as against 19/100,000 for NSW as a whole) and in the Far West health district, this rises to 38/100,000. (It should be noted that suicide among women in Western NSW is lower that the State average for females.) The attempted suicide figures for Western NSW are five times the completed suicides in the age group 15-34.

In looking at the situation for males in 1992, for the age group 15-24, the completed suicide rate was 33/100,000 as against 21/100,000 for the NSW urban rate. In the 25-34 age range, it was 32/100,000 compared to 25/100,000 for the corresponding urban rate. These figures accord with Michael Dudley's follow-up study in which he cites rates of up to 44/100,000 for young men aged 15-24 in towns greater than 4,000 and 33 per 100,000 in towns less than 4,000 in the period 1989-1991 (Dudley, 1994). This represents a further 100 percent increase in deaths since 1986 and a 1,250 percent increase since 1966.

While all suicide figures are a cause for concern, these are a cause for alarm. And there is no evidence to suggest they have plateaued, let alone decreased. Figures from the US seem to corroborate the NSW data. While the research there into rural youth suicide is limited, Forrest in 1988 cites a study by the US National Institute of Mental Health involving 2,200 15-19 year old adolescents in south west Minnesota (see Forrest, 1988). Some 3 percent had attempted suicide in the previous one month, whilst the national average is 2 per 1,000. Depression scores on the youth from Minnesota were greater than those scores from adolescents hospitalised at the EUCLA Neuropsychiatric Institute. Furthermore, when Rosenberg, in 1986, repeated the study in two other rural communities in the same State, the findings were similar (Forrest, 1988).

Why should this be so? It appears to me that those causal factors most often cited seem to have greater impact in rural areas. While there has been limited research overseas, and (typically) virtually none in this country on the relationship between rural environment and causation of adolescent youth suicide, some factors, even anecdotally, seem worth mentioning.

US research by Rosenberg suggests that confiding in a friend becomes a primary coping mechanism in times of high stress (Forrest, 1988). In rural environments, stress results in limited interaction with the family unit, and neighbours are infrequently utilised for support, according to another study (Forrest, 1988). There is no reason to suggest that similar findings would not apply to the Australian rural setting.

For the country adolescent without a close confidant, life can be almost a living hell. Routine coping mechanisms become ineffective, resulting in increased vulnerability and a further increase in feelings of alienation. It may then become a downward spiral.

And it would appear (anecdotally) to this observer that those rural adolescents most unable to find a confidant in small-town environments in which they live are often likely to be gay. Urib and Herbeck in their study (1992) suggest that those who attempt to hide their gayness will typically experience damaged self-esteem, distancing from family and peers and self-conscious attempts to avoid disclosure. 'Passing as straight' incurs significant cost to their developmental processes and sense of identity. Those, who 'come out' face the possibility of rejection and conflict with parents, friends and school authorities. They face social ostracism, religious condemnation and (sadly) even threats to their physical safety.

This isolation has very much to do with family interaction. Remafedi (in Proctor and Groze, 1994: 506) reported that when he looked at risk factors among gay/lesbian and bisexual youth, he found the 44 percent of suicide attempts were attributable to family problems; 33 percent to personal or interpersonal turmoil, and 22 percent to hassles with peers.

Conversely, Savin-Williams' study (Proctor and Groze, 1994) revealed that self-esteem among young males was highest when they felt that parents were accepting of their (son's) sexual orientation. Gay males in this study who exhibited the highest self-esteem 'reported satisfying relationships with both parents, and having a mother who knows their sexual orientation.

Not surprisingly, poor family relationships also destroy self-esteem. Many studies have shown that lesbians and gay men have to contend with an oppressive social environment, including a rising incidence of violence. Hunter writes that he found that 46 percent of young gays and lesbians reported violence being perpetrated against them, and of these attacks 61 percent were at the hand of their own family members (Proctor and Groze, 1994: 507). A recent Australian study of young gay and lesbian homeless youth suggests that 70 percent of them 'had experienced some form of violence from their family' (Irwin *et al.*, 1994: 31) and 57 percent of males as identifying 'their sexuality as one of the major reasons for leaving home (Irwin *et al.*, 1994: 30). These frightening figures are in line with a further two Australian studies: A Report by Gay Man and Lesbians Against Discrimination (GLAD, 1994) (a Victorian group) and The Lesbian and Gay Anti-Violence Project in NSW.

In Hammelman's (Due, 1993: xl) study, 29 percent of respondents had attempted suicide, with over half of the attempts occurring before the age of 20. Hammelman identified four risk factors:

- discovering same-sex preference early in adolescence
- experiencing violence due to one's lesbian or gay identity
- using drugs or alcohol in an effort to cope
- being rejected by family members as a result of being lesbian or gay.

All of this is compounded in 'the bush'.

The country boy who is a gay has no role models and he has no-one in whom he can confide. There are no social outlets. He is young and alienated. Usually he is at school or unemployed, but either way, he is socially trapped. He feels personally isolated and *is*, indeed, geographically isolated. He knows only too well how vulnerable he is. He is the proverbial goldfish in a very small bowl.

Furthermore, he cannot reveal himself as he seems himself. This continual facade is a continual stress, and, as the certainty of a gay orientation increases, so too does the effort to conceal - often with decreasing success.

It seems to this observer of rural life that the age of highest incidence of youth suicide among young men - 17 years of age - is no coincidence. Seventeen might well be the age when earlier confusion over sexual identity is (for better or worse) finally dispelled. The irreversibility of the fact becomes abundantly clear. The realisation of who we are seems to finally dawn. This does not mean (necessarily) that we accept it then - quite the contrary. For most, years of angst still have to be experienced. It seems that seventeen is a crucial age, an age of extreme vulnerability. Nicholas, the young man from Dubbo, was seventeen. Nicholas killed himself, I would suggest, not because he was *confused*. Rather, he was so despondent precisely because he was *not confused*. It was clearly evident to him that he was gay; and that he did not conform to society's expectations or to those of his family. It was clearly

91

evident to him that his homosexuality was to be a life-long companion. What was unclear to him was what he could and should do about it.

A study by Gibson (1989) for the US Department of Health states that:

> suicide is the leading cause of death among gay male, lesbian, bisexual and transsexual youth...Gay males were six times more likely to make an attempt than heterosexual males. Lesbians were more than twice as likely to try committing suicide than the heterosexual women in the study. A majority of the suicide attempts by homosexuals took place at age 20 or younger, with nearly one-third occurring before age 17 (Gibson, 1989: 3).

The US National Centre for Health reported that of over 5,000 annual suicides by young men and women between 15 and 19, over 30 percent of these suicides may be directly related to emotional turmoil over sexual preference issues and societal pressures surrounding same-sex relationships (Gibson, 1989: 3). The US Department of Health's *Taskforce on Youth Suicide Report* reiterated this evidence.

But this is not new data! In their 1978 study, Bell and Weinberg found, like Gibson a decade later, that the majority of suicide attempts took place before the age of 20 and about one third before the age of 17 (Proctor and Groze, 1994: 506). As far back as 1973, Saghir and Robins indicated that five out of six homosexual men sho had attempted suicide had done so by the age of 20 (Proctor and Groze, 1994: 506).

In Australia, no studies have been done linking homosexuality and youth suicide, much less homosexuality to rural youth suicide. Thankfully, research is beginning to be conducted, with Western Australia leading the way. But if overseas evidence is a guide, then it would seem that perhaps the majority of rural male youth who kill themselves *may* identify as gay. And we should remember that the figures quoted above refer to city-based gay youth. One can only speculate on the incidence of suicide among young gay men on the prairies of America and the plains of Australia.

Final thoughts

Some eleven years ago, Garry Bennet (1983: 62) wrote that one of the ways to reduce the internal and external hostility that gay and lesbian youth feel is hurled at them is to institute

> community education programs that bring about an improvement
> in societal attitudes and knowledge.

Up to now society has rightly put resources, however meagre, into programs that target and support the *object* of societal hostility, that is, gays and lesbians themselves. But we have not, to now, put resources into programs that target the *sources* of hostility towards gays and lesbians. This dichotomy is well reflected in Barry Lowe's play, *Relative Merits*. Here, we readily acknowledge that the gay brother has a problem, but we overlook of bypass the fact that, in reality, it is the straight brother who also has a problem in coming to terms with the homosexuality (and concomitant right to a lifestyle reflective of that sexuality) of his football-hero brother. This poignancy of this is often lost.

Remafedi found that a third of the suicide attempts in his study group took place in the same year the youth had self-identified as gay or lesbian, and that, in fact, an inverse relationship existed between self-identification and suicide attempts - the later you know, the better. 'With each year's delay in self-labelling, the odds of suicide attempt declined by more than 80 percent (Due, 1995: xxi).

Gibson, in an interview, points out that this is a blessing in disguise. He asserts that, 'once people get some support and acceptance around being homosexual, those suicidal feelings are largely reduced' (Due, 1995: xxii). Helping suicidal gay and lesbian youth is more a matter of altering consciousness and perceptions and self-esteem than looking at drug abuse, gun control or whatever.

So, we must take resources and ingenuity into the schools and onto the streets. We must tell young gays and lesbians that it is 'okay to be gay'. But equally, we must tell their peers (and ours) the same thing, because if we can dispel the homophobia at its sources - namely, some families, many straight kids in schools and all the churches - then we can assist/eliminate the problems for the object of that homophobia, that is, gay men and lesbians.

We must acknowledge that our children are sexual beings and we must accept that their sexuality is irrevocably set at an early age. We must accept, too, that being gay or lesbian is part of the wonderful spectrum of wholesome sexuality in society. Therefore, we have to accept that gay and lesbian youth exist and have the right to be who they are. They have the right to have an inner sense of being a good and decent person; they have a right to be visible, they have a right to a wholesome identity. That is the challenge to our society. And we cannot afford to wait. Another Nicholas is one too many.

References

Bennett, G. (1983) *Young and Gay: A Study of Gay Youth in Sydney*, Surrey Hills, Twenty-Ten Publications.

Diekstra, R. (1989) Suicide and Attempted Suicide: An International Perspective, *Acta Psychiatrica Scandinavica* 354: 80.

Dudley, M. (1994) *Suicide Among Young Australians, 1964-1991: Urban-Rural Trends*, unpublished.

Dudley, M. *et al.*, (1992) Youth Suicide in New South Wales: Urban-Rural Trends 1964-1988, in McKillop, S. (ed.) *Preventing Youth Suicide: Proceedings of a Conference*, Canberra, Australian Institute of Criminology.

Due, L. (1995) *Joining the Tribe: Growing Up Gay and Lesbian in the 90s*, New York, Anchor Books.

Fitzsimmons, G. (1995) *An Overview of Suicide in Western NSW*, Sydney, Westlink.

Forest, S. (1988) Suicide and the Rural Adolescent, *Adolescence* 23, 90.

Gibson, P. (1989) Gay, Male and Lesbian Youth Suicide, in Feinleib, M. (ed.) *Report of the Secretary's Task Force on Youth Suicide*, Volume 3, Washington, US Department of Health.

GLAD (1994) *Not a Day Goes By: Report into the GLAD Survey into Discrimination and Violence Against Lesbians and Gay Men in Victoria*, Melbourne, University of Melbourne.

Irwin, J. et al., (1994) *'As Long As I've Got My Doona': A Report on Lesbian and Gay Youth Homelessness*, Sydney, Australian Centre for Lesbian and Gay Research.

Lester, D. (1988) Youth Suicide: A Cross Cultural Perspective, *Adolescence* 23, 92: 965.

McKillop, S. (ed.) (1992) *Preventing Youth Suicide: Proceedings of a Conference*, Canberra, Australian Institute of Criminology.

Mason, G. (1990) *Youth Suicide in Australia: Prevention Strategies*, Canberra, Department of Employment, Education and Training.

Meneese, W. and Yutrzenka, B. (1990) Correlates of Suicidal Ideation Among Rural Adolescents, *Suicide and Life-Threatening Behaviour* 20, 3: 206-212

Miller, N. (1989) *In Search of Gay America*, New York.

Montgomery, B. et al., (1994) Church Blamed for Gay Suicides, *The Australian*, 29 April: 3.

O'Sullivan, J. (1994) Gays in the Bush, *Daily Liberal*, 22 January.

Penley, K. (1993) *Ignore Them and They'll Go Away: Gay, Bisexual and Lesbian Young People and Suicide*, Unpublished.

Proctor, C. and Groze, V. (1994) Risk Factors for Suicide Among Gay, Lesbian and Bisexual Youths, *Social Work* 39, 5: 506.

Urib, V. and Herbeck, K. (1992) Addressing the Needs of Lesbian, Gay and Bisexual Youth: the Origins of Project 10 and School-Based Intervention, in Herbeck, K. (ed.) *Coming Out of the Classroom Closet*, New York, Haworth Press.

Chapter 8

Ideas of rural property in Australia

Malcolm Voyce

Prologue

> She said she hoped to goodness they would have no trouble with
> Indians. Mr Scott had heard rumours of trouble. She said, 'Lord
> knows, they'd never do anything with this country themselves. All
> they do is roam around over it like wild animals. Treaties or no
> treaties, the land belongs to folks that'll farm it. That's only common
> sense and justice'.

> Laura Inglis Wilder, *Little House on the Prairie*, 1935, (1981: 142).

I was bought up on a dairy farm in central North Island, New Zealand. Across our
farm boundary lay rich rolling land, owned by Maori people. This land had never
been ploughed and grassed but lay in its natural condition of scrub and fern. My
father often lamented that it was a great pity the land was not properly farmed and
lay wasted.

In later years I realised how typical was my father's attitude towards Maori land.
Many white farmers resented the fact Maori land owners underused their land by not
adopting European methods of farming. Many farmers politically agitated for
underused Maori land to be confiscated (Voyce, 1987) and used productively.
Essentially, what was at stake here was European ignorance or intolerance towards
traditional Maori attitudes towards land (Voyce, 1987; Tully, 1994).

Many years later I was reading *Little House on the Prairie* by Laura Inglis
Wilder to my daughter. This story was about a pioneer family in the 1870s in the
United States settling in new lands. In reading this story to my family I re-
encountered this typical attitude that land belongs rightfully to those who work it.
What intrigued me was, what was the history and source of such a common
European attitude found both in New Zealand and United States?

Furthermore, I wondered what psychological dimension of working 'owned
land' (as against rented land) gave to the formation of individuality and identity.

Introduction: Property as an iceberg

> The idea of property is like an iceberg. It is more complicated than it looks, and much of its significance is submerged (Minogue, 1980:10).
>
> The meaning of property is not constant. The actual institution, and the way people see it, and hence the meaning they give to the word, all change over time. We shall see that they are changing now. The changes are related to change in the purposes which society of the dominant classes in society expect the institution of property to serve (Macpherson, 1978:1).

Social ideas about ownership of land are like an iceberg: beneath the 'social surface' are a collection of values, or discourses, regarding gender, work, identity and law.

While the notion of an iceberg is suggestive to indicate that property is dependent on an array of other ideas emanating from different sources, knowledge of property come from both official and popular culture. In fact, popular notions may subtly constitute official notions (or vice versa). While ideas of property at official as well as popular levels seems self-evident, this approach is problematic as it implies the ideas of two separate spheres and inhibits analyses of the complex way notions of property are produced.

The dominant liberal critique tells us little of the social life of those who hold property or who depend on property. The reason for this is that the liberal idea of property rights regards only those who own assets (things) as being subjects before the law. Subjects are regarded as equal, but the actual distribution of assets is not (Cotterrell, 1987).

The concerns of property law, and the ideas of possession and exclusion obscures or mystifies the private area where owners have powers over others. Most property writers, like Macpherson, have analysed property in terms of power relations in the sense that property provides access to valued goods of life (Symes, 1987). Under this analysis property, as an individual right, becomes essentially the individuals share in political power (Macpherson, 1975).

Before I develop how I wish to examine what I tentatively call the 'social side' of property, several comments are appropriate.

Firstly, we must not develop essentialist notions of property. Some indeed argue that we are in an era where ideas about property are dissolving and no clear conception has emerged. (Macpherson, 1975; Grey, 1980; Edgeworth, 1988). Rather than speak of property (singular) we should speak of the notion of *properties* (plural) to emphasise that property should be seen as not having a definite finite eternal meaning but should be seen as emerging as a result of economic, social, legal and historical discourse.

Secondly, I am not interested in defining property in a legal sense. This is the lawyer's functionary role as hired professional. In other words I accept that the reader understands the hallmarks of modern landed property. Likewise, I am not interested in the history of property: the decline of feudalism and the rise of capitalism, the notion of 'possessive individualism' (Macpherson, 1962), the 'new property' (Reich, 1964) or the so-called 'disintegration of property' (Grey, 1980).

Thirdly, this paper is not a critique of the political theories of property or the justification for private property. A review of these theories of property whether they be the classical natural rights case based on Lockean liberalism or the Hegalian notion of personality, or other theories of property, is outside my scope. I only comment on these theories I have noted here to the extent they are part of the local discourse of farmers and become constituted knowledge as regards property.

Is property a social construction or does property-related behaviour have an innate basis? The evidence from Australia

In line with my approach to understand property it is tempting to review the various philosophical, political and psycho-social theories that have been advanced often by intellectuals to explain or justify property. I intend to classify the approaches into two categories, that of the 'social constructionist approach' and the 'personal knowledge' approach. I make this distinction to provoke the question of whether or not property-related behaviour has an innate basis or whether property related behaviour is socially constructed and defined (Loewental, 1976).

(i) Property as innate behaviour

In her biographical novel of her pastoralist pioneering family, Judith Wright traces the history of her grandfather who had developed a property in central Queensland. Wright's work concerned many themes; the concern for the Aboriginals, the environment, the significance of her grandfather and her concern to personally exemplify his life.

In the section below she talks of the affect the land was having on her ancestor, Albert Wright.

> In the years he had spent in that heart-breaking stubborn toil, the country had begun to set its mark in his bones. He would never love it, for he was of the lost first generation, brought up on stories of a country they had never seen; yet in the fight to master the land, it had in fact begun to master him. The long occupation of his whole mind and life with the problems it set had made him more its own than he realised; the ways of thought it imposed on him had become the yardstick by which he measured what was strange or foreign to him. His struggle with it was forcing him into an even narrower intensity of focus (Wright, 1995:114).

> But Albert had begun to nourish an idea. He had come to respect this country, which at first had seemed to him so uninviting. And he had the contours of the run clear in his head; he could see how it should be worked and what its virtues were. It had become a unit to him: the spread of the country along the creeks, to the range and beyond, out to the Island and back to Mimosa. He felt it as a piece of knowledge that ought not to be wasted, the map in his head, the

experience he had gained of the seasons, the rainfall and the distribution of feed and water. It was good cattle country, he knew now, though hard and uncompromising. He did not like the idea of raping and leaving it (Wright, 1995: 51).

This extract introduces the idea that landscape (property) may have a formative interactive force which may shape, or be part of, people. Accordingly, I introduce the idea of landscape or property as 'personal knowledge' to attempt to formulate a method of understanding how humans may perceive land. I acknowledge that such understandings may be coloured by a particular social context.

I introduce this concept of 'personal knowledge' out of the recognition that farmers frequently have an intimate wisdom of the land based on an appreciation of the natural cycles of the seasons and the capacity of the human life cycle to work with it. The recognition of the formative forces of landscape, attitudes of stewardship or the notion that landscape shapes personality, may be contrasted with exploitative attitudes to land.

(ii) Property as a social construction

Some writers conclude that the category of property reflects the social order and those who are in a position to manipulate social meaning. I perceive Foucault's work to be consistent with this approach in that property is the product of political domination (Cohn and White, 1990). The implication of this approach is to acknowledge that everything humans know to be true is conditioned by power.

On interviewing farmers I noticed the importance of pioneer narratives. Family stories of land development and settlement are important because through 'staking a claim in land' farmers develop institutions which reinforce family identity, hierarchy and gender allocation. Narratives create a commonality within a family as the 'audience' becomes part of the community as the tale develops. The meaning of gender is ensconced in these stories which do not really describe social events but create them (Rose, 1990).

These stories along with socialisation of children into work roles create hierarchy, gender roles and the allocation and definition of property. Importantly dominant masculine ideas of work construct the notion of work as deserving and who is to be marginalised (Parker, 1992; Miller, 1993).

What seems to be happening in frontier societies is that 'personal' knowledge about property has become culturally shaped. In other words, personal ideas of work and identity may be ideologically or socially interpreted through categories of thought or power networks.

The influence of John Locke

Philosopher John Locke saw the historical development of societies from the pre-monetary stage to the introduction of money and to an enlargement of possessions and land. Locke regarded that this ethic of development was found in its superior form in modern society. The process of development was legitimised by the ethic of industriousness.

In contrasting native society with its limited possessions and the desire for European societies for unlimited possessions, Locke was seeking to see a distinction between market and non-market societies and their different degrees of motivation. Cultivation of land was seen as the criteria of industriousness and rational use, in contrast to the 'waste' and lack of cultivation of native hunting and gathering societies.

Locke's four stage theory developed the idea of a historical progression in land use from subsistence hunting, and gathering through pastoralism to agriculture and thereby to civilisation and trade (Meek, 1976; Frost, 1981; Coltheart, 1982).

The vital leap according to Locke, between subsistence and industry, happened when people mixed their labour with the earth, thus entitling them to the fruits of their labour. Thus, bread, wine, cloth or silk the product of labour, were the symbols of property in the land used to produce them. Acorns, leaves and moss were the products of nature.

In Australia the ideas of John Locke and Vattel and the four stage progression of societies were seen as justifying Aboriginal dispossession. Earlier European observation of American Indians seemed proof of this hypotheses. Later some European histories recounted Australian history as 'in large part the story of the progressive mastery of land' (Coltheart, 1982).

These ideas took the form in the Gove case in a reaffirmation of the doctrine of *terra nullius* (land belonging to no one), the consequence being that firstly, all land was regarded as being vested in the crown; secondly, that the crown did not recognise pre-existing native title; and thirdly, native peoples had to show a proprietary interest in land ownership to have a legal interest in land (in the European sense of having boundaries).

That these ideas have been rejected in *Mabo* is not the point. Pastoral opinion has not shifted from the idea that native title should not be given to Aboriginals (Way, 1993).

While ideas of the supremacy of European political institutions and the idea of the primacy of commercial agriculture generally (see Tully, 1993) have been displaced or at least questioned what I proposed to take out of Locke is not necessarily a reading as to a juristic-discourse of rights as regards property but an ideology of work which attributes virtue to people who are industrious and diligent. In short the essence of humanity is to work (Hundert, 1972; Dean, 1992). I am interested in how discourses of work, discipline, habit and self-formation are linked to property.

What was the notion of 'property' which was transplanted to Australia and which formed the matrix of knowledges constituting property? In trying to seek an analysis of cultural underpinnings of European society, Heathcote offered the following as a view as to the background beliefs of early settlement.

A rationalistic non-scientific concern for the description of nature as a phenomenon to be studied in its own right was being complemented by the romantic movement with it concern for a wilder aesthetic nature. To these were added beliefs in Darwin social evolution and the doctrines of laissez-faire economics and capitalism. A belief in progress and the improvement of nature by labour and capital (Heathcote, 1975).

Coltheart has argued that the Victorian age presented a characteristic set of values which she likens to a lens through which the Australian continent can be viewed. She argues that the exigencies of Empire and the assumptions of the political theory of liberalism were the essential elements from which this lens was ground (Coltheart, 1982).

The relationship of Christianising, civilising and colonising indicate the role of religion as the dynamic. But, in this process, the promise of redemption was replaced by the promise of progress as the major force in shaping the landscape in the late nineteenth century (Coltheart, 1982; Williams, 1989).

The social construction of rural households: The role of work in structuring rural identity

In this section I attempt to critique the historical and sociological construction of masculine identity in rural Australia. I use the idea of masculinity in rural Australia to understand the discourse of male hegemony and the sexual division of labour which forms the basic underpinning for the understanding of the division of property on divorce and inheritance.

(i) The historical portrayal of rural identity

Farming in Australia has usually been portrayed as a man's realm, with women being background figures in the landscape. Farming identity is seen to be based on the acceptance of male hegemony, domestic ideals for women, a commitment to self-sufficiency and individualism and self-determination without government interference (Alston, 1993). To some extent this portrayal has been the result of our frontier colonial past and the political construction of the image of the free-wheeling bushman and the values of mateship (Pringle, 1993).

Lake has argued that in the 1890s the 'bushman' was lifted to a heroic status and that this elevation amounted to masculinist politics which defined itself against the effeminate cult of English domesticity (Lake, 1994). This model of masculinity had firm views about the place of women and a rejection of the idealisation of domestic man.

The turn of the century was also important as the state created a new ideology of femininity, extolling new forms of social control for women such as the 'consumer' housewife and an ideology of motherhood. Part of this campaign was the official government action that disfavoured women's agricultural work (Deacon, 1985).

I argue that this idealised historical image of the bushman together with the growing notion that women should be restricted to the private realm helped reinforce the ideology behind the sexual division of labour and its power structure based on male hegemony.

(ii) Sex and gender and the role of work

Sex and gender are the foundations of the individual and social identity. While sex is biologically determined as either male or female, gender roles are cultural constructions. It follows that what constitutes the notion of masculine and feminine varies from one culture to the next. Thus, men and women play gender roles according to what is deemed appropriate for masculine and feminine. One essential attribute assigned to gender is the sexual division of labour and the way men and women divide work among themselves (Reiter, 1975; Faragher, 1979).

The study of work, and who does 'what', is important as in a general sense 'work' shows how people experience, control/autonomy, power/powerlessness so essential to gender relations (Share, 1994). In particular, a study of work relates to kinship and property revealing how work constructs women as subordinate and marginalises and renders women's labour as 'unproductive' or 'invisible'.

(iii) The allocation of work in rural households

In Australian households Australian women appear to bear the primary responsibility for unpaid work in the home. It is also clear that the many technological aids to housework have not decreased the amount of work that women do in the home (Game and Pringle, 1983). It is also clear that women are responsible for the bulk of domestic labour in rural households and that part-time or full-time work by women has done little to change the traditional divisions of labour. Nor do men cross over and help women in the house (Alston, 1993).

Recent research has also shown that women actively work alongside their husbands on farms but that such contributions are not accepted as work because such contributions are only seen as 'helping out' (Gibson, 1990). Thus, women actively participate in 'men's work' but do so in a subsidiary role. The ideology that women do not help in farms, despite proof to the contrary, is instructive because it reveals the strength of male hegemony (Gibson, 1990).

It appears that younger women want a change in the sexual division of labour and a sharing of roles. Women in this regard have been influenced by the wider community and in particular by government bodies like the office for the status of women or the Anti-Discrimination Board (Alston, 1993).

Finally, it appears that the increasing pattern of women seeking part-time work, as a necessary step to support farm income, has not changed at the allocation of labour (Alston, 1993).

(iv) The implication of the sexual division of labour on 'divorce and inheritance'

The rate of rural divorce in Australia is increasing. Part of the responsibility for this may be the challenging of the rigid allocation of labour by younger women. Women's labour on farms has been devalued in legal cases reflecting rural attitudes to women's work. The law reinforces a particular masculine construction of property. Because of the strong ideology behind the sexual division of labour, daughters are not regarded as 'farmers', nor are they regarded as suitable persons to inherit the farm (Alston, 1990). The dominant practice is that farms are inherited by sons and normally only through marriage may a daughter become involved in farming.

Conclusion

Ideas of property change over time and even within the context of an individual's life. Towards the end of his life Albert Wright, looking back with a sixth sense of his own approaching death, wrote:

> The name she had chosen for the run, out of the Dawson Valley dialect, showed the strength of the bonds she was forging for them: translated, Wongwibinda meant 'stay here always'.
>
> He knew all this, and acquiesced in it; if he could have given her more yet, he would have delighted in the gift. But it set his responsibilities even closer on his shoulders. They had put so much money, so much trust, in this doubtful piece of land that it was now his burden to justify them both. Every step he took, every decision he made, was now desperately important; it might mean the difference between triumph and ultimate defeat in the struggle that engaged him. This new tension shut him off from taking pleasure, as May could, in the growth of the house or of the garden, or in the cool bright weather and the green landscape that so much delighted her; his eyes could scarcely spare time for them from his preoccupation with the goal.
>
> The importance of that goal, now, he would hardly have known how to question. The struggle for possessions and security, wealth and position, had become more and more central in his life as luck and the seasons had seemed to conspire against him. Now, he felt, was the final test of his abilities; the next few years would determine whether he could indeed justify the risk they had taken, whether they would in fact stay here always, or again be driven out (Wright, 1985:162).

This extract indicates that within Albert Wright's life his understanding of property shifted from a formative-interactive sense to property as being synonymous with personal achievement and social acceptance.

Albert Wright's life provokes the thought that the generations of men in farming Australia have not been numerous enough to develop any deep linkages with the soil. Likewise my brother, who took over my father's farm, now has more tolerant views of Maori land claims and the workings of the Treaty of Waitangi Tribunal which, to some extent, has recognised land and fisheries. In Australia the *Mabo* decision reflects a tension the shifting of pastoral opinion on Aboriginal land use. Little progress has been made on the granting of native titles and the coalition policy on this issue does not seem encouraging.

In Australian, European settlement had proceeded without concessions to native culture settlement patterns or land use - 'the survey lines and the fences could run straight for hundreds of miles as though they crossed vast sheets of blank paper' (Reynolds, 1987: 194). With the globalisation of the economy, fewer farmers identify with the phrase 'farming as a way of life' and increasingly, see farming as a business where families regard the farming property like any other asset that can be sold off (Voyce, forthcoming). Thus, an increasing group of farms are unsentimental about farm retention and can be seen to be subscribing to a capitalist ideology and a full participation in the market economy.

The dominant and most persuasive critique of Australian history has argued that agriculture from the beginning was capitalistic. Davidson and Wells concluded that the consensus on individual property rights was so strong that the right of 'getting one's land and working on it without hindrance' forced a political compromise that pastoralists should have access to extensive pasture (Davidson and Wells, 1984:107). Thus, in the Australian colonies:

> capitalist rationality, middle class morality, populist demands and liberal political economy apparently coincided on one essential point: property ownership, public and private should generate the rewards commensurate with the energy and sacrifice exhibited by the producer (that is, the capitalist producer). (Davidson and Wells, 1984:108).

The dominant view of Australian property is that the state endorsed the liberal Whig view of history enshrined in Locke and reflected in agrarian ideas of land: that land was to be mastered by men and that agriculture was the precursor of civilisation and commerce (Coltheart, 1982). Under this view ideas of European agriculture and labour were seen as supreme over Aboriginal ideas of property.

At a grass roots level the ideas of pastoralism in Australia were underpinned by notions of the rightfulness of industrious giving respectability to ideas of ownership. Under these views the state eventually reflected both popular and elite views of property, which enshrined the development ethos of the pioneer age. As part of the package of these notions lay the central idea of property, as a reward for male labour, the merit of individual autonomy, and the public and private sphere.

References

Alston, M. (1993) A Study of Farm Women, unpublished PhD, Kensington, University of New South Wales.

Cohn, E. and White, S. (1990) *Legal Socialisation: A Study of Norms and Rules*, New York, Springer-Verlag.

Coltheart, L. (1982*) Australia Misere: The Northern Territory in the Nineteenth Century,* unpublished PhD, Brisbane, Griffith University,.

Cotterrell, R. (1987) Power, Property and the Law of Trusts: A Partial Agenda for Critical Legal Scholarship in P Fitzgerald (ed.) *Critical Legal Studies,* London, Blackwell.

Deacon, D. (1985) Political Arthmetic: The Nineteenth Century Australian Census and the Construction of Woman 11, 1 *Journal of Women and Culture* 11, 1: 127-47.

Dean, M. (1992) A Genealogy of the Government of Poverty, *Economy and Society* 21, 3: 215-257.

Edgeworth, B. (1988) Post-Property: A Post Modern Conception of Private Property, *University of New South Wales Journal* 11: 87.

Faragher, J. (1979) *Women and Men on the Overland Trail,* New Haven, Yale University Press.

Frost, A. (1981) New South Wales as Terra Nullius: The British Denial of Aboriginal Land Rights, *Historical Studies* 19: 513-523.

Game, A. and Pringle, R. (1983) *Gender at Work,* Sydney, Allen and Unwin.

Gibson, D. *et al.,* (1990) Beyond the Dichotomy: The Paid and Unpaid Work of Rural Women in M Alston (ed.) *Key Papers No 1, Rural Women,* Centre for Rural Welfare Research, Wagga Wagga, Charles Sturt University: 8-20.

Grey, T. (1980) The Disintegration of Property, in Dennock, J. and Chapman, J. (ed.) *Nomos XXII,* New York University Press: 69.

Heathcote, R. (1975) *Australia,* New York, Longman.

Hundert, E. (1972) *The Making of Homo Faber: John Locke Between Ideology and History* (n.d.).

Lake, M. (1994) The Politics of Respectability: Identifying the Masculinist Context in S. Magarey *et al.,* (ed.) *Debutante Nation: Feminism Contests the 1890's,* Sydney, Allen and Unwin: 1-15.

Loewental, K. (1976) Property, *European Journal of Social Psychology* 6, 3: 343-351.

MacPherson, C. (1962) *The Political Theory of Possessive Individualism: Hobbes to Locke,* Oxford, Oxford University Press.

MacPherson, C. (1975) Capitalism and the Changing Conception of Property, in *Feudalism, Capitalism and Beyond* (ed.) Kamenka, E. and Neale, R. (n.d.).

MacPherson, C. (1978) *Property: Mainstream and Critical Positions,* Oxford, Basil Blackwell.

Meek, R. (1976) *Social Science and the Ignoble Savage,* Cambridge, Cambridge University Press.

Miller, P. (1993) Genealogies of Calculation, *Accounting Organisations and Society* 18, 7/8.

Minogue, K. (1980) The Concept of Property and its Contemporary Significance in Property, *Nomos xxii* (ed.) Pennock, J., New York University Press: 27-33.

Parker, H. (1992) Engendering Identity(s) in Rural Arkansas Ozark Community, *Anthropological Quarterly* 65, 3: 148.

Pringle, R. (1993) Putting Sex and Gender on the Centre State 100 Years Ago, *Campus News* 2 December: 11.

Reich, C. (1964) The New Property, *Yale Law Journal* 73.

Reiter, R. (1975) *Towards an Anthropology of Women*, New York, Monthly Review Press.

Reynolds, H (1987) *Frontier, Aboriginals and Land*, Sydney, Allen and Unwin.

Rose, C. (1990) Property as Storytelling: Perspectives from Game Theory, Narrative Theory, Feminist Theory, *Yale Journal of Law and the Humanities* 2, 37: 37-57.

Share, P. (1994*) 'Tickle it with a Hoe and it will Laugh with a Harvest!' Discourses of Closer Settlement in Australia 1898-1988*, unpublished PhD, School of Sociology and Anthropology, Melbourne, LaTrobe University.

Symes, P. (1987) Property, Power and Dependence: Critical Family Law, *Journal of Law and Society* 14, 2: 199-215.

Tully, J. (1993) Placing the Two Treatises, in Phillipson, N. and Skinner, Q. (ed.) *Political Discourse in Early Modern Britain*, Cambridge University Press: 253-280.

Tully, J. (1994) Rediscovering America: The Two Treatises and Aboriginal Rights, in Rogers, J. (ed.) *Locke's Philosophy Content and Context*, Oxford, Clarendon Press: 165-196.

Voyce, M. (1987) Native Doctors in New Zealand: Rua Kenana and the Tohangra Suppression Act 1907, *paper delivered to the Law and History Conference*, La Trobe University, 8 May.

Voyce, M. (forthcoming) Inheritance and Family Farm Ownership, in Lees, T. (ed.) *Family Farm in Australia*, Rural Development Centre, Armidale, University of New England.

Way, N. (1993) Rumblings within the NFF over Mabo, *Business Review Weekly* 28, 10 December.

Williams, R. (1989) Documents of Barbarism: The Contemporary Legacy of European Racism and Colonialism in the Narrative Traditions of Federal Law, *Arizona Law Review* 31: 237.

Wright, J. (1995) *Generations of Men*, Sydney, Imprint.

Chapter 9

Technological change and communications in a sparsely settled community: A case study in remote rural Australia

Roger Epps

Introduction

The development of a viable wool industry in the western portion of New South Wales was, in large part, dependent upon technological developments which occurred in the first half of the nineteenth century. Following Sturt's exploration of portion of the inland river system in 1829-30, steam powered paddle boats (introduced several decades later) provided a very cost-effective means, although inherently reliant upon seasonal conditions upstream, for transporting wool down the Darling River to ports such as Port Elliot and Victor Harbour. Another technological development redirected the wool marketing focus of the area once the Sydney-to-Bourke railway link was established.

Much of the hinterlands of Bourke and Wilcannia had very poor surface water supplies which curtailed the extent of grazing away from permanent water such as the Darling River and other inland watering points. The general aridity and unpredictable rainfall determined that the grazing of large runs was less intensive until reliable water could be located in much of this corner of NSW. Due, again, to technological developments, stock water supplies were located through the use of improved bore sinking equipment which released the bounty of artesian water (Shaw, 1987). Stock-feed - normally only accessible during wetter times - could now be utilised regardless of seasonal conditions. This fostered an increase in populations of both livestock and those that attended them.

Shortly after, the Homestead Lease provisions of 1884 provided the opportunity for additional families to be established in this region - a trend that was sharply reversed quite shortly afterwards. A series of droughts through until the end of 1902 took its toll on the fragile environment, the livestock, and the population. A somewhat more appropriate carrying capacity of the land was realised and restricted further significant growth. Due to the nature of the management of grazing properties, however, relatively high numbers of staff (stockmen, boundary riders, and general station hands) were involved in running the large stations except during the war years. The wool boom in the early 1950s witnessed some increase in population, but a portion of this was due to a high level of property improvement, including homesteads, woolsheds, yards and fencing. Since then, there has been a steady reduction in the population associated with the pastoral industry, particularly in the far north west of NSW.

There are many economic, environmental and political factors that have induced change in the more remote areas of rural Australia. In particular, global markets have had an increasingly significant impact on the viability of agricultural industries. At the same time, successive Australian governments have significantly reduced subsidies and other forms of support with the exception of drought relief and agricultural research. In the context of these harshening circumstances, this study focuses on the impact of technology on the community and neighbourly interaction in part of the far west of NSW.

Technology and quality of life in remote areas

For those living in the remote rural areas through the 20th century, there were many innovations that led to improvement in the living conditions including refrigerators, electric generators and electrical appliances, basic manual exchange telephones, radio, School-of-the Air and television. For those without telephones, regular schedules by two-way radios ensured that contact was maintained between remote homesteads. The introduction of the Royal Flying Doctor Service has been a major comfort to many living hundreds of kilometres from the nearest doctors and hospitals. In regard to the management of extensive grazing properties, probably the most dramatic changes have followed the introduction of motor vehicles and, more recently, motorbikes for mustering.

Whilst many innovations have reduced the time necessary for carrying out basic domestic duties and the need for additional help at the homestead, the deteriorating economic conditions prevailing over the last three decades have prompted a major reduction in the number of stationhands, or employed farm staff, from most inland agricultural holdings. It has been fortunate that the evolution of labour-efficient means to carry on normal activities on rural holdings have matched the need to reduce the number of farm employees. Now, many large holdings in the far west of New South Wales, particularly those over 100,000 hectares, use aircraft, helicopters or gyrocopters to enable them to muster their livestock, thereby maximising the effectiveness of labour. One person in the air and another on the ground in a four wheel drive vehicle or on a motorbike who is in radio contact with the spotter above, can quickly and efficiently muster single paddocks of 10,000 hectares or more, even when covered by scrub (low trees). In many instances, this is carried out by a husband and wife team, or other family members including teenage children who are at home during school holidays.

The role of the telephone

Communication by telephone has played an important role in remote areas. In the past, most homesteads were connected through manual exchanges to the outside world and a small proportion were linked via radio-phone. In many rural regions, the homesteads were often linked to the exchanges via telephone lines that they constructed and maintained themselves. They were sometimes primitive; the top wire in a fence was occasionally used although the line often became ineffective in wet or humid conditions. As the homesteads were generally at considerable distances from exchanges, many shared a single phone line. These 'party lines' as they were called, required the exchanges to transmit a call sign, generally a morse code signal, so that the required party would take the particular call. Some properties, were not directly connected to the exchanges, but used another intermediate homestead to relay messages.

Although some people had reservations about the lack of privacy of party lines, manual exchanges, and particularly relayed messages, these technologies provided an effective personal communication network within each area. They promoted a strong sense of community, both via the frequent use, and maintenance, of lines. Local news was readily transmitted, people were always aware of whether their neighbours were at home, and, in times of emergencies, the role of the exchange operator was central in coordinating operations.

Times change - as do technologies and their costs. In 1984, the national provider of telephone communications, Telecom, declared 'that Australians who require a phone, no matter where they live in the outback, will have access to the world communications network at reasonable rates' (Telecom, 1984: 16). This signalled a new era. Following a period when transitional technology was used, remote homesteads were connected to the digital radio concentrator system (DCRS) and the manual exchanges were eliminated by 1992. Each homestead had its own private telephone station that was linked to a line of radio repeaters, each with a range of 50 kilometres. This was achieved by a major cross subsidy from the metropolitan users. The justifications were that the system would save lives and provide 'for many rural and remote users, the only practical method of communication between their home and the outside world' (Commonwealth of Australia, 1986: 71).

The role of mobile radio communications

In the large outback stations, mustering in the 1960s was sometimes carried out with a light aircraft spotting the sheep and a message, literally being dropped to the ground, directing a stationhand with a motorbike. As the VHF (very high frequency), or citizens' band, two-way radio became available, it replaced not just this primitive method of communication, but provided an invaluable link between the homestead and others working on the property. Although its performance wavered in the heat of the day, it nevertheless had sufficient coverage to provide conversation between neighbouring properties, particularly since only a few channels were used. Most people in the vicinity new what was going on in their area, and cooperation between neighbours was regular.

In the 1980s, the UHF (ultra-high frequency) sets replaced the VHF. The FM based technology provided a much improved voice quality and did not suffer from interference and extremes of climate. It did, however, as a consequence of its higher frequency, have a more limited range than the VHF. In addition, each property used its own designated 'private' channel, which meant that neighbours would have even less opportunity of following activities.

The benefits of communication in the rural context

Siu (1968) felt that technological innovations would lead to significant social benefits and List (1969) expectantly waited for improved communications that would allow people to work effectively, but without being in close physical proximity. Further anticipating the evolution of telecommuting, Tofler (1980: 204) foresaw a 'return to cottage industry on a new higher, electronic basis, and with a new emphasis on the home as a centre of society'. Gold (1991: 328) suggested the proponents of the information revolution believed it would offer:

> opportunities for economic regeneration, for greater leisure time due to decentralized working patterns, for cultural enrichment from ubiquitous, and multi-channeled cable networks, for increased choice through electronic banking and shopping, and even for enhancement of democracy by instant (voting).

It is suggested by Cavill and Fidler (1991) that communication services will become more pervasive and that the technologies will erode geographical specificity. They will encourage the dispersion of people and activities and help rural communities better to cope with the special problems of their economies. Perhaps providing further incentive for decentralisation and/or population deconcentration, Newton (1991: 228) sees improved technology as opening 'a new era in relation to the relative attractiveness of rural communities for manufacturing production'.

There have been many concerns that communications are not necessarily serving the needs of society. The electronic media have a pervasive effect and there has been considerable debate about both the degree of censorship and the constraints that should be imposed upon the ownership of television and/or print media corporations. In Australia, in response to concerns about the ownership, access and delivery of propaganda, and standards of content on telephone message services (Jennings, 1983; Commonwealth of Australia, 1992), restrictions have been placed on some aspects of these operations. Through controls, and improvements in communications interfaces Biocca (1993) argues that provided technology is subordinate to society and does not direct it, there is undoubted scope for technology further to meet the needs of individual users and society as a whole.

Perhaps the concerns of Jennings and others about electronic media, information and telephone services do not go far enough, particularly in remote rural areas. Hamelink (1986: 8) contended that the information society is a 'post-society', and would lead to 'a break with previous values, social arrangements and modes of production'. In addition, Gold (1991: 327) states, 'social transformation through technological advance is still very much alive'. It may well be that, in addition to providing scope for improvement in the quality of human life, some aspects of technology may essentially be dismantling society as it has existed and offering a global, people-free, virtual reality.

In rural Australia, there has been a long tradition of independence, particularly amongst the agriculturalists. This has, in part, been a consequence of their relative isolation, both from each other and from support from urban centres. Holmes (1985: 13) argued that 'technology has altered, but not destroyed, the pattern of self-sufficiency'. However, he also claimed that 'high mobility and improved communications have further aided self-sufficiency by expediting shared work between neighbours in mustering and livestock work in yards'. This indeed was the situation during the 1960s when groups from neighbouring properties worked cooperatively on tasks such as fencing and lamb-marking (when lambs are tail-docked, their ears given an owner's distinctive marking, and male lambs castrated). The latter operation - carried out on mobs of up to 2,000 - needs to be finished early in the day to ensure that the young lambs will find their mothers before evening, and benefits from a large number of helpers, maybe from as many as five neighbouring properties. In a laudable spirit of cooperation these helpers would move to each property in turn assisting with the speedy completion of lamb-marking.

As indicated earlier, grazing properties started to dispense with permanent staff and, in the 1960s, began to contract teams of specialist operators for many purposes in much the same manner as teams were employed for shearing. This necessary development has led to a trend which has continued into the 1990s, fostered by the tendency for grazing properties to become larger through amalgamation. This study - reported below - reviews aspects of the changes to neighbourhood interaction with particular focus on the influence of new communications technology in this context in the far north west of NSW.

The study

The study area is located to the west of Wanaaring, 970 kilometres by road to the north west of Sydney and extending almost to Tibooburra, 840 kilometres north north-east of Adelaide (see Figure 1). Within this area - approximately 160 kilometres east to west and 160 kilometres north to south - interviews were carried out with all contactable property owners who were at home at that time (March/April, 1993). No contact was possible with three homesteads, but meetings took place with owners of the 26 remaining properties. The land is all leasehold, administered by the Western Lands Commission, but has been tenured by some families for several generations. The leasees own their livestock and the value of the 'improvements' including fencing, water and buildings.

Figure 1
The study area

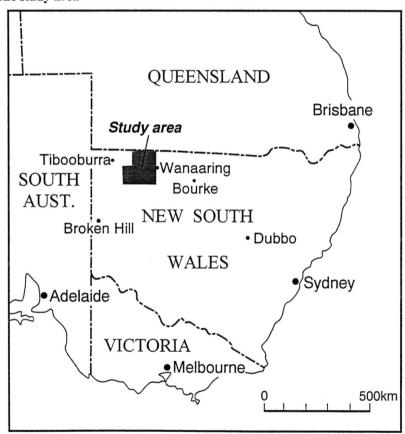

While properties average over 75,000 hectares, the modal size is some 40,000-50,000 hectares. All properties run breeding merino sheep and most carry some cattle when the season is appropriate. In addition, the majority of properties had significant populations of kangaroos and feral goats which reduce the number of sheep that can be carried, further exacerbating the economic and environmental problems confronting the landholders. Feed shortage was critical, at the time of the interviews, due to the prolonged drought and heightened by extensive growth of woody weeds (shrub-like inedible native vegetation) that has colonised much grazing land as a consequence of the disruption of the natural ecosystem.

Because of the physical dimensions of the grazing properties, there are extensive distances between homesteads, typically about 30 kilometres, and most travel is by four wheel drive vehicles. Names of the leasees were acquired from the Western Lands Commission and each homestead was contacted before visiting to ensure that the members were at home. It also served the purpose of alleviating their concerns at seeing a strange vehicle in areas where visitors are infrequent.

The interviews included questions about the frequency of visits to towns and major centres, the problems of isolation, and the frequency of contact and cooperative work with neighbours. Interviews also covered issues related to the quality of life of the families, whether their children intended to return to the property or become established on the land, and whether they intended to remain on the land themselves. These questions were all open-ended, giving the respondents ample opportunity to deal with issues they saw as important.

Results

Before reviewing the impact of changing communications technologies, a brief profile of the households interviewed provides an appropriate contextual background to the discussion.

Family structure

Nine of the 26 families interviewed had one or more children at home receiving schooling and a further five had children away for educational purposes. Two households consisted of single people, four couples had children who had settled away from the area, and six couples had adult children working with them on the property. One property had a governess to attend to the children, helping them with schoolwork, and also employed a permanent stationhand. The financial circumstances of this family were atypical of the general population of the area. Two families employed governesses on a casual basis. One property was managed by a non-family member. All other properties relied on family members for stationhand assistance and contractors for activities including shearing, some stock work, fencing and well sinking.

Quality of life

When given the opportunity to comment on the quality of life, some people contributed a number of responses whilst others appeared limited in their opinions. In response to the questions that asked what were the best and worst features of their living environment, the most prominent advantages, in terms of the number of times cited, were seen to be:

Lifestyle	15
Ideal for family	7
Challenge of the life	7
Isolation	5
Independence	4

The respondents could only offer half the number of disadvantages about living in this remote rural area. The most important was seen to be schooling (seven) followed by tourists (three) and the costs associated with distance (three). All except one family and the employed property manager expected to remain living where they were, but one couple qualified that by declaring that they will move away when they reach the age of 65.

When asked the likelihood of their children returning to the land, of the 18 who were in a position to answer this, there were seven whose children had or were about to do so, nine who believed their children would, and only two who felt their children would not. Of those who saw their children's return as a possibility, two commented that they and others would do their best to talk the children out of their intentions!

Travel to other centres

Travel by the respondents to local towns and further afield to capital cities is particularly limited. There are no significant settlements for as much as 400 kilometres for most of the sample. Travel to towns such as Broken Hill or Bourke are relatively infrequent with the average interval being monthly, but with some people visiting such centres only four times per year. Trips to these centres are multi-purpose, but purchasing of stores and equipment are the essential reasons. The majority of families managed one trip per year to either Adelaide or Sydney. The purpose of these trips was predominantly for a holiday, contact with other family, medical reasons and, in some instances, taking children back to boarding school.

Isolation

Living in remote rural areas with infrequent travel to towns could be particularly disturbing for people unaccustomed to geographic isolation. Isolation is a component of the way of life. Only two households considered that isolation was a frequent problem, whilst ten felt that it was never a matter of concern. Half of those interviewed acknowledged that they were not normally troubled by isolation, but that it occasionally caused anxiety. The circumstances fell into three general categories: roads being cut at times of flooding; crisis situations such as major illness; and lack of contact with family and other friends.

Contact with neighbours

Questions regarding the change in the interaction with neighbours and the extent of cooperative work established that there was a particularly marked decline in this form of contact. Over 80 percent did not undertake any form of work sharing, except in emergency or other one-off occurrences. Of the remainder, all stated that contact was only occasional or out of necessity, and certainly nothing like it used to be. The reasons why this situation had evolved included mention from 22 of the respondents of the following:

Difficulty in scheduling other activities into their own time	2
People use machines wherever possible and fend for themselves	2
Some people rely fully on regular contractors	5
Not many people left in the area	8
Most people are too busy	9
There is little communication between neighbours, regardless of whether it is about work or social matters	9

Two predominant issues appear here. One is the response to the reduction in the rural work force, its substitution by contractors and labour saving devices, and the extent to which people's time is taken up attending to essentials. It appears not to recognise the possibility that some efficiency may be achieved through cooperative work, but this matter may partly be linked to the second issue - the reduction in the level of communication between neighbours.

Discussion

The initial comments relating to the reasons as to why there was a reduction in cooperative work tended to relate generally to the reduced local population and associated consequences (26 comments) versus a reduction in communications (nine comments). Most of those who mentioned the latter were able, after some consideration, to offer some explanation as to why this situation had evolved over a period when, ironically, there had been many technical improvements in electronic communications. The following discussion draws on components of information volunteered, or indirectly offered, by 18 of 26 respondents.

Four specific influences were identified as weakening the reduction in contact with neighbours and the community in general. These were:

- the elimination of the manual telephone exchanges and party lines;
- the displacement of regular HF (high frequency) radio contact schedules in remote areas by DCRS telephone communications;
- reception of television via satellite dishes and availability of video tapes; and
- the adoption of UHF transceivers in place of VHF.

Ironically all these innovations were designed to facilitate electronic communication yet have tended, in part, to reduce the degree of work-related and social interaction.

Telephones

Prior to the introduction of automated systems, the exchange operator was unofficially involved in forwarding messages and, in an area devoid of local newspapers, a source of up-to-date information about community matters. The operator would often be informed if somebody was going away and also take a mental note of phone activity as an indicator of the subscribers' welfare. In crisis situations such as flooding and fire, warnings, recruitment and coordination were the obvious unofficial responsibility of the exchange operator.

The introduction of new DCRS telephones, where calls were charged on the basis of time, was resented by users who were accustomed to free use of party lines and minimal fees for local calls. Relative to the high costs of installation and service fees, the cost of local calls remains low. Despite this, several respondents said that they had restricted their telephone use as a consequence of cost.

The elimination of the joint maintenance of party lines by neighbours was also another, although small matter, that had reduced community contact. However, the overwhelming change to the level of local communication was the loss of the manual exchanges which had left the operators, as may be expected, feeling particularly isolated.

The elimination of routine radio schedules

The introduction of the DCRS telephones also ended a tradition of routine daily calls via high frequency (HF) radio that had existed from the earliest days of radio in the outback. In a more structured fashion than the telephone exchange operator's unofficial check on people's welfare, each household was contacted on a routine basis in a regular timeslot. This evolved through the necessity for many radio users to be using pedal-operated generators to provide power and radios could not be left on standby. Needless to say, it has been many years since other generator systems began to power the radios but, until telephones made HF radios superfluous, there remained a routine community interaction covering all matters ranging from urgent orders, through local news to medical advice.

The advent of TV and video players

Even if work-related contact was declining, recreational activity still involved frequent contact with neighbours or the local community at a variety of social events. With the advent of television, this situation changed considerably. Remote areas were without television until 1984 when the satellite transmission of signals enabled those with satellite dishes to receive normal programs. In addition, the availability of videoplayers, with the rental of video tapes made available through the mail system, provided most remote households with entertainment comparable with that of city dwellers. Rather than contemplate a visit to neighbours or the nearest small town for social contact, it became more convenient, cheaper, and less time consuming to sit at home and view a recent movie or television show.

Several of the respondents identified another significant trend - one based largely on the introduction of television - as reduction in their knowledge of local affairs. Due to the immediate, global, coverage of many television programs, such as news and current affairs, regional newspapers lose much of their interest, particularly if delivered by mail on a weekly basis. In addition, as a consequence of the physical and financial constraints of covering news items from remote areas, television viewers tend to become less well-informed about local issues than they are on national and international matters, particularly if neighbourly interaction is reduced. As one householder declared, she 'knew more about the war in Sarajevo than what was happening in White Cliffs' - the nearest town just over 60 kilometres away via a rough unsealed road.

The introduction of UHF transceivers

The reliability and reception quality of the UHF transceivers represented a major improvement over distances up to about 30 kilometres, depending upon topography and the height and location of the base aerial. For communication within individual properties, they are ideal. In order to reduce interference for satisfactory transmission/reception, each property uses its 'own' channel from the 40 available in the appropriate segment of the UHF band. Thus, each property has good, reliable, communication on an individual channel. This represented a marked change from the pattern of usage on the VHF band where there was, admittedly at poorer quality, a higher degree of intercommunication and neighbourly awareness of activity. Again, a change to more sophisticated technology, giving improved verbal exchange, has weakened another aspect of social interaction.

Conclusion

Unquestionably, technological improvements in electronic communication have, in particular, enhanced the potential for information distribution and interchange, especially in remote rural regions such as the study area. There is the distinct possibility that further developments, such as forms of electronic shopping, may reduce the need for some household members regularly to visit urban centres for the purpose of purchasing many essentials. This may appear to be beneficial through saving considerable travel time and associated costs. All facilities represent a reduction in the 'tyranny of distance', such an important factor in remote areas.

However, despite this dwindling of the impact of long distances and enhanced communication potential, there has been a substantial reduction in work-related and social interaction between homesteads in the study region. Admittedly, this is partially a function of reduced populations and also (due to limited labour resources) there is less flexibility in scheduling cooperative activities. However, often tasks tackled by a team can represent a more efficient utilisation of labour. Yet, because of the elimination of incidental contact via telephone party lines, radio schedules or use of transceivers, the opportunities for catalysing spontaneous cooperative work and social arrangements have also been reduced. The provision of entertainment and news via videos and satellite television further reduces the stimulus for social contact. It remains to be seen if, in the longer term, there is some return to the past levels of physical contact or whether the trend will continue towards the possible 'people-free virtual reality' in remote areas.

Note

This chapter draws upon a paper entitled 'Technology Changes and the Implications for the Sustainability of Social Networks in Remote Rural Australia', presented to the *IGU Study Group Conference on the Sustainability of Rural Systems*, Tsukuba, Japan, 19-26 August 1995.

References

Biocca, F. (1993) Communication Research in the Design of Communication Interfaces and Systems, *Journal of Communications* 43, 4: 59-68.

Cavill, M. and Fidler, G. (1991) Towards an Australian Vision: Capitalising on Telecommunication Advancements, *Urban Policy and Research* 9, 4: 237-241.

Commonwealth of Australia (1986) House of Representatives Standing Committee on Expenditure, *Poles Apart - Telecom's Zonal and Charging Policies in Rural and Remote Areas,* Canberra, AGPS.

Commonwealth of Australia (1992) Senate Select Committee on Community Standards Relevant to the Supply of Services Utilising Telecommunications Technologies, *Report on Telephone Message Services,* Canberra, AGPS.

Gold, J. (1991) Fishing in Muddy Waters: Communications Media and the Myth of the Electronics Cottage, in Brunn, S. and Leinbach, T. (eds) *Collapsing Space and Time: Geographical Aspects of Communication and Information,* London, Harper Collins Academic.

Hamelink, C. (1986) Is There Life After the Information Revolution?, in Traber, M. (ed.) *The Myth of the Information Revolution: Social and Ethical Implications of Communication Technology,* London, Sage.

Holmes, J. (1985) Policy Issues Concerning Rural Settlement in Australia's Pastoral Zone, *Australian Geographical Studies* 23, 1: 3-27.

Jennings, L. (1983) The Human Side of Tomorrow's Communications, in Cornish, E. (ed.) *Communications Tomorrow,* Bethesda, USA, World Future Society.

List, B. (1969) The Goal: a Communications System that Replaces Person-to-person Contact, The Tools: Satellites, Facsimiles, Computers, Telephones and the Microwave, *Electronics,* November: 80-87.

Newton, P. (1991) Telecommunications and Spatial Restructuring: an Australian Perspective, *Urban Policy and Research* 9, 4: 227-229.

Shaw, M. (1987) *Yancannia Creek,* Melbourne, Melbourne University Press.

Siu, R. (1968) Role of Technology in Creating the Environment Fifty Years Hence, in Ewald, W. (ed.) *Environment and Change: the Next Fifty Years,* Bloomington, Indiana University Press.

Telecom Australia (1984) *Telecommunications in the Outback,* Sydney, Telecom.

Tofler, A. (1980) *Future Shock,* London, Bodley Head.

Chapter 10

Accessibility changes in South Australia and the country town network

Peter Smailes

Introduction

Among the many aspects of rapid social change in contemporary rural Australia, two of the most fundamental are demographic change and the increased speed of access to major cities. Demographically, a division is developing between those (mainly coastal, accessible or environmentally attractive) rural areas experiencing in-migration, and those (mainly inland and based on non-irrigated farming) experiencing selective out-migration. In much of inland Australia, demographic depletion has been accompanied by low incomes due to the rural recession. In South Australia's case, this has been in progress since the middle 1980s, though interrupted by occasional good years, leading to the serious incidence of rural poverty by the early 1990s (Parliament of South Australia: Social Development Committee, 1995). Taken together, these factors have eroded the economic support base available for the service activities in the country towns around which social life and sense of community are focused. This chapter is concerned primarily with the potential for survival of the rather small locality-based communities which have long formed the basis of the rural social fabric in Australia. It examines the fortunes of country towns as shopping centres, not from the viewpoint of the economic geography of retailing, but as an indicator of the economic viability of communities. The relationships between changes in population, income, personal mobility and country town economic performance are complex, and as the former two have been dealt with in detail elsewhere. (Hugo and Smailes 1992; Smailes 1996, in preparation) the present chapter concentrates on mobility/accessibility and country town performance, inevitably against the backdrop of demographic change.

Accessibility and mobility

The present paper aims first to demonstrate empirically the extent to which patterns of accessibility have changed in South Australia over the past 25 years - in particular, the accessibility of the metropolitan area for rural households. Second, this is compared with the changing extent to which Adelaide's trade shadow has affected retail spending, over a 25 year and a 10 year period. Third, the changes in the fortunes of the network of country towns as shopping and service centres will be examined over the same time span to establish the extent to which these are related to changing accessibility and to aspects of demographic change.

Following Moseley (1979), it is important to distinguish between the related concepts of accessibility and mobility. Mobility, an attribute of rural persons or households, expresses the ease or difficulty involved in overcoming distance - in this case, distance expressed in terms of kilometres, dollars or minutes. Accessibility is an attribute of a desired target destination and expresses its degree of availability, openness and reachability. High mobility of the person is a necessary but not sufficient condition for high accessibility of the target destination, which is also affected by such things as opening hours, cost and social restrictions. Important recent studies attempting to quantify patterns of rural access to urban centres in Australia have been provided by Faulkner and French (1983) and more recently by Griffith (1992, 1994) and for New South Wales by Nichols (1993), while the Commonwealth government has provided a methodology for the measurement of remoteness by which rural areas can be classified (Commonwealth of Australia: Departments of Primary Industries and Energy, and Human Services and Health, 1994). These methodologies provide potential benchmarks for current patterns of accessibility and the promise of measuring future change. To go backward in time to assess change which has already occurred, however, insights gained from the replication of a regional study after a long time interval can be very useful. This has been attempted in this chapter.

During 1968/69 I undertook a study of the South Australian urban system and the extent of Adelaide's dominance over it (Smailes, 1969). Results, based on a postal questionnaire covering 630 rural households (53 percent response rate) allowed the construction of a map of the state showing respondents' reported driving time to Adelaide. In a similar but larger postal survey conducted in 1992/93 (2,000 households, 61 percent response rate) the same question was asked, and a new map constructed. The technique used was to use a moving grid window covering one degree of Latitude by one degree of Longitude, moving the window half a degree each time and counting the average of driving time responses for respondents within each location of the window, in order to construct isopleths of average reported travel time (Figure 1). In the interests of space saving, the 1969 map is not reproduced, but Figure 2 illustrates the *difference* between the 1968 and 1992/3 surfaces in hours. (Kangaroo Island is omitted because in 1968 there was no rapid car ferry to the mainland.) It should be noted that the driving times to Adelaide reported by rural people are generally a lot faster than the driving times published by the motoring organisations, for the benefit of tourists and using official speed limits. A trip to Adelaide is generally a direct, purposeful and limited-stop undertaking done in the most favourable time for driving, and speed is not seen as one of the seven deadly sins, but as a matter of what the car will safely do, tempered by common sense. It should also be noted that as distance from Adelaide increases, so too does the variability in the reported driving times, clearly dependent on such things as the age of the respondents and of their cars. There is a strong relationship between mean driving time from the city and the standard deviation of responses within the grid window locations, which should be borne in mind when interpreting Figures 1 and 2.

Figure 1
Average reported driving time to Adelaide, 1992/93

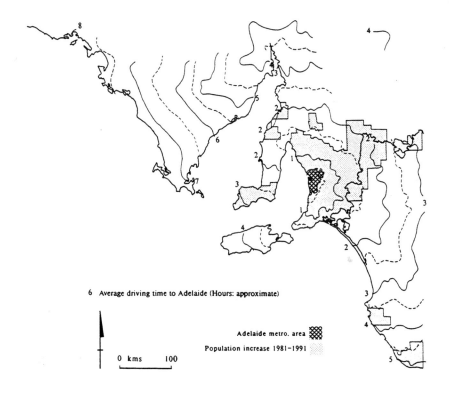

6   Average driving time to Adelaide (Hours: approximate)

Adelaide metro. area
Population increase 1981–1991

0   kms   100

Source: author's postal survey of rural households, 1992/3; Australian Bureau of Statistics, 1981 and 1991 population censuses.

Figure2
Reduction in reported driving time (in hours) to Adelaide, 1968 to 1992/93

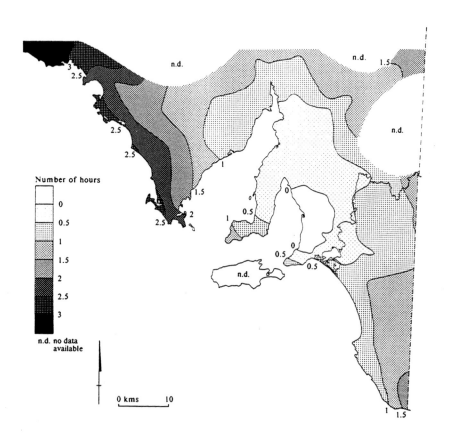

At least three significant points emerge from Figure 2. First, although the entire period under review has well and truly been in the motor age with almost universal access to at least one car per household, there has been a general tendency for driving times to Adelaide to be reduced. Second, as would be expected, this reduction has been greatest in the peripheral areas. At the outer limits of the settled areas, from Ceduna westwards, three hours or more has been cut from the average reported driving time between the two dates. This represents a very significant shrinkage of the distance barrier. Third, in the central core area of the state, from about Victor Harbour to Port Germein near the head of the Spencer Gulf, there has been very little saving of driving time. Indeed, up to about one hour's non-rush hour drive from central Adelaide, there has been no saving at all reported, and indeed it appears likely that the increased density of traffic within this area may have slowed the average rate of movement, wherever this has not been countered by road improvements.

Before concluding on the net outcome of the distance shrinkage which has taken place over the last quarter century, Figure 3 needs to be examined. This shows the *percentage* reduction in reported travel time over the period. The topography of Figures 2 and 3 is not necessarily related, for a fairly small reduction in travel time at a short distance from Adelaide may still produce a substantial percentage reduction, while on the remote periphery a much larger absolute reduction in travel time is needed to produce the same percentage change.

Figure 3
Percentage reduction in average reported driving time to Adelaide, 1968 to 1992/93

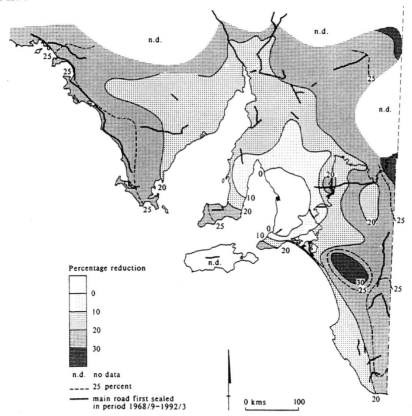

Source: author's postal surveys of rural households, 1968 and 1992/3; various road surface maps.

The results from Figure 3 do show a general relationship between percentage reduction in travel time and distance from Adelaide, but with several unforseen variations and changes. The maximum reduction in reported travel time of about 30 percent, which occurs in the Upper Murray and Upper Southeast rather than the far West Coast. Even in the late 1960s travel speeds on the Eyre Peninsula were already fairly fast, due to relatively light traffic, straight roads and low population densities. Nevertheless the 20-25 percent reduction in reported travel times over much of western Eyre Peninsula represent a significant change in the region's remoteness. The pattern of percentage changes in the southeastern quadrant of the State is much more complex, with a tongue of relatively low reported change (below 20 percent reaching right down the Coorong and coastal belt to the far Southeast. At the same time improvements of 20, 25 and even 30 per cent along the Duke's Highway (main Adelaide-Melbourne road) were reported at relatively short distances from Adelaide. Most of the eastern Murray Mallee and Upper Murray has experienced a 20 percent reduction or better, including a small patch of formerly ill serviced territory east of the Adelaide Hills escarpment.

The quoted surveys did not seek information on the reasons for these changes, but clearly there are three main factors involved - road sealing, the improvement of already sealed roads, and the greatly improved economy, comfort and performance of the newer generation of cars. Of the three, new road sealing has played a less significant part than might be expected within the settled areas, although it has made major improvements on the far West Coast, the Flinders Ranges and the main routes to Broken Hill, Alice Springs and Perth with the sealing of large tracts of the Eyre, Flinders, Stuart and Barrier Highways (Figure 3). However, a surprisingly large part of the South Australian network had already been sealed by 1969, and (although direct evidence has not yet been collected) most of the improvement in travel time has almost certainly come from the other two factors. It is a very different proposition driving an air-conditioned 1990s Commodore or Falcon along a well-graded, well aligned, three to four lane bitumen highway, than it was following a narrow bitumen strip, often pocked along the edges, in an equivalent vehicle of the mid-1960s. The fact that very many South Australian farmers and country people have been unable, due to the rural recession, to replace old cars, is likely to contribute substantially to the wide scatter about the means of reported driving times.

In sum, the evidence presented so far indicates that the principle of the 'elastic mile' is very appropriate in South Australia. The friction of distance clearly increases from the periphery toward the central core of the State. Even in 1969, calibration of gravity model predictions of trade areas showed that to fit empirical observations, a much higher distance exponent was required in the core area of the State than in the periphery (Smailes, 1969). What we are witnessing is a kind of on-going logarithmic transformation of physical space.

Changes in Adelaide's dominance of the State's retail and services provision

The next step in the analysis is to investigate whether the demonstrated reduction in travel times has favoured Adelaide and deepened the trade shadow it casts over the whole State. In 1968/9 the Adelaide central business district cast a very heavy shadow over the country areas (Smailes, 1969), taking over half of the country householders' business for items other than day-to-day standard items over large parts of the State, according to two different measures.[1] By the early 1980s, the pattern revealed by a second (1982/83) postal survey was similar in outline, but at a much lower level of Adelaide dominance. Since then further substantial changes have occurred, and as both the 1982/3 and 1992/3 surveys were based on about 1,200 respondents and used identical methods, we can be fairly confident that real changes are in progress. Since 1982/3, Adelaide's relative share of rural spending has in fact *declined* substantially. The 50 percent 'trade shadow' area of the State, in which respondents on the average estimate they incur over half their expenditure in Adelaide, has been reduced from a very dominant area in 1968/9 to a more limited zone in 1982/3, including only the southern end of Yorke Peninsula and Kangaroo Island plus a belt extending from around Gawler to the Upper Southeast (Figure 4). By 1992/3, this had been further reduced to just Kangaroo Island and Southern Yorke Peninsula.

These changes, however, are the result of complex causes, and certainly can not be explained simply by changes in the speed of personal access to Adelaide - indeed, the results are counter-intuitive. Another, and probably more important, factor has been the changing structure and location of the State's retail industry over the last quarter century (Table 1).

Table 1
Proportions of retail and selected service turnovers by location type, 1968/9 to 1991/2

Location	1968/9		1973/4		1985/6		1991/2	
	$000	%	$000	%	$000	%	$000	%
City of Adelaide	263,639	26.5	389,391	23.5	1,125,677	15.4	1,120,552	15.3
Rest of Metro area	473,386	47.7	876,635	53.0	4,631,716	63.3	4,684,135	63.8
Total, Adelaide Statistical Division	737,025	74.2	1,266,026	76.5	5,757,393	78.7	5,804,687	79.1
Rest of the State	256,218	25.8	388,380	23.5	1,559,923	21.3	1,537,545	20.9
TOTAL STATE	993,243	100.0	1,654,406	100.0	7,317,316	100.0	7,342,232	100.0

Source: Australian Bureau of Statistics: Retail Censuses, 1968/9, 1973/4 and 1991/2.

Clearly, although the central business district (which accounts for the great majority of the City of Adelaide turnover) is still by far the largest single retail complex in the State, it steadily lost ground in terms of its dominance over the rest of the metropolitan area. Whereas in 1968/9 the CBD and the country areas (such as the State exclusive of the Adelaide Statistical Division) each had about a quarter of the total retail turnover, by 1991/2 both had suffered heavy relative losses, while the proportion of the turnover spent in suburban and satellite locations within the Adelaide SD rose from less than half to almost two thirds. The change in the balance occurred rapidly between 1973/4 and 1985/6.

Figure 4
Changes in Adelaide's reported 50 percent trade shadow area, 1968-1992/3

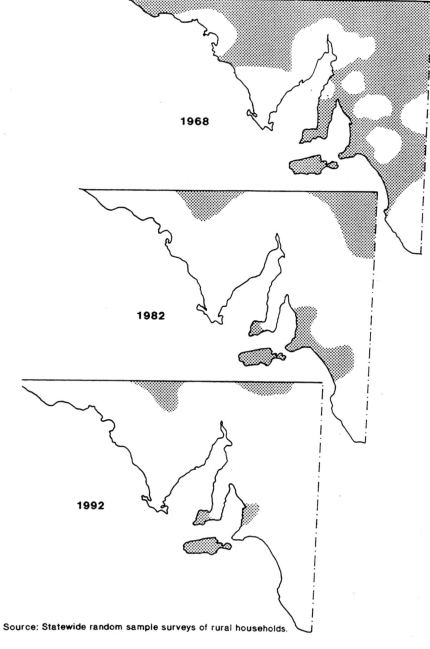

1968

1982

1992

Source: Statewide random sample surveys of rural households.

This burgeoning growth of large suburban shopping complexes has thus provided a new element of competition for retailers in country locations. In

126

1968/9, I was able to show that the suburban shopping centres, then in the early stages of their development, had a negligible impact on the shopping habits of country people. By 1992/3, however, they were drawing in many rural customers from well beyond the metropolitan commuting zone, who may previously have patronised the Central Business District. This competition has clearly reduced central Adelaide's dominance in the more accessible rural districts, but there are several other potential reasons why reduced travel time has not increased the City's retail hegemony:

1   The general drop in rural incomes has reduced discretional spending on major items typically supplied in the CBD.
2   In the context of low rural incomes, travel time reduction has not been matched by equivalent reduction in travel cost.
3   The increased speed of travel has benefited the larger regional centres, as well as Adelaide.

To assess some of these suggestions, the focus now changes to the level of the individual community.

Measuring change in regional shopping centres and the country town network

It is not a simple task to measure and analyse change at the level of the individual country town for the entire urban system of South Australia. This is due, partly, to the lack of data on small size country towns, and partly due to constantly changing definitions. The retail census is the most suitable vehicle for analysing business performance, since it gives data on turnover, workforce, number of establishments and floor space for the same set of locations in each census year. Retailing is, of course, only one of the many tertiary service activities contributing to the economy of country towns, but it is probably the most important in terms of employment and is a vital element in forming the image of a rural community. In the absence of data on the performance of other sectors at an adequate scale of spatial resolution, the retail censuses are taken as an adequate surrogate for the general health and performance of the service sector.

These data have several shortcomings however, notably the facts that there have been numerous changes in both the definitions of what types of services are included, and in what is required to qualify an establishment for inclusion. Further, the smallest area for which data are available for each census year is the LGA, and most of these contain more than one town or suburban centre. For this study, retail census data for each LGA have, therefore, been apportioned *pro rata* to towns (or major regional shopping centres, in the case of suburban LGAs) within it, using the Universal Business Directory information on numbers of establishments in each town for 1968/9. For 1991/92, the more exact data on the numbers of retail businesses for each individual postcode area from the ABS Business Register, as at March 1994, were used for the pro rata allocation. Following this, to qualify for inclusion in the analysis country towns were also required to

- have at least 10 retail establishments in 1991/2;
- have their own postcode; and
- have a town population of at least 200 at the 1971 and 1991 population censuses (forming at least a 'bounded rural locality' CCD in both censuses).

Figure 5
Percentage share of total State retail employment, by town, 1991/92

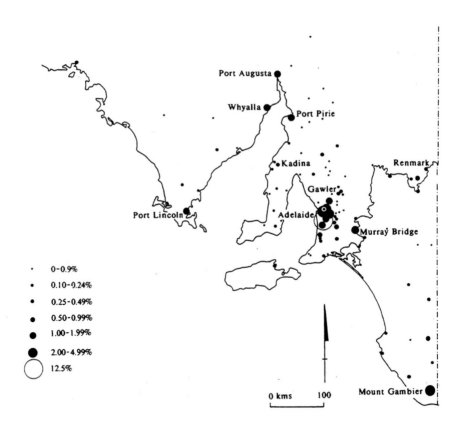

Source: Census of Retailing in South Australia, 1991/92.

Resulting from these criteria, 83 country towns were included (Figure 5). A further 17 towns had at least 10 establishments in 1968/9, but had dropped below the threshold by 1991/2, while only one new qualifier had emerged by that date. In addition, included in the analysis are the City of Adelaide and eight regional shopping centres within metropolitan Adelaide which were identified as being used by the 1992/3 postal survey rural respondents. Where the latter were contained within large LGAs that had substantial shopping outside the main regional centre, they were separated out *pro rata* from the total LGA In order for the retail census data to be comparable from year to year despite the various changes in definitions, the town data for each year have been converted from absolute numbers of shops, employees and dollars of turnover to *pro mille* shares of the State total in each case.

Service provision as at June 1992

Figure 5 provides a snapshot view of the status of retailing in 1992. Of the three available indicators, employment in retailing has here been taken as the best indicator of provision, since the number of establishments gives no indication of the scale of provision, while the volume of sales is more variable from year to year, dependent *inter alia* on the level of regional (particularly farm) incomes.

The immediate messages of the Figure are first, that despite its relative decline Adelaide city continues to dominate the State. The 12,292 persons employed in retailing there at 31 June 1992 outnumbered the entire resident population of the city. Second, the enormous growth of regional shopping centres within the metropolitan area (Adelaide statistical division) has seen the biggest of them outstrip all country centres except Mt Gambier. Third, the growth of the competing regional centres of relevance to country shoppers has been heavily concentrated on the northern side of the city, where Elizabeth, Salisbury and increasingly Gawler have attracted much custom from rural residents to their north. The influence of the Marion and Noarlunga regional centres to the south is so far much more limited. Fourth, when the present pattern of retail provision is compared with the 1992/3 map of Adelaide's trade shadow, the country centres with apparently the greatest success in keeping Adelaide at bay appear still to be Port Lincoln, Port Augusta, Whyalla, the remote town of Ceduna, and above all Mount Gambier where Adelaide's average reported share of consumer spending falls below 10 percent.

While Figure 5 shows the extent of retail provision, it gives only a very indirect indication of the *relative* performance of each town, and Figure 6 therefore provides a performance indicator. Since the town retailing data are arranged by postcode, it has become possible to estimate the proportion of locally earned income which is going through local businesses. To the extent that turnover approaches or even exceeds 100 percent of locally earned income, the town is clearly acting as a successful central place. On the other hand, a low percentage indicates that the town is either not able to provide an adequate suite of services, or is suffering business leakage through competition by other centres.

Examination of Figure 6 shows that, once again, Adelaide, with retail turnover at 1,320 percent of the taxable income of the city's resident population, emerges as the dominant central place. Only five of the other centres studied have turnovers that exceed 100 percent of the taxable income

Figure 6
Retail turnover as a percentage of local taxable income, by town and postcode area, 1991/92

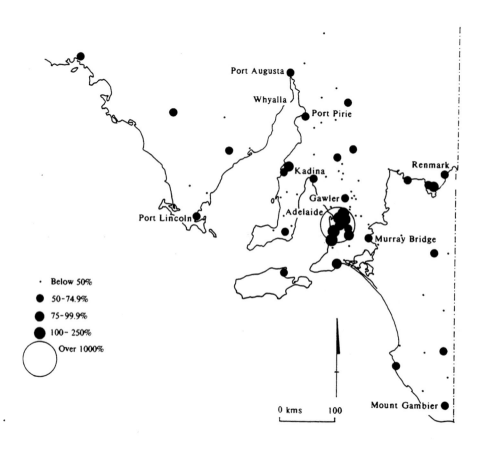

Source: Australian Bureau of Statistics, Census of Retailing in South Australia, 1991/92; Annual Report of Commissioner of Taxation, 1991/92 tax year.

being earned within their postcode areas, and all these are major regional shopping centres within the metropolitan area - Noarlunga Centre, Marion, Elizabeth, Salisbury and Tea-Tree Plaza. Once outside the metropolitan area, though, there is no necessary relationship between size of town and successful exploitation of the local market potential. Towns with turnover exceeding 75 percent of local taxable income include some quite small places, such as Yorketown on Yorke Peninsula and Berri, centrally located in the irrigation areas of the Riverland region, as well as the more dominant local centres of Kadina, Mount Barker and Victor Harbour, while some of the largest country towns - notably Whyalla, Port Pirie, Port Lincoln and Mount Gambier - fail to reach the 75 percent level. Figure 6 also shows the tendency, particularly on Eyre Peninsula, for a small number of strategically located and evenly-spaced towns to take over trade from their neighbours. In particular, two of the most successful small communities are Cleve and Wudinna, which despite their inland location are well placed to share dominance of the Peninsula with the larger towns at the three corners of the triangle - Port Augusta, Port Lincoln, and Ceduna. The performance of Cleve is particularly striking, for it is located well off the main highways, has no industry and very little tourism. In the central and eastern wheat belt regions of the State too, the most successful towns are widely scattered. The influence of tourist income in boosting turnovers is apparent in a number of coastal centres, though this is more limited than might have been expected. Robe, Victor Harbour, Moonta, Kingscote and Port Broughton have large retirement/tourism functions though there is obviously some contribution from tourism in the others. Kingscote on Kangaroo Island is a special case where the heavy loss of trade to Adelaide for high order items is compensated by its tourism function and insulation from competition for low-order goods.

Changes in retail performance 1968/9 to 1991/2

Turning from the current situation to actual changes in retailing over the past 25 years, Figure 7 reveals a very striking pattern of change which strongly reflects the increasing differentiation between core and periphery. For each town, the map shows the 1992 percentage share of the total State retail *employment* as a ratio of the 1968 share; the results for *turnover* (not presented here) are spatially almost identical. The picture is clear, stark and simple. A core area of relative growth in the share of the State's retail business extending from the Barossa Valley to the coastal resorts of Victor Harbour and the other Encounter Bay towns is offset by relative decline throughout the rest of the rural areas, with just a single notably successful outlying centre in each corner of the settled areas - Ceduna, Port Lincoln, Berri and Mt. Gambier. Beyond this, only a couple of tourism/retirement centres stand out. At first sight, Figure 7 appears to give a clear answer to the question of whether change in country shopping centres has been linked to changes in their accessibility to Adelaide. The great majority of country towns showing growth have high absolute accessibility, and have experienced negligible percentage change in driving time to Adelaide over the period, nearly all lying within about 90 minutes' driving time from the city. Thus, it would appear that for most towns, a large increase in accessibility to Adelaide correlates with a declining share of the State's retail turnover and employment The observed changes in retailing may simply reflect, however, the differential population growth and decline between the accessible and the peripheral rural areas.

131

Figure 7
Ratio of share of State employment in retailing 1991/92 to share in 1968/69, by town

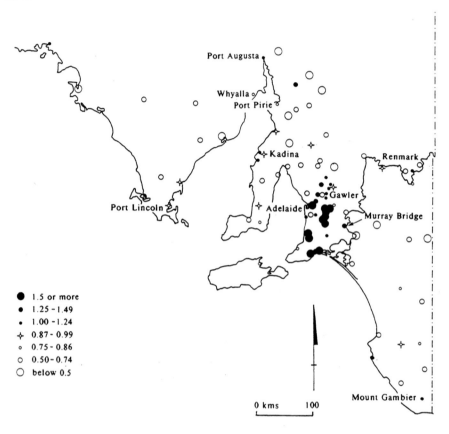

Source: Australian Bureau of Statistics: Census of Retail and Selected Service Establishments, 1968/69; and Census of Retailing in South Australia, 1991/92.

In order to test this assumption it is necessary to control for the effects of population change, and this is done by examining the change in location quotients of retail turnover: for each town at a given point in time, its share of the State retail turnover is expressed as a ratio of its share of the State's total urban population. A ratio (location quotient) above 1.0 indicates that the town has a greater turnover than would be 'expected' from its population share. Change in the location quotient over time then indicates whether or not the town is improving its performance relative to its population base, independent of population change. This procedure stretches the less than ideal data base to the limit: results may not be reliable for individual small places. However, the overall spatial picture should be correct and shows some consistent and interesting features (Figure 8).

Figure 8
Retail turnover change, 1968/9 to 1991/2: ratio of location quotient 1991/2 to location quotient 1968/9

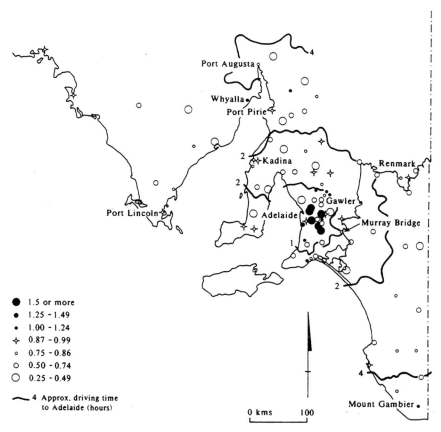

Source: Australian Bureau of Statistics: Census of Retail and Selected Service Establishments, 1968/69; and Census of Retailing in South Australia, 1991/92.

Over the full 23 year period from 1968/9 to 1991/2, by far the dominant feature was the growth of outer suburban and satellite regional shopping centres around the periphery of the metropolitan area. That the retail sales in these places has grown even faster than the substantial growth of their own populations indicates that these places have siphoned off a substantial part of the spending of both suburban and rural households within about a 90-minute radius of Adelaide, so that population growth in these areas has not been reflected by a proportionate increase in trading in the smaller towns. Nevertheless, the country towns which have improved their position are practically all within a little over an hour's drive from Adelaide, apart from the largest regional centres (Whyalla, Mount Gambier). Other towns which have almost held their own over the longer period appear on Figure 8 with a cross-like symbol. These show location quotient changes better than the non-metro average of 0.86 but below the State average of 1.00, and are mostly located about 1.5 to 2.5 hours from Adelaide - outside the immediate pull of the satellite centres - or are important outlying centres, including Port Lincoln, Port Pirie, Ceduna and Berri.

Turning to Figure 9, however, it is clear that a significantly different pattern of change in the location quotients has developed in the last seven years of the study period. This coincides with a period of rural crisis, as well as the nation-wide 'depression we had to have', and it is somewhat unexpected to find that a much larger number of country centres have improved their share of retail turnover in relation to their share of the State's urban population in this period. Some reasons are suggested below.

Figure 9
Retail turnover change, 1985/6 to 1991/2: ratio of location quotient 1991/2 to location quotient 1985/6

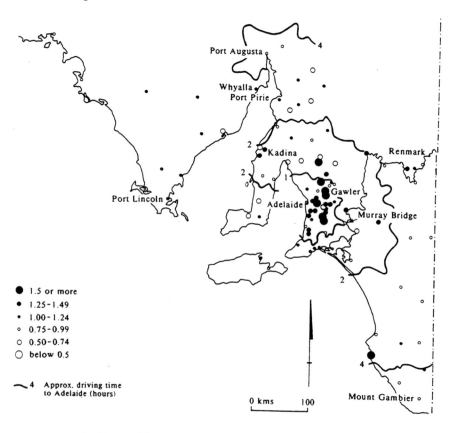

Source: Australian Bureau of Statistics: Retail Industry Small Area Statistics, South Australia 1985-86; and Census of Retailing in South Australia, 1991/92.

First and most importantly, it was during the period 1968/9 to 1985/6 that the major satellite shopping centres were building up their share of trade vis-à-vis the CBD and country areas. By the mid 1980s this process had run its course, and the turnover share of the Adelaide Statistical Division outside the City proper hardly changed up to 1993 (Table 1). Second,.the trade shadow effect of the CBD had been reduced by 1992/3 and although the slack had been taken up by metropolitan satellites or the country regional centres (Figure 4), many smaller centres located in relatively accessible or environmentally attractive areas were beginning to feel the benefits of population growth resulting from the continued if selective counterurbanisation trends. Third, this same counterurbanisation trend was reflected by relatively higher average incomes in the affected rural areas, offsetting in part the depressed state of farm incomes in a spatially selective manner. Thus most country centres within an hour's non-rush hour drive, and a selection of those within about 90 minutes, have improved their relative status.

Brief mention is needed of a number of small inland wheat belt towns which have improved their location quotients on Figure 9 not by increasing their share of the State's turnover, but because their share of the total urban population has fallen faster than their turnover share. This is the case with nine small inland towns[2]. Apart from these, Figure 9 confirms the strong emergence of a core-periphery structure in the distribution of country centres.

To what extent, then, have changes in personal mobility and accessibility affected rural communities as service centres, as compared with the effects of demographic change? Before drawing conclusions, the visual evidence given in Figures 1-9 is supplemented by brief presentation of more quantitative data on the relative strengths of some of these relationships. The three dependent variables used are change in the town's share of the State's retail and special services (a) turnover, (b) employment, and (c) establishments, from 1968/9 to 1992/3. These are compared with one pair of accessibility and two pairs of demographic independent variables (Table 2)

Table 2
Correlations of three measures of retail change in country towns, 1968/9 to 1991/2, with selected independent variables (Pearson's *r*).

	Change, 1968/9 to 1991/2, in share of State retail and special services:		
	(a) turnover	(b) employment	(c) establishments
Driving time to Adelaide, 1968	-0.325	-0.331	-0.290
Change in travel time to Adelaide, 1968-92	-0.349	-0.386	-0.264
Town population, 1971 census	0.002	-0.006	0.001
Change in town population, 1971-1991	0.715	0.661	0.573
Surrounding rural population density, 1981	0.433	0.488	0.558
Rural population density change, 1981-91	0.557	0.522	0.411

Source: Author's survey data; Retail Censuses 1968/9, 1991/2; Population Censuses 1971/ 81/91.

The table reveals several interesting features. In a highly unicentric state, relative location with respect to Adelaide at the outset of the time period is a significant factor for a country town. First, as would be expected from Figures 8 and 9, both accessibility variables show weak negative correlations with all the measures of retail performance. The greater the distance from Adelaide in travel time at the outset of the period, the more likely that the town has experienced a decline in its share of the State's retail turnover, employment and establishments. Similarly, because the remotest centres have experienced the biggest reductions in travel time to Adelaide, a large reduction in travel time over the 23 year period correlates with low or negative growth in the town's share of retail activity. The correlations are weak, however, with r^2 values showing that the accessibility variables account only for between about 7 and 15 percent of the variance, and other important factors are obviously involved.

Turning to the demographic variables, these have been separated into two pairs, one relating to the population of the *town itself*, the other to the *rural service population* in which it is embedded. As to the former, it might be expected that towns which were large at the start of the study period, with a head start, would tend to improve their share of retail activity relative to their smaller competitors. In fact, there is absolutely no relationship: some of the largest centres have lost ground, while many small places, particularly those closer to the city, have shown healthy increases (Figure 7). Looking at urban population change 1971-1991, however, the correlations are at their strongest, particularly in the case of turnover share. Turnover responds quickly to a change in town population, while in small country businesses employment changes are slower and the actual closure or opening of new businesses is subject to considerable inertia. To say that the service sector in a country town is sensitive to change in the town population is not very meaningful, however, for both these factors are interrelated and probably both are responding together to other causative variables.

In many ways the most interesting variables shown on Table 2 are those relating to the rural or dispersed population surrounding the town. The absolute size of a service population cannot be determined due to the overlap and hierarchic nature of service areas for different types of goods and services. Instead, the *density* of rural households is used. This is a useful measure, acting as a surrogate for many factors, including the intensity and nature of farming, usually also the rainfall and with it often the age of settlement and environmental attractiveness. Comparable data were not available here for the full period, but generally speaking, rural areas with a high initial density have attracted further in-migration while those with initially low density have suffered further losses over the period 1981-1991. Densities in 1981 ranged from four-five occupied dwellings per 100 Km^2 in the outlying marginal wheat/pastoral areas, to over 500 per 100 Km^2 in the Riverland irrigation areas and parts of the Adelaide Hills. This variable is a reasonably good predictor of growth in the retail sector, and notably the relationship here is strongest for growth in the share of retail establishments, rather than turnover - a longer-term indicator of growth.

Conclusions

Accessibility is a complex variable, whose role in affecting country town businesses is not easy to separate out from other causative factors. The present analysis would have been much improved by the inclusion of further measures incorporating change in access to large centres other than the capital city - a task awaiting attention. However, the interaction surface linking the periphery with the capital is by far the dominant feature of the intra-State space economy in South Australia. Although there is a central core area of the State of about 70 km radius in which driving times have shown negligible change over the past quarter century, the insulating effects of distance - both as a barrier and a protector - have fallen by up to three hours' average reported driving time, and by over 30 percent in some peripheral rural areas.

This reduction, however, has not resulted in the central city of Adelaide increasing the strong grip it had on rural shopping patterns in 1968/9. In fact, the reverse has happened, and central Adelaide's trade shadow has paled as major outer suburban and satellite city planned shopping centres have developed. The major country towns have also increased their accessibility and seem to have captured some trade in the outlying areas. The main period of satellite centre growth was between the 1968/9 and 1985/6 retail censuses.

Despite problems with the definitional changes and the relatively coarse spatial resolution of the retail censuses, it has been possible to demonstrate the main features of change at the level of the 83 country towns. The possibility of error for individual places should be borne in mind, but the overall spatial patterns are consistent and revealing. Whereas the absolute size of retailing provision still corresponds roughly with the population size of country centres, the relative success of towns in terms of their ability to attract spending from outside their own postcode areas shows the process of competitive selection at work within the urban system, and Figure 6 shows that many strategically placed small centres are doing *relatively* well in this competition despite the rural recession, as well as most of the 'regional capitals'.

The examination of change among the country towns over the quarter century shows unequivocally that a very clear differentiation is developing between core and periphery, whether or not one controls for the independent effects of population change. The greater part of the relative decline of country centres to date occurred in the period up to the mid 1980s.

A correlation analysis carried out to supplement the spatial evidence found that the accessibility variables have weak negative correlations with all indicators of change in retail performance: thus, long driving time to Adelaide, and large improvements in its accessibility over time correlate, albeit weakly, with low or negative change in share of State retail activity. The initial, urban, population size of country towns has been shown to have absolutely no predictive value on the likely change in retail share over time, but the initial density of the rural population in which the town is embedded, and the growth or decline of this over time, have been shown to be much better predictors of likely change in the town's retail trade share. Thus, while accessibility is a complex and important variable affecting the fortunes of country towns, demographic factors have a more direct impact. But the two, in conjunction, are tending to create an ever sharper distinction between core and periphery in the State.

Notes

1   The question on which Figure 4 is based is 'Excluding ordinary day-to-day or weekly needs such as food and drink, soap, petrol, cigarettes etc, how much of your expenditure on more important shopping items (eg. furniture, radio or TV, best clothes or footwear) is normally incurred in Adelaide? Please tick.'
2   These are Wudinna, Kimba, Cleve, and Cummins (Eyre Peninsula), Booleroo Centre and Peterborough (Upper North), Snowtown (Mid-North), Karoonda (Murray Mallee) and Penola (South-East).

References

Commonwealth of Australia: Departments of Primary Industries and Energy, and Human Services and Health. (1994) *Rural, Remote and Metropolitan Areas Classification: 1991 Census Edition*, Canberra, AGPS.

Faulkner, H. and French, S. (1983) *Geographic Remoteness: Conceptual and Measurement Problems*, Canberra, Bureau of Transport Economics.

Griffith, D. (1992) *Development of a Spatial Model of Disadvantage in Rural and Remote Areas of Australia*, Darwin, NT Department of Education, Unpublished Paper.

Griffith, D. (1994) *A Northern Territory Approach to Quantifying 'Access Disadvantage' to Educational Services in Remote and Rural Australia*, Darwin, NT Department of Education, Unpublished Paper.

Hugo, G. and Smailes, P. (1992) Population Dynamics in Rural South Australia, *Journal of Rural Studies* 8: 29-51.

Moseley, M. (1979) *Accessibility: The Rural Challenge*, London, Methuen.

Nichols, M. (1993) *Development of Indices for Measuring Potential Accessibility in Rural New South Wales*, Sydney, NSW Roads and Traffic Authority.

Parliament of South Australia: Social development Committee (1995) *Rural Poverty in South Australia*. Eighth Report of the Social Development Committee, Adelaide, SA Government Printer.

Smailes, P. (1969) A Metropolitan Trade Shadow: the Case of Adelaide, South Australia, *Tijdschrift voor Economische en Sociale Geografie* 60: 329-345.

Smailes, P. (1986) Trade Areas, in Griffin, T and McCaskill, M. (eds) *Atlas of South Australia*, Adelaide, Wakefield Press: 102-103.

Smailes, P. (1996, in preparation) Demographic Response to Rural Restructuring in South Australia, 1981-1991, submitted for publication.

Chapter 11

Rural restructuring and uneven development in the Western Australian wheatbelt

Matthew Tonts
Roy Jones

Introduction

Contemporary processes of global economic restructuring, together with recent state and federal government policy changes have had a profound effect on the social and economic well-being of rural Australia. The international farm crisis, farm amalgamation, labour market adjustments and the deregulation of the Australian agricultural economy have fuelled increasing concerns for the sustainability of family farming and for the small country towns which service agriculture. Over recent years, these processes of decline have been exacerbated by a shift in government policies from those based upon social equity towards economic efficiency. One outcome, in many rural areas, has been the rationalisation and withdrawal of basic services, such as schools and health facilities, together with a retreat from state-driven regional development strategies, as governments seek ways of ensuring greater efficiencies.

Increasingly, rural communities are being required to meet their own basic social and, to a large extent, economic needs through local development strategies and employment initiatives. While local development strategies have enabled some communities to reverse the pattern of decline (Conroy, 1987; Wildman *et al.*, 1990), a reliance upon such initiatives, as opposed to effective regional strategies, has the potential to increase competition between localities within rural areas, rather than improve economic and social well-being on a wider regional scale. The outcome is a pattern of uneven development: those communities which have sufficient social, economic and human capital, together with effective local leadership, are able to 'develop' at the expense of nearby localities. This paper discusses this emerging pattern of uneven development in the Central Wheatbelt of Western Australia, in light of current processes of economic restructuring and shifts in government policy.

Economic restructuring

Since the end of the World War Two, rural Australia has become increasingly integrated into global systems of production, distribution and exchange (Fagan and Webber, 1994). Significant early manifestations in this globalisation process were the internationalisation of capital flows (Massey, 1995), the growth in the number and influence of transnational corporations (Fagan and Webber, 1994) and the establishment of international trading blocs, such as the European Union (Dicken, 1992). However, the strongest impetus for the shift towards a global economy, and for the consequent processes of economic restructuring at the national, as well as at the state and local levels, was provided by the economic and political developments of the early 1970s.

According to Marsden *et al.*, (1993) the collapse of the Bretton Woods agreement in 1971, together with the rapid oil price increases and accelerating inflation during the 1970s, was instrumental in ending the post-war boom and triggering a long wave of recession. Processes of fundamental political and economic restructuring in both the private and the public sectors appeared as a response to the international economic crisis. The relationships between this process of restructuring and the current status of rural communities can be conceptualised within the framework of regulation theory (see Brenner and Glick, 1991; Lipietz, 1992).

The basis of the regulationist approach lies in the integration of the patterns of production, consumption and exchange (the *regime of accumulation*) with the role of political and social relations (the *mode of social regulation*), which serve to secure the integrity and cohesion of the accumulation process (Tickell and Peck, 1992). The restructuring of the regime of accumulation was originally interpreted as a transition from Fordism to flexible specialisation (post-Fordism), although more recently other spheres, such as those of consumption, distribution and exchange have been considered (Wilson, 1995). Studies of the restructuring of the mode of social regulation, which includes government legislation, welfare, social institutions, and behavioural and cultural norms, are relatively underdeveloped within the regulation approach, although parallels have been drawn with the transition from a welfare to a post-welfare state (Brenner and Glick, 1991).

The effects of the emergence of a post-Fordist regime of accumulation have been profound for rural Australia. The shift towards a post-Fordist agriculture suggests that the global economy is moving away from mass production and mass consumption towards a system based upon consumer demand for differentiated products requiring more flexible modes of production (Gray, 1994). Consequently, Australian wheat-sheep farmers who, during the post-war boom, became specialised in the mass production of standardised agricultural commodities were, and continue to be, faced with the need to adjust to new market demands.

This shift in the regime of accumulation has been accompanied by changes to the mode of social regulation. Since the end of the post-war boom in the early 1970s and the demise of the US dominated Fordist-Keynesian model of capitalism, there has been virtually no regulation of capital movements on an international scale (Tickell and Peck, 1992). Consequently, the potential for economic activity and capital flows to escape from highly regulated nation states, such as Australia, could be realised more easily than hitherto (Fagan and Le Heron, 1994). In Australia, the government reacted to these changes by deregulating financial and commodity markets, reducing tariffs and import restrictions, and removing state marketing monopolies (Lawrence, 1990). Swyngedouw (1992) argues that this deregulation at the national level is now being replaced by a transfer of regulatory power to international institutions such as the World Trade Organisation. However, as Lawrence (1994) points out, the deregulation of Australian agriculture has not yet been accompanied by the emergence of legitimate and effective global regulatory practices, and has thus exposed family farmers to the vagaries of the global economy (see also Le Heron, 1993).

At the local level, these developments have produced a farm financial crisis, as the increasing cost of capital inputs, rising interest rates and lower commodity prices reduce net-farm incomes and lower cash operating surpluses (Bryant, 1992). In order to remain viable and to improve efficiency, Australian farmers have been forced to increase economies of scale, resulting in farm amalgamations as small family farms are replaced by larger and more flexible operations. While this has reduced the number of farming families, the application of new technologies in agriculture has also reduced the need for farm employees, thus further reducing the agricultural population in rural areas.

These structural changes in Australian agriculture go well beyond the family farm and have a profound effect on many of the country towns which service the farming industry. As Lawrence and Williams (1990: 40) point out, 'a more productive agriculture is coming to mean less productive and viable rural communities'. In many of the country towns which have traditionally existed to service the farming industry, population losses associated with agricultural restructuring have reduced the demand for services, eroded local employment opportunities and undermined the viability of many local social organisations.

While the initial changes in the mode of social regulation were directed at liberalising the flow of capital between nation states, more recently such changes have come to encompass public policy, service provision and strategic planning. Increasingly, the public sector has been characterised by the privatisation of government services, short term policy goals rather than long term strategies, policies based upon economic efficiency rather than social equity, reduced cross subsidisation of services in rural areas, and an increasing focus on rural communities meeting their own needs (Rolley and Humphreys, 1993). Jessop (1994: 264) argues that the role of federal and state governments has been 'hollowed-out', as the key scale for economic regulation is shifted to international bodies such as the Asia-Pacific Economic Community, with the responsibility for community well-being devolved to local authorities and organisations. These processes of rationalisation have radically altered the nature of state and federal government involvement in rural Australia.

141

Policy change in rural Western Australia

For much of this century the rural policies of the state and federal governments were directed not only at developing the agricultural economy, but also at meeting, and even anticipating, the needs of rural people (Jones, 1993). The provision of services, such as schools, hospitals and recreational facilities, together with a comprehensive transport and communications infrastructure, was seen as instrumental in the development of stable rural communities. Since the early 1980s, however, agricultural restructuring and the emergence of government policies based upon economic rationalism, together with the devolution of responsibility for community well-being to local governments, have undermined the viability of many wheatbelt settlements. For Tickell and Peck (1992), this shift to policies of economic rationalism is an attempt to develop a 'neo-competitive' mode of social regulation which, Rolley and Humphreys (1993) argue, has commodified rural people while removing many support measures from the political agenda. The outcome of this process has been the development of policies which fail to consider human needs, values and preferences.

The Western Australian Government's adoption of the principles of economic rationalism, as advocated by a recently released report on the State government's financial operations (McCarrey, 1993), has resulted in massive cuts in total government expenditure, and rather a commitment to economic efficiency. Following a major electoral redistribution in 1989, which reduced the level of malapportionment and, therefore, the political lobbying power of rural areas, it is not surprising that the impact of the McCarrey report and the subsequent policy responses have been severe in the wheatbelt. The largest cost-cutting measures adopted by the Western Australian government have been directed at the major expenditure areas of education, health and transport.

While hospitals in some of the larger regional centres, such as Northam, have been maintained and at times upgraded, hospitals in the smaller wheatbelt settlements have generally experienced a rationalisation of budgets, facilities and beds. Furthermore, services such as geriatric care are currently under threat of privatisation or closure in a number of small towns, while travel assistance for out-patients in remote areas has also been severely reduced. This rationalisation of health services has occurred despite the lower health levels and rapidly ageing structure of the rural population. Levels of suicide, stress, chronic illness, domestic violence and work-related accidents are all higher per capita in rural areas than urban centres. While these differences can in part be associated with the rural lifestyle and environment, the shortage of rural health services also contributes to these problems (Rolley and Humphreys, 1993).

Education services have also been targeted by the Western Australian government in the pursuit of economic efficiency. The State government is currently deliberating on the closure of a number of schools in the wheatbelt (Jones and Tonts, 1995). While the closure of these schools may help meet efficiency goals, government policy has failed to consider the wider ramifications of such action. Small schools in the wheatbelt not only provide education, but retain young people in the local community, provide a local centre for social interaction and help to overcome problems of lengthy travel for students. Rural children already perform less well in basic competencies, have fewer subject options and experience more limited career opportunities than their urban counterparts (Lawrence, 1987). Furthermore, the financial hardships associated with the current rural crisis has meant that many households cannot afford to maintain their children at boarding schools in large regional centres or in Perth.

Rationalisation has also occurred in the transport industry, as railway infrastructure has been removed from parts of the wheatbelt and job numbers reduced. Further massive employment cuts were experienced earlier this year when the State government subcontracted the maintenance of the remaining lines to the private sector. While the government has claimed that resourceful and entrepreneurial former employees could tender for the maintenance contracts few, if any, retrenched workers have the necessary capital, equipment or skills to undertake such a task (*Narrogin Observer*, 10 May 1995). Consequently, most of the maintenance contracts have been filled by metropolitan-based operations, further reducing employment opportunities in country towns.

The outlook for many rural communities in the Western Australian wheatbelt, in socio-economic terms, appears uncertain. While there is some evidence that the rate of farm amalgamation has slowed (Gow, 1994) and that some towns have experienced marginal population growth and increases in economic activity (Tonts, 1995), many areas remain in steady decline. While this is partly a response to economic restructuring, current State government policies continue to undermine the socio-economic sustainability of many rural communities. Although service and infrastructure rationalisation and withdrawal enable governments to cut costs in rural areas, such policies can result in costs of another sort, namely poor education, health, unemployment and increases in crime (Lawrence and Share, 1993). The downgrading of basic services in the wheatbelt will continue to disadvantage those sections of the population which are least able to cope with such changes, notably the aged, the unemployed and young people (Rolley and Humphreys, 1993).

The shift towards local development

The responsibility for ensuring the well-being of rural communities is increasingly being devolved to local authorities. Many services which were previously provided by state and federal government are now the responsibility of extremely small, and usually declining, country shires. In the Western Australian wheatbelt local governments are now providing, or at least facilitating, services such as geriatric health care, public housing, telecommunications infrastructure and Home and Community Care (Clements, 1995; Tonts and Jones, 1996). While the delivery of these services at the local level can be successful and responsive, they are not necessarily provided in all wheatbelt communities. Decisions on which services will be provided where and to what extent are generally made by the individual authorities and often depend upon the availability of sufficient funding, resources, and the support of those in positions of political power. As such, there is a danger that some services, which might be accepted as essential in urban areas, will not be provided by some local governments, thus increasing the likelihood of social inequalities between localities within rural areas, and more generally between rural and urban areas.

Alongside the devolution of responsibility for the provision of services and infrastructure to local government, there has also been a reduction in the involvement of state and federal governments in economic development strategies at a regional level (Sorensen, 1993). Increasingly, rural communities are being forced to initiate their own local development strategies if they are to remain economically and socially sustainable. Local employment initiatives, main-street beautification and revival projects, and free land grants for newcomers are just some of the strategies adopted by wheatbelt communities in order to remain viable (Tonts, 1995). While local initiatives are constrained within the impositions of economic restructuring and are generally small in scale, their impact in some wheatbelt towns has been positive and has prompted further entrepreneurial development (Clements, 1995). The result has been marginal population growth and a small increase in the number of private services in some towns (Tonts, 1995). Despite the significance of local development strategies in contributing to the revival of several wheatbelt towns, there is a danger that their success is merely at the expense of neighbouring communities and that they will provide a political smokescreen for a further reduction of national and state assistance to rural areas (Fagan, 1987; Cox, 1995).

The shifting focus of government policy towards communities meeting their own needs has increased the importance of effective local leadership for ensuring the viability of rural communities (Sorensen, 1993). In many cases, however, the resources of local leaders are being directed at retaining existing services under threat of closure or rationalisation, such as the school, hospital or police station, rather than initiating new projects which will enhance the local community and/or economy. There are also indications that effective local leadership has enabled some rural communities to perform better in economic terms than nearby centres, further contributing to uneven development in rural areas at the local scale (Sorensen and Epps, 1994).

While local leadership is of considerable importance in ensuring the sustainability of rural communities, the devolution of power to the local level has the potential to increase inequalities within communities. As Gray (1991) points out, local governments in rural Australia tend to be elitist and controlled largely by small-business and property owners (see also Wild, 1974; Dempsey, 1990). Gray (1992) further argues that, although local government has the potential to increase public participation in decision making processes, high status groups tend to participate more frequently than lower status groups, thus reinforcing the power of the middle and upper class. As such, those groups or individuals who execute local political power are in a position to address their own local interests, rather than the needs of the community as a whole, thus enhancing the potential for what might be termed a micro-scale process of uneven development. In the emerging policy environment, where local authorities have increased official authority or power, individuals in local government have even more potential to serve their own needs at the expense of other 'communities of interest' within rural areas. With increasingly limited funding available for local government, services and facilities for minority groups such as young people, Aboriginal people or the aged, might be overlooked in favour of projects which benefit those in positions of power and influence.

Uneven development in the wheatbelt

The process of rural restructuring and recent state and federal government policy shifts have resulted in a pattern of spatially uneven economic and social development in the Western Australian wheatbelt. While there have always been some social and economic inequalities between wheatbelt towns, the shift away from effective state-driven regional development strategies towards communities meeting their own needs has increased the competition between localities and produced a pattern of 'winners' and 'losers'. Rural communities are now forced to compete for government funding, public services, tourist dollars and even for social institutions such as churches if they are to remain viable and to reverse the pattern of economic and demographic decline (see McKenzie, 1994; Jones and Tonts, 1995).

In 1991, the population of the Central Wheatbelt (see Figure 1) of Western Australia was 9,585, which is 5,001 or some 34 percent less than the total population in 1966 when the region's population peaked at 14,586. Between 1966 and 1991, the workforce declined from 6,376 to 4,412, a fall of 1,964 or 30.8 percent. During this period, the population engaged directly in agriculture declined from 3,593 in 1966 to 2,057 in 1991, a fall of approximately 42.7 percent, as economic and technological restructuring changed the face of family farming. This decline was accompanied by significant falls in Building and Construction (-86.9 percent), Transport and Communication (-48.8 percent), Personal Services (-43.7 percent) and Commerce (-31.7 percent).

These changes at the regional level mask the trends occurring in individual wheatbelt towns during this period. Between the 1947 census and the mid-to-late 1970s, most of the larger wheatbelt towns which were the administrative headquarters for local government experienced a pattern of steady population growth (Jones, 1993). In line with this growth most towns also experienced an increase in the number of public and commercial services until the late 1970s, albeit frequently at the expense of smaller nearby 'non-shire headquarters' settlements (Jones, 1993; Tonts, 1995). By 1981, however, the effects of severe population decline in the farming sector had begun to impact upon even the larger wheatbelt towns. The negative multipliers associated with this trend resulted in the contraction of local economies, the closure of local businesses and depopulation of the country towns. Alongside these changes, increasing personal mobility associated with higher levels of car ownership and improving transport technologies, concentrated economic and social activity in larger regional centres and the Perth metropolitan area (Rolley and Humphreys, 1993; McKenzie, 1994).

Figure 1
Towns in the central wheatbelt of Western Australia

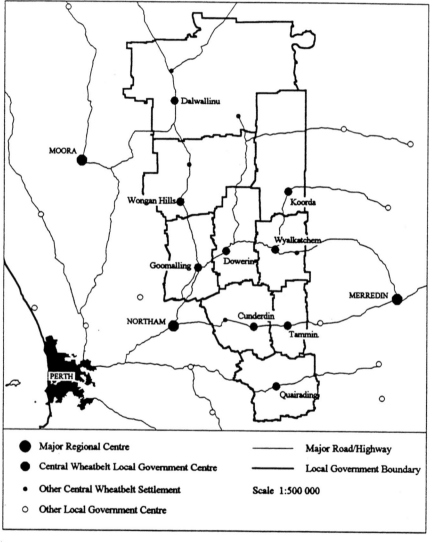

During the 1981-1986 intercensal period, eight of the nine towns in the Central Wheatbelt experienced demographic decline (Table 1). Only the small settlement of Tammin recorded population growth, increasing by 11 persons (4.3 percent). This pattern of population decline was accompanied by reductions in the levels of service provision in most towns (Table 2). The settlements of Wongan Hills, Tammin and Wyalkatchem remained stable, while most other towns experienced a decline in the total number of services. This pattern of decline was confined largely to the private sector, as state and federal governments continued policies of ensuring equitable levels of access to public services and infrastructure. During much of the early 1980s, services such as schools, hospitals and justice facilities were maintained, public recreational facilities were upgraded, and communications infrastructure improved. Since the mid 1980s, however, as federal and state governments began to adopt policies based on economic rationalism and increased the focus on communities meeting their own needs, a pattern of uneven development in the Central Wheatbelt has become increasingly evident.

Table 1
Population change in central wheatbelt urban areas, 1981-1991

	Population			Percentage Change	
	1981	**1986**	**1991**	**1981-1986**	**1986-1991**
Cunderdin	731	696	688	-4.8	-1.1
Dalwallinu	639	571	597	-10.6	4.6
Dowerin	410	377	374	-8.0	-0.8
Goomalling	600	569	535	-5.2	-6.0
Koorda	378	331	344	-12.4	3.9
Quairading	741	654	696	-11.7	6.4
Tammin	254	265	226	4.3	-14.7
Wongan Hills	947	826	890	-12.8	7.7
Wyalkatchem	453	429	410	-5.3	-2.3

(Source: Australian Bureau of Statistics Census Reports)

Over recent years, a number of small towns in the wheatbelt have initiated local development projects to address the problems of depopulation, service withdrawal and the contraction of the local economy. Wongan Hills, Quairading, Dalwallinu and Koorda have initiated strategies such as shopping precinct redevelopment and beautification schemes; the formation of local cooperatives to purchase and restore derelict commercial premises which are offered at subsidised rates to new businesses; the development of retirement villages to retain local retirees; and the provision of free housing and industrial land for households and businesses willing to relocate to small towns. While the impact of these projects is generally small in scale, their effect is often cumulative, and in some cases they have been responsible for reversing the economic and social decline of small towns. However, towns which fail to initiate local strategies due to lack of local leadership, insufficient human or economic capital, or simply through a lack of desire to change have tended to continue their pattern of decline.

During the 1986-1991 intercensal period, four settlements in the Central Wheatbelt began to increase their population, while the remaining five remained stable, or continued to decline. In addition to these changes in population trends between 1986 and 1991, the total number of services began to show signs of stabilisation in some towns (Table 2). Between 1986 and 1994, the number of services in Wongan Hills continued to increase, while Quairading, Dalwallinu and Cunderdin recorded slight rises in their number of services following decline during the 1980-1986 period. In line with their static or declining populations, the number of services in the other Central Wheatbelt towns was either stable or in decline.

Table 2
Changing number of public and private services in central wheatbelt towns, 1980-1994

	1980	1986	1994	Change 1980-1986	Change 1986-1994
Cunderdin	57	51	52	-6	1
Dalwallinu	49	40	44	-9	4
Dowerin	33	32	32	-1	0
Goomalling	45	42	39	-3	-3
Koorda	29	24	24	-5	0
Quairading	46	38	42	-8	4
Tammin	18	18	15	0	-3
Wongan Hills	60	64	72	4	8
Wyalkatchem	36	36	32	0	-4

(Source: Tonts, 1995)

Some light can be shed on the nature of this pattern of uneven development by examining employment trends in the Central Wheatbelt. Between 1986 and 1991, those settlements which experienced an economic and population turnaround recorded significant increases in the size of the total labour force. The towns of Quairading, Wongan Hills and Koorda all recorded growth in excess of 5 percent, while the work-force in Dalwallinu increased by 4.8 percent (Table 3). On the other hand, Goomalling and Tammin, which recorded the highest rate of population decline between 1986 and 1991, experienced a significant contraction of the labour-force, declining by nine percent and 18.8 percent respectively. While all settlements experienced a loss of primary industry workers, the towns which recorded significant employment growth did so mainly in the Manufacturing sectors, with small increases recorded in the Community Services and Transport sectors (Tonts, 1995).

Table 3
Employment trends in central wheatbelt towns, 1986-1991

	Labour Force			Unemployed		
			Percentage			Percentage
	1986	1991	Change 1981-91	1986	1991	Unemployment 1991
Cunderdin	307	283	-7.8	19	15	5.3
Dalwallinu	291	305	4.8	27	25	8.2
Dowerin	180	174	-3.3	16	15	8.6
Goomalling	234	213	-8.9	25	38	17.8
Koorda	175	185	5.7	14	16	8.6
Quairading	272	292	7.3	35	28	9.6
Tammin	96	78	-18.8	15	22	28.2
Wongan Hills	405	425	4.9	34	28	6.5
Wyalkatchem	203	194	-4.4	21	27	13.9

(Source: Australian Bureau of Statistics Census Reports)

Levels of unemployment also varied considerably between settlements in the period 1986 to 1991. While levels of unemployment were low throughout much of the wheatbelt during the 1970s and 1980s (Jarvis, 1979), more recently unemployment levels between settlements have begun to vary considerably. While a clear pattern is difficult to discern, it is clear that the three towns which experienced the most significant population and service decline, Tammin, Wyalkatchem and Goomalling, also experienced the highest levels of unemployment (Table 3). In 1991 each of these settlements recorded unemployment levels greater than the Western Australian average of 12.1 percent. In contrast Wongan Hills - which experienced the strongest economic and demographic growth - recorded only 6.5 percent unemployment.

While much of the literature dealing with uneven development has considered problems of population change, labour force adjustment, unemployment and levels of economic activity (see Massey, 1994; 1995; Pratt, 1994), more recently important social and cultural aspects of restructuring have been considered (Jones and Tonts, 1995). In many of the declining settlements of the wheatbelt, local social institutions have become less viable, undermining the local 'sense of community' and breaking down local social networks. In Tammin, the local Australian Rules football club has been forced to amalgamate with a club in a nearby town due to dwindling numbers, while the local tennis club has recently closed. In other declining settlements, organisations such as Rotary and Lions have gone into recess and church services are now only held once a fortnight. On the other hand, social institutions in the larger growing towns are expanding. The Wongan Hills bowling club has been extended, a new town hall was recently opened, while a new indoor sporting facility is currently under construction. This emerging pattern of uneven social development has been accompanied by recent calls for the amalgamation of local governments in many parts of rural Western Australia (McCarrey, 1993)

Recent local government amalgamations in eastern Australia and New Zealand have been directed at improving the efficiency of service delivery, resource and assets usage, and resulted in the transfer of responsibility for community well-being to the emerging 'regional councils' (Moran, 1992; O'Toole, 1994;). While local government amalgamations may help to meet the goals of economic efficiency, they can prove to be a severe blow to the local sense of identity and erode community social sustainability (Moran, 1992). This was confirmed by Jones (1993) who found that very few towns in the Western Australian wheatbelt which were not the headquarters for local government were capable of remaining economically or socially viable in the long term. Local shires are significant employers and facilitate considerable economic and social activity. The removal of this activity in a process of amalgamation has the potential further to undermine the viability of country towns. Evidence from New Zealand indicates that the towns which become the headquarters for local government following amalgamations tend to be in a stronger position both politically and economically than nearby the non-shire headquarters towns (Moran, 1992), enabling them to compete more effectively for resources and facilities, thus exacerbating the process of uneven development.

Conclusion

Uneven social and economic development does not merely reflect the varying degrees to which local communities are capable of meeting their own needs. While local factors such as development projects, employment initiatives, and local leadership each play a critical role, the pattern of uneven development in rural areas is largely tied to wider economic and social processes. Declining farm incomes, rising costs and farm amalgamation associated with economic restructuring and the regulation 'crisis' in the world trade arena (Lawrence, 1994), continue to erode the viability of family farming and, consequently, the economic and social viability of many country towns. Furthermore, the problems of rural communities have been exacerbated by a shift from government policies based upon spatial equity towards those based on economic rationalism. As Rolley and Humphreys (1993) point out, the wellbeing of people living in rural areas can only be assured by policies which acknowledge that people matter. However, current policies which result in the withdrawal of education, welfare, justice and primary health services, without providing adequate alternatives, clearly fail to take into account that 'geography matters' and thereby discount the basic needs of wheatbelt residents and threaten the sustainability of many rural communities.

In the emerging policy and economic environment, rural communities have become increasingly responsible for ensuring their own long term social and economic viability. The problem for many of these communities is that rural restructuring, public and private service withdrawal, and severe depopulation have eroded many of the economic, social and human resources necessary to make self-determination possible and local strategies viable. At a wider regional level, however, significant resources do exist and it may be that an integration of human and economic capital on a regional basis will help avoid the 'survival of the fittest' approach to rural development. While a cooperative approach is not new, and has the potential to be plagued with problems of parochialism and localism, it can be progressive and can offer a genuine alternative for rural communities provided that it receives adequate state and federal government support (Stilwell, 1994). This approach would not only preserve community identity and belonging, but has the potential to encourage collective strategies for economic and social development at a regional level, using local people and local knowledge. Currently, however, attempts to form regional cooperatives are hindered by the increasing pressure being placed upon local government resources as they attempt to deliver services and infrastructure previously provided by the state and federal governments. If the problem of widening social and economic inequalities between rural communities is to be successfully addressed, governments must adopt a more holistic development framework, which not only provides spatially equitable access to basic services, facilities, and infrastructure, but also actively encourages and supports locally and regionally initiated economic and social development.

References

Brenner, R. and Glick, M. (1991) The Regulation Approach: Theory and History, *New Left Review* 188: 45-120.

Bryant, L. (1992) Social Aspects of the Farm Financial Crisis, in Lawrence, G., Vanclay, F. and Furze, B. (eds) *Agriculture, Environment and Society: Contemporary Issues for Australia*, South Melbourne, Macmillan.

Clements, A. (1995) *Employment Growth and Housing Shortage: A Case Study of Wongan Hills*, Unpublished BA Honours Dissertation, Perth, Curtin University of Technology.

Conroy, J. (ed.) (1987) *An Evaluation of Local Area Economic Strategy Studies*, Canberra, Australian Government Publishing Service.

Cox, K. (1995) Globalisation, Competition and the Politics of Local Economic Development, *Urban Studies* 32, 3: 213-224.

Dempsey, K. (1990) *Smalltown: A Study of Social Inequality, Cohesion and Belonging*, Melbourne, Oxford University Press.

Dicken, P. (1992) *Global Shift: The Internationalisation of Economic Activity*, (Second Edition), London, Paul Chapman.

Fagan, R. (1987) Local Employment Initiatives: Long Term Strategy for Localities or Flavour of the Month?, *Australian Geographer* 18, 1: 51-56.

Fagan, R. and Le Heron, R. (1994) Reinterpreting the Geography of Accumulation: The Global Shift and Local Restructuring, *Environment and Planning D: Society and Space* 12: 265-285.

Fagan, R. and Webber, M. (1994) *Global Restructuring: The Australian Experience*, Melbourne, Oxford University Press.

Gow, J. (1994) Farm Structural Adjustment, *Rural Society* 4, 2.

Gray, I. (1991) *Politics in Place: Social Power Relations in an Australian Country Town*, Cambridge, Cambridge University Press.

Gray, I. (1992) Power Relations in Rural Communities: Implications for Environmental Management, in Lawrence, G., Vanclay, F. and Furze, B. (eds) *Agriculture, Environment and Society: Contemporary Issues for Australia*, South Melbourne, Macmillan.

Gray, I. (1994) The Changing Structure of Rural Communities, *Rural Society* 4, 3/4: 17-21.

Jarvis, N. (ed.) (1979) *Western Australia: An Atlas of Human Endeavour*, Perth, State Government of Western Australia.

Jessop, B. (1994) Post-Fordism and the State, in Amin, A. (ed.) *Post-Fordism*, Oxford, Blackwell.

Jones, R. and Tonts, M. (1995) Rural Restructuring and Social Sustainability: Some Reflections on the Western Australian Wheatbelt, *Australian Geographer* 26, 2: 133-140.

Jones, R. (1993) Country Town Survival: Some Anglo-Australian Comparisons, in Wilson, M. (ed.) *Proceedings of the Prairie Division, Canadian Association of Geographers*, Saskatoon, Department of Geography, University of Saskatchewan.

Lawrence, G. and Share, P. (1993) Rural Australia: Current Problems and Policy Directions, *Regional Journal of Social Issues* 27: 3-9.

Lawrence, G. and Williams, C. (1990) The Dynamics of Decline: Implications for Social Welfare in Rural Australia, in Cullen, T., Dunn, P. And Lawrence, G. (eds) *Rural Health and Welfare in Australia*, Wagga Wagga, Centre for Rural Welfare Research, Charles Sturt University.

Lawrence, G. (1987) *Capitalism and the Countryside*, Sydney, Pluto Press.

Lawrence, G. (1990) Agricultural Restructuring and Rural Social Change in Australia, in Marsden, T., Lowe, P. and Whatmore, S. (eds) *Rural Restructuring: Global Processes and Their Responses*, London, David Fulton.

Lawrence, G. (1994) Rural Adjustment Revisited: In Defence of a Sociological Approach, *Rural Society* 4, 3/4: 11-16.

Le Heron, R. (1993) *Globalized Agriculture: Political Choice*, Oxford, Pergamon.

Lipietz, A. (1992) *Towards a New Economic Order*, Cambridge, Polity Press.

Marsden, T., Murdoch, J., Lowe, P., Munton, R., and Flynn, A. (1993) *Constructing the Countryside*, London, University College London Press.

Massey, D. (1994) *Space, Place and Gender*, Cambridge, Polity Press.

Massey, D. (1995) *Spatial Divisions of Labour* (Second Edition), London, Macmillan.

McCarrey, L. (Chair) (1993) *Agenda for Reform: Report of the Independent Commission to Review Public Sector Finances*, Perth, Western Australian Independent Commission to Review Public Sector Finances.

McKenzie, F. (1994) Population Decline in Non-Metropolitan Australia: Impacts and Policy Implications, *Urban Policy and Research* 12, 4: 253-263.

Moran, W. (1992) Local Government Reform, in Britton, S., Le Heron, R. and Pawson, E. (eds) *Changing Places in New Zealand: A Geography of Restructuring*, Christchurch, New Zealand Geographical Society.

Narrogin Observer (10 May 1995) *Westrail Make Final Job Slash*, 17, 817: 1.

Pratt, A. C. (1994) *Uneven Re-Production: Industry, Space and Society*, Oxford, Pergamon.

Rolley, F. and Humphreys, J. S. (1993) Rural Welfare: The Human Face of Australia's Countryside, in Sorensen, T. and Epps, R. (eds) *Prospects and Policies for Rural Australia*, Melbourne, Longman Cheshire.

O'Toole, K. (1994) Replacing Rurality with Human Services in Victorian Local Government, *Rural Society* 4, 1: 22

Sorensen, T. and Epps, R. (1994) *The Links Between Leadership and Local Economic Development*, Perth, Paper delivered to the 18th Australian and New Zealand Regional Science Association Annual Conference.

Sorensen, T. (1993) The Future of the Country Town: Strategies for Local Economic Development, in Sorensen, T. and Epps, R. (eds) *Prospects and Policies for Rural Australia*, Melbourne, Longman Cheshire.

Stilwell, F. (1994) Economic Rationalism, Cities and Regions, *Australian Journal of Regional Studies* 7: 54-65.

Swyngedouw, E. (1992) The Mammon Quest: Globalisation, Interspatial Competition and the Monetary Order, in Dunford, M. and Kafkalas, G. (eds) *Cities and Regions in the New Europe: The Global-Local Interplay and Spatial Development Strategies*, London, Belhavan Press.

Tickell, A and Peck, J. (1992) Accumulation, Regulation and the Geographies of Production: Missing Links in Regulationist Research, *Progress in Human Geography* 16, 2: 190-218.

Tonts, M. and Jones, R. (1996) *Policy Change and Social Sustainability: The Case of the Western Australian Wheatbelt*, Tsukuba, Japan, Proceedings of the International Conference on the Sustainability of Rural Systems, Tsukuba University Science Report Series.

Tonts, M. (1995) *Rural Restructuring and Community Adaptation in the Western Australian Wheatbelt*, Newcastle, Unpublished paper delivered to the Institute of Australian Geographers Annual Conference.

Wild, R. (1974) *Bradstow: A Study of Class Status and Power in a Small Australian Town*, Sydney, Angus and Robertson.

Wildman, P., Moore, R., Baker, G. and Wadley, D. (1990) Push from the Bush: Revitalisation Strategies for Smaller Rural Towns, *Urban Policy and Research* 8, 1: 51-59.

Wilson, P. (1995) Embracing Locality in Local Economic Development, *Urban Studies* 32, 4/5: 645-658.

Chapter 12

The nature of leadership in rural Australia: A case study of four central western Queensland towns

Roger Epps and Tony Sorensen

Background

Fundamental to the well-being of individuals in rural Australia is the availability of employment or business opportunities and access to goods and services in the broadest sense (see Rolley and Humphreys, 1993). Whilst substantial developments in communication technology have eroded the 'tyranny of distance' (see Blainey, 1966), physical isolation still restricts much of the population's access to a range of employment, post-secondary education, health care and shopping opportunities in inland rural areas. Although some facilities have improved through time, others have deteriorated. More importantly, with some exceptions, the contrasts between access to goods, services and transport in most inland rural areas and the better serviced metropolitan and developing coastal regions has steadily increased. These exceptions include such major regional centres as Toowoomba, Bathurst/Orange and Albury/Wodonga to name a few.

Many factors are responsible for the 'relative' decline in access to goods and services throughout inland regions and these are most pronounced in either the smaller centres and/or towns struggling to maintain their population. They include:

- the growing expectations of the community in terms of access to high quality goods and services whose high demand thresholds preclude their delivery from small places;
- the rising real cost of providing some services, especially in health and education (note that the per capita cost of supplying some other public services like electricity, phones and sealed roads also rises as remoter and less densely settled areas are connected);

- the reluctance of the community to pay higher taxes to sustain or acquire more public services (the reluctance to pay higher prices appears to be less obvious in the private sector, even when it comes to petrol prices and bank fees);
- the consequent deterioration in the ability of various tiers of government to provide services demanded, leading to the spread of the user-pays principle (although typically the charges for postal and telephone communications services and school bus and rail transport, still do not truly reflect full costs);
- the retraction, through 'rationalisation', of some services such as banks and hospital care, especially in smaller centres - due to organisational needs to optimise the quantity of services delivered from a given budget or to maximise profits;
- arising from the above points, the lack of employment prospects and quality lifestyle opportunities or expectations;
- while probably always present to some degree historically, increasing inter-town competition as each place manoeuvres to maximise its portfolio of goods and services, capture community project funding, and attract businesses or government agencies;
- rising scale economies that enlarge the hinterlands needed to sustain many private and public enterprises;
- the weakening of traditional rural enterprises (due *inter alia* to continuing unfavourable trends in many sectors' terms of trade, increasing scale economies in the farm sector too, lagging diversification of output, and reluctance by governments to provide expensive financial support for agriculture) has served to reduce the population size, and therefore market demand, of many town hinterlands; and
- the reduced political clout throughout inland rural Australia (for elaboration on such issues, see Sorensen and Epps, 1993; Epps, 1995).

Rural locations were favoured by:

- their ability to attract population and associated infrastructure investment;
- opportunities for agricultural diversification, particularly in horticulture, through access to irrigation supplies and transport;
- the trend in lifestyles of many Australians and their preference for coastal locations;
- the tourism and retirement industry (see also Holmes, 1994).

Quite apart from local factors that are impinging upon rural communities, there is a range of other, largely autonomous, elements over which the population and government may have little control. These include:

- international affairs;
- domestic macro-economic settings;
- private and corporate actions;

155

- inventions, innovations and technological change;
- demographic and lifestyle change;
- physical environmental constraints;
- cultural change.

Within this complex framework, and particularly due to governments' increasing reluctance (and perhaps inability) to provide an extensive slate of readily accessible, uniformly priced basic services (effectively subsidising smaller centres) to all population centres, there is a pseudo-Darwinian process taking place with some towns emerging as survivors, better able to win in the struggle for expansion. On the one hand, some services, including school education, are formula-based and are still provided in basic form wherever the threshold levels for those services prevail (although the range of courses available in smaller high schools will be limited). In other respects, where towns are faced with the opportunity to compete in order to attract business, industry, cultural facilities, government agencies and infrastructure, for example, there are clear indications that some places are more successful than others (see Sorensen, 1993: Beer *et al.*, 1994).

Assume a scenario in which several towns with similar locational, environmental, social, and economic characteristics are contesting such development. Should one town perform better than others, this could be due hypothetically to one of three factors:

- it manages, in a technical sense, its resources more efficiently;
- it has benefited from an element of chance (for example, a government's decision to invest in some optic fibre cable, dam or research facility; an entrepreneurial decision to invest in a factory; or the production of some local invention); or
- local leadership seizing endogenous or competitive development opportunities.

Although unconfirmed and in need of basic research, it is likely that towns which lag persistently on these conditions will have difficulties sustaining their services, quality of life, and population size in the longer term. Our purpose here is to assess the potential importance of local leadership to local development, although admittedly the three factors are, to some extent, inter-connected, along with a raft of other considerations including accumulated wealth, entrepreneurial ethos, demographics and citizen profile.

The role of leadership

Several overseas studies have acknowledged the important role that community leaders may assume in regional economic development (see Judd and Parkinson, 1990; Pigg, 1991; Bowler *et al.*, 1992). Despite this, leadership has received little attention in Australia. Instead, the focus is on local employment initiatives (LEIs) and especially the role of infrastructure provision, information supply, business advisory services, the availability of capital, and the responsibilities of various tiers of government to provide subsidies of one kind or another (Sorensen and Epps, 1996).

The McKinsey Report (1994) is one of the few Australian documents that specifically identifies the importance of local leadership in regional development. Disappointingly, it does not explore the nature of this key element in any depth. The McKinsey analysis suggests that leadership is almost a resource that is on-line once the decision has been made to utilise it.

> The first step to increase investment in a region is forming a strong committed leadership group and agreeing on a clear vision of where the region's future lies (McKinsey, 1994: 77).

The report has little further to add except that leadership should be encouraged, 'the "vision thing" is not well understood' and that 'leadership must be reinforced by symbolic actions' (McKinsey, 1994: 79). It identifies the role of leadership but does not explore its nature. The overseas studies cited above confirm McKinsey's prescription and, logically, one anticipates its appropriateness in some circumstances to rural Australia.

The nature of leadership

This raises the crucial question about the nature of leadership. Byrt (1978: 3) considers that leadership is an 'imprecise, general, emotional, value laden term' and therefore open to some degree of interpretation. The popular conception of a leader is one of :

> a forceful and dynamic personality who really leads from the front; an architect and implementer of strategy; a mediator in conflict situations; an integrator who assures the climate of the organisation; a person able to motivate subordinates and who, by persuasion, compulsion or example to others, succeeds in getting others to follow the leader's wishes. In this regard, leadership is a process (Sorensen and Epps, 1996).

Hodgkinson (1983) emphasises the importance of knowledge and intelligence and the need for leaders to have a strong sense of what is morally correct, despite the obvious historical examples which would suggest otherwise. However, this latter point is of less consequence if Chemers (1984) claim, that the leader's traits need to be consistent with those of their followers, is accepted. A synopsis of literature and field work suggests that a leader can provide growth and development not only in terms of economic, but also in social and cultural, outcomes. Effective leadership results from:

- developing a clear and practical vision of the future that leads, *inter alia*, to a well reasoned and integrated set of goals;
- enlisting the strong support of key community groups for the vision and its related goals; and
- motivating key actors in the community to deliver the strategy's main components - infrastructure, investment, quality management and so on (Sorensen and Epps, 1996).

The performance of a leader is also highly dependent on the particular circumstances prevailing at any time. Such circumstances may include rivalry among potential leaders, the nature of the task, the community and the presence of secondary leaders or executives (see Figure 1).

Figure 1
Attributes of effective leadership

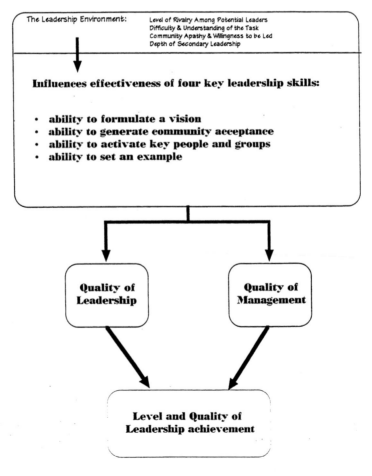

The Leadership Environment: Level of Rivalry Among Potential Leaders
                             Difficulty & Understanding of the Task
                             Community Apathy & Willingness to be Led
                             Depth of Secondary Leadership

Influences effectiveness of four key leadership skills:

- **ability to formulate a vision**
- **ability to generate community acceptance**
- **ability to activate key people and groups**
- **ability to set an example**

Quality of Leadership

Quality of Management

Level and Quality of Leadership achievement

The case study

To test the hypothesis that there may be a link between the quality of local leadership and economic and socio-cultural development in rural towns, we initiated a case study in which the judicious selection of a group of towns with relatively comparable geographical, economic, social and environmental conditions enabled us to focus on the significance of actions by communities and their leaders for local development. The structure of the study enabled us to investigate not only the nature of local leadership, but also to differentiate between business and community leaders, and to assess the relative effectiveness of individual versus collective or group leadership (see McKinsey, 1994). One step involved the identification of key leadership tasks to provide a benchmark against which to assess which members of the local community played a significant leadership role. For the purposes of our research project, and on the basis of relevant literature (see Judd and Parkinson, 1990), the key leadership functions are considered to be:

- formulation of a *vision* of the community's economic and social development;
- the *generation* of community acceptance of, and support for, that vision;
- the *motivation* of key people and groups to work in an organised fashion towards that vision;
- the setting of an *example* to the community through the leader's commitment and action.

The capacity of an individual to lead in these directions is aided by possession of several key personal qualities. While there is the potential for speculation about just which qualities may be important in different situations, the following list, again based on the leadership literature, includes some of the most significant, a situation that was verified during the course of the study:

Intelligence	Knowledge	Respect	Resources
Energy	Originality	Persuasiveness	Synoptic thinking

To detract from random 'noise' that could mask leadership effects, we selected towns which were comparable. Ideally towns should:

- function largely as service centres for surrounding agricultural enterprises;
- be subject to the same state and regional policies and initiatives;
- have similar populations in size and demographic composition;
- be located in similar geographic situations;
- have comparable capacity to access information, garner investment, etc.;
- have minimal external influences (such as a neighbouring large regional centre);
- be sufficiently far apart so that they may largely function independently of each other.

Although, it is unlikely that any part of Australia meets these ideal laboratory conditions, a group of four Central Queensland towns (Barcaldine, Blackall, Longreach and Winton) approximated them sufficiently (see Figure 2). Their populations are as shown in Table 1.

Figure 2
Location of the study area

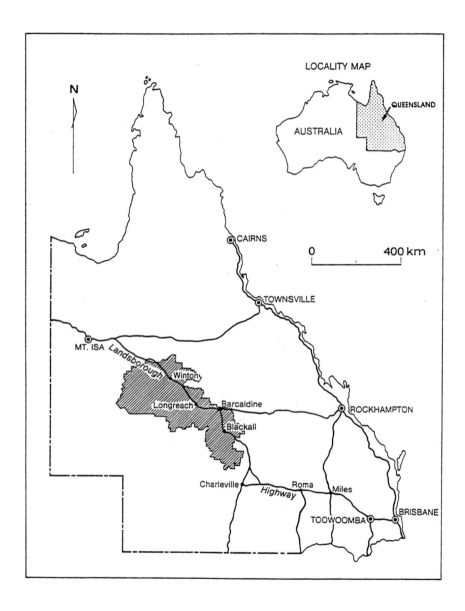

Table 1
Population and population change (1986-1991) of the four towns (shires)

Place	1986	1991	Absolute Numbers	Percent
Barcaldine (S)	1779	1813	+34	+1.9
	1427	1530	+103	+7.2
Blackall (S)	2070	2045	-25	-1.2
	1497	1578	+81	+5.4
Longreach(S)	3871	4369	+498	+12.9
	3159	3607	+448	+14.2
Winton (S)	1986	1877	-109	-5.5
	1281	1156	-125	-9.8

Note: Figures in italics are for the main urban centre in the respective shires. Urban centres have the same names as their surrounding shire (S).
Source: ABS 2703, *Census Counts for Small Areas, Queensland.*

Field research for the project was carried out in two stages. Following preliminary investigation through which many of the key community persons were identified, the first visit (September, 1993) involved interviews with these individuals, local government executives and other people active in community organisations identified during the course of the interviews. This trip provided the researchers with a provisional list of community leaders and an appreciation of who, in the community, would be in a likely position to assess their capabilities. The research also provided further useful information about the economic and social development of the towns.

The second trip (March, 1994) had, as its objective, the interviewing of both perceived leaders and those who had worked with them. Forty-five formal, structured interviews were carried out, typically lasting about an hour each, and details taken in note form. Only one requested interview was refused (due to the illness of that person) and interviewees were very candid, partly due to the fact that nearly all had been interviewed earlier on general issues by the researchers and also as confidentiality in relation to their comments was guaranteed.

The interviews commenced with questions about perceptions of leadership. The interviewees were then asked who the local leaders were, their significant qualities, and what particular characteristics differentiated them as leaders. Whilst those previously identified as leaders were asked the same questions, they were also asked to identify what they saw in themselves as being important leadership qualities. The interviewees were also requested to assess the degree to which the leaders networked amongst themselves, the level of interest and support of the community, and the extent to which these matters were important. Opinions were also sought about the change in the local community over time and some speculation about how the other towns in the study differed from their own. This also provided an opportunity for the researchers to identify leaders with regional prominence.

The contents of the interviews from each town were transferred to a matrix. The analysis of the data first involved an assessment of the leadership functions and personal attributes of each nomination, and a record of their achievements. Whilst some degree of weighting for each quality could be justified in other circumstances, it was considered appropriate for this study to apply a simple scoring system with a point for each function/attribute (as listed above) evident in each leader.

Results

A simple ranking of the results indicates that Blackall's average rank of its leaders was superior, ahead of Longreach, followed by Winton and Barcaldine. However, in terms of gross 'leadership mass', or the number of leaders multiplied by their average score, Longreach surpassed Barcaldine, Blackall and Winton. In some respects, this result is not surprising as Longreach had a larger population than the other centres. Essentially, such a basic summary is suggesting that, within the four towns, Blackall had several good leaders but Longreach, by comparison, had more individuals identified as leaders. However, the result for Longreach was strongly biased by one first rate leader who had, by far, the highest individual ranking within the region. It is also significant to note that, from the results of associated research, Longreach had performed better in terms of economic development and population growth than all other towns over the period since 1980 (see Sorensen and Epps, 1995).

The analysis of leadership in these towns provides valuable insights into the nature of leadership in moderate sized rural towns. The fact that 23 individuals were identified from the interviews as having some degree of leadership capacity is indicative that the region has many individuals playing significant roles in these towns. However, with the one notable exception from Longreach, they were not archetypal leaders but individuals falling into the general categories of: working largely in the domain of their own business (and indirectly to the benefit of their town); working with a government agency; or community-minded individuals, generally working as part of a collective leadership. There was an element of spatial differentiation. Winton, for example, was seen to have its strength amongst its business leaders, whilst Barcaldine had a large number of strongly community-minded individuals in the collective leadership category. From the field work, it is possible to construct a classification of leadership situations (Table 2). Not every category of leadership was evident in the study area, and, in some cases, the examples were indicative rather than strongly represented. Nonetheless, Table 1 provides a conceptual framework of the match between leadership in the four rural towns studied and leadership as it may be found elsewhere.

Table 2
Categories of leadership and their representation in the study area

	Individual	Collective
Government		
Bureaucracy (advisory/implementation)	*	not evident
Political (decision-making)	**	not evident
Community	**	***
Corporate	*	*
Private	**	

* Poorly represented
** Moderately represented
*** Well represented
Note: A single person may well fill two or more of these roles simultaneously.

From the survey itself, and from a general appraisal of the functions of the four towns, it became obvious that the region had active community leadership, on both individual and collective bases. This was also the case with private sector leadership, which mainly came from local small enterprises. Although private and public leadership are demonstrably crucial to community welfare, the scale of the activity in both sectors was to be relatively low key. Corporate leadership, which is now the source of much rural investment, appeared largely absent from the region and this could possibly be linked to the region's lagging economic development. However, a realistic assessment of the area suggests that any major corporate opportunities are matched currently by more profitable opportunities in more favoured locations, especially the coastal zone.

As expected, the local government arena supplied several important leaders at the time of the survey, though none matched the exceptional qualities of one now retired shire chair. Surprisingly, local government had not furnished a greater number of competent leaders given its significant employment and infrastructure role in the regional economy and its 'officiality'.

In order to emphasise the role that a key leader might play in local economic and social development, we focus attention on Longreach's long serving leader. Of all the individuals interviewed, he was the only one who could provide a comprehensive definition of leadership, which suggests to us that takes a strong leader to fully recognise the dimensions of the task. In his personal and somewhat vernacular view, leadership involves:

- commonsense in taking initiatives
- the role of dealer and establishing links
- not being cautious about borrowing money
- the importance of flexibility

- no handouts or kickbacks
- a fair dinkum attitude and a good track record
- using people to build a reliable team
- commitment

This same leader acknowledged battles both in the political arena and with various other people. He has been described by those interviewed as being a good communicator, having access to information, a reasonable element of vision, dogged, often not receptive to ideas of other people, focused and realistic. Interestingly, there were mixed opinions on many issues including whether he was a charismatic leader or not. However, due primarily to his efforts, Longreach gained, amongst other things, an agricultural college, a pastoral research station and the Stockmen's Hall of Fame.

The study established that there was a clearly identifiable echelon of secondary leaders who are particularly effective in bringing about important community developments. These individuals are those who either volunteer for or are co-opted into committee positions. In each town, there appeared to be a small group that filled key positions in a number of organisations. In some respects, these people are executives rather than leaders. Although often lacking the vision and synoptic thinking abilities of a classical leader, they are generally dedicated to the betterment of their communities and, without their efforts, the towns would have little to offer in terms of general well-being, particularly in areas of sporting activities, community welfare and cultural activities.

For those who have lived in a number of locations, perhaps are well educated and possibly have travelled overseas, a move to a small rural town can be particularly depressing. This can be due to many factors including distance from friends and relatives, lack of educational opportunities, a lack of community, sporting and cultural activities, and often an acute sense of not belonging (see Epps, 1991). Those who are employed by corporations and government agencies, and who often move on to more senior positions elsewhere, are described as spiralists (see Montague, 1981, for specific references to Barcaldine). They are rarely able to take dominant leadership roles in rural towns of the type included in the study area. However, particularly if these people are parents who have their families with them, they may be highly effective in fulfilling key roles in the echelon of secondary leaders. Unfortunately, many of these have the potential to be competent archetypal leaders but, because they are considered outsiders, do not receive wide community support (see Epps and Sorensen, 1995).

Conclusion

As the financial constraints on governments pressure them to continue rationalisation, a process that appears to have a greater impact in remote areas with relatively low populations, there will be greater need for rural towns such as those in the study area to call on effective leaders to both win government support for local initiatives and services and to attract business investment. Only in this manner will there be a chance of maintaining the existing population and level of well-being. Alas, leaders of this calibre are also a scarce resource. More commonly, individuals with potential to take a prominent role do not possess the mandatory long-term resident status that appears to be a necessary prerequisite for widespread community support.

Fortunately for the towns studied, there are many in the community who work diligently in many facets of the functions within the towns to ensure that sporting, community and cultural activities provide a reasonable level of well-being. Whilst there was a handful of successful business entrepreneurs, some of whom were major benefactors in terms of enhancing the quality of life in their towns, there was neither evidence of significant corporate enterprise that is likely to lead to major job creation, nor the presence of those who could be actively and effectively selling the merits of their particular locations. Most businesses are, quite logically, being attracted to coastal regions already boasting impressive population growth.

There are initiatives around the nation that are trying to develop leadership skills in individuals, particularly from rural areas. Implicit in this matter is the hypothesis that leaders can be created. There is no question that, with a modicum of training, the potential for some individuals to be seen as a leaders may be increased. However, the research conducted indicated that in the context of effective leadership that produces significant outcome, the attributes of knowledge, vision, synoptic thinking, flexibility, ability to motivate and generate acceptance by the community, and commitment are all essential. It would be unlikely that an individual could develop such abilities through a series of training sessions. Some towns may have a long wait until the necessary leader evolves from within.

References

Beer, A. Bolam, A. and Maude, A. (1994) *Beyond the Capitals: Urban Growth in Regional Australia*, Canberra, Australian Government Publishing Service.

Blainey, G. (1966) *The Tyranny of Distance*, Melbourne, Sun Books.

Bowler, I. Bryant, C. and Nellis, M. (eds) (1992) *Contemporary Rural Systems in Transition: Vol. 2, Economy and Society*, Wallingford, CAB International.

Byrt, W. (1978) *Leaders and Leadership*, Melbourne, Sun Books.

Chemers, M. (1984) The Social, Organisational and Cultural Context of Effective Leadership in Kellerman, B. (ed.) *Leadership: Multi-disciplinary Perspectives*, Englewood Cliffs, NJ, Prentice-Hall.

Epps, W. (1991) An East-West Transect: Attitudes to Travel, Isolation and Environment, *Australian Journal of Social Issues* 26, 1: 51-67.

Epps, R. (1995) The Sustainability of Australian Agricultural Production Systems: A Realistic Objective or Simply a Desirable Aim? *Australian Geographer* 26, 2: 173-179.

Epps, R. and Sorensen, T. (1995) Local Leadership in the Rural Heartland, *Central Queensland Journal of Regional Development* 3, 4: 44-47.

Hodgkinson, C. (1983) *The Philosophy of Leadership*, Oxford, Basil Blackwell.

Holmes, J. (1994) Coast Versus Inland: Two Different Queenslands, *Australian Geographical Studies* 32,.2: 167- 182.

Judd, D. and Parkinson, M. (1990) Urban Leadership and Regeneration, in Judd, D. and Parkinson, M. (eds) *Leadership and Urban Regeneration: Cities in North America and Europe*, London, Sage.

McKinsey and Company (1994) *Lead Local Compete Global*, Sydney, McKinsey and Company.

Montague, M. (1981) Community Structure and Mobility in a Queensland Country Town, in Bowman, M. (ed.) *Beyond the City*, Melbourne, Longman Cheshire.

Pigg, K. (ed.) (1991) *The Future of Rural America: Anticipating Policies for Constructive Change*, Boulder, Westview Press.

Rolley, F. and Humphreys, J. (1993) Rural Welfare - the Human Face of Australia's Countryside, in Sorensen, T. and Epps, R. (eds) *Prospects and Policies for Rural Australia*, Melbourne, Longman Cheshire.

Sorensen, T. (1993) The Future of the Country Town: Strategies for Local Economic Development, in Sorensen, T. and Epps, R. (eds) *Prospects and Policies for Rural Australia*, Melbourne, Longman Cheshire.

Sorensen, T. and Epps, R. (1993) (eds) *Prospects and Policies for Rural Australia*, Melbourne, Longman Cheshire.

Sorensen, T. and Epps, R. (1995) The Changing Economic Structure of Four Central West Queensland Shires, paper presented to the *Annual Conference of the Australian and New Zealand Regional Science Association*, Brisbane, December.

Sorensen, A. and Epps, R. (1996) Community Leadership and Local Development, *Journal of Rural Studies* (in press).

Chapter 13

Agro-industrialisation and rural restructuring: A case study of the Australian poultry industry

Kristen Lyons

Introduction

Attempts have been made by numerous theorists to understand the changes occurring within industrial capitalist production, distribution and consumption networks. Regulationists, proponents of Fordist and post-Fordist theories, and most recently, advocates of the notion of food regimes, have all attempted to conceptualise these changes. It is difficult to approach some general consensus between scholars in attempting to understand these changes. However, this paper focuses largely on theories of Fordism and post-Fordism, and what they offer in attempting to gain a greater understanding of the changes affecting current agri-food restructuring. Of particular importance is the applicability of the notion of Fordism in understanding accumulation and production regimes, and consequent social changes occurring within the Australian poultry industry.

In addition, processes of agro-industrialisation, including appropriationism and substitutionism will be discussed, as will the role they have played in commodification as well as integration of agriculture within the wider circuit of capitalist accumulation. By facilitating integration within the capitalist system, these processes have validated the use of concepts such as Fordism and post-Fordism in understanding changes that have occurred within agricultural production. In contrast, Mathews and Marsden have claimed that Fordism is outdated in its understanding of modes of production, and Watts and Goodman have also proposed that it is inappropriate to talk of food production in these terms. The Australian poultry industry will be highlighted to show that Fordist production persists in certain industries. It will also be concluded that the integration of agricultural production into the wider circuits of capitalism suggests the desirability of employing such terminology when discussing food production and its associated social implications.

The history of industrial capitalism within agriculture

Historically, mechanisms of industrialisation have resulted in dynamic changes throughout all industrial production processes, with the rate of industrialisation varying between different industrial sectors. Within agriculture initial processes of industrialisation were dependent upon variable conditions imposed by nature, thus reducing the rate and predicability of industrialisation. Such natural barriers include the biological conversion of energy, involving the reliance upon solar energy for the transformation of raw inputs into food, as well as the rate of biological time in plant growth and animal gestation (Goodman, Sorj and WIlkinson, 1987). Agricultural production was also dependent upon biological production processes that determined yield, the structure of plants and their efficiency at nutrient uptake. The amount of land available for production also limited the quantity of agricultural outputs (Goodman, Sorj and Wilkinson, 1987).

Processes of agro-industrialisation, including appropriationism and substitutionism, enabled capitalist infiltration within production and served to reduce this dependence upon nature, as well as increasing the rate of agricultural production. Such agro-industrialisation mechanisms have effectively served to integrate agriculture within industrial production, and consequently into the wider circuit of capitalist relations. It is important to consider these processes in more detail, particularly due to the important role they have played in the industrialisation of poultry production.

Goodman, Sorj and Wilkinson (1987: 2) define appropriationism as

> the discontinuous but persistent undermining of discrete elements
> of the agricultural production process, their transformation into
> industrial activities, and their re-incorporation into agriculture as
> inputs.

Initial appropriationist strategies within agriculture involved the adoption of mechanical innovations, which were closely followed by chemical and genetic innovations to supplement, modify or replace biological production processes (Goodman, 1991). This has resulted in the increased use of fertilisers, hybridised seeds, as well as the emergence of biotechnologies in order to increase agricultural production efficiency (Goodman, 1991). Appropriationist strategies in the form of biological innovations have replaced natural production processes, further removing nature as a constraint to production. These appropriationist strategies are clearly evident in the case of poultry production.

At the same time, adoption of mechanical and biological innovations within agriculture also facilitates increased corporate intervention throughout the various stages involved in the agricultural production process (Clunies-Ross and Hildyard, 1992). This is because adopted off-farm inputs enable agro-industrial capitals - which own the technical and biological innovations - to exert increasing control and influence over decision-making related to agricultural production. As a result, suppliers of farm inputs, including chemical and machinery industries, are establishing a position of hegemony throughout the agricultural production process.

Just as with appropriationism, substitutionism has also facilitated corporate intervention and dominance by agro- and chemical industries throughout agricultural production. Substitutionism requires the infiltration of industrial and mechanical processing and manufacturing applications between the growing of agricultural commodities and their final consumption (Goodman, Sorj and Wilkinson, 1987). These applications modify agricultural commodities, resulting in their reassemblance to industrial products, exhibiting particular properties characteristic of industrial outputs (see Friedmann in Friedland *et al.*, 1991). Consequently, food commodities may hold particular traits, including specific dietary qualities, taste, colour and texture via these processes of industrial activity. The application of industrial characteristics to agricultural outputs has facilitated their commodification, and further product differentiation. As a result, mechanical skills and scientific research can be applied to reproduce these same characteristics without reliance upon nature (Berlan, in Friedland *et al.*, 1991).

These mechanisms of appropriationism and substitutionism have led to radical changes in production regimes and in the consequent food commodities produced. Such agro-industrial development, facilitating the increased production of standardised agricultural goods, have contributed to the commodification of agricultural products as well as product differentiation (Friedmann in Friedland *et al.*, 1991). As a result of these changes within capitalism, agricultural goods have become increasingly standardised and mass produced.

The nature of Fordism and its application to agriculture

Marsden (1992) and Kim and Curry (1993), have fitted the nature of modern agricultural production (that production reliant upon appropriationist techniques and substitutionist strategies) into the wider framework of Fordist and post-Fordist production and accumulation strategies. They suggest that these regimes of accumulation and modes of regulation that persisted throughout the post World War II period, identified by Jessop (1992), Aglietta (1979) and Lipietz (1987), are applicable to the production of certain agricultural commodities.

The characteristics of each of these regimes of accumulation are outlined in the table below. This table (see Buttel, 1993) is not intended to be exhaustive. Rather it provides a summary of the main features of Fordism and post-Fordism.

Kim and Curry (1993) argue strongly that Fordist tendencies persist in certain agricultural sectors and they highlight the case of the US broiler industry. Marsden (1992) also suggests that Fordism continues in numerous industries, including battery farming (intensive, highly concentrated production of animals) and fast food. The fast food industry clearly highlights the use of Fordist production strategies in order to maintain the mass production of standardised commodities for mass consumption.

Table 1
Differences between Fordism (social-democratic society) and post-Fordism (neo-conservative society)

Characteristics	Fordism	Post-Fordism
regime of accumulation	intensive	transitive
time period	1945 - early 1970s	emerged early 1970s
consumption patterns	mass consumption	highly differentiated consumer styles
production concept	international mass production	computer integrated manufacturing flexible batch production
mode of production	assembly line production	production via flexible specialised machinery
employment	full employment homogeneous mass workers	job losing growth individual decentralised markets
market	world market	'Triad' markets (North America, EEC, Pacific Rim)
government policies	Keynesian socioeconomic policies, welfare state, social democracy	deregulation, self-servicing society, neo-conservatism

Source: Adapted from Buttel (1993:16)

However, numerous theorists including Piore and Sabel (1987), Mathews (1992) and Marsden (1992), suggest that the collapse in social conditions that maintained Fordism have, in turn, undermined that particular system of accumulation. Marsden (1992) identifies these crises as the decline in US hegemony, the collapse of the Bretton Woods Agreement, as well as the US oil shocks. In conjunction with changing social conditions, Friedmann (1991) also identifies the integration of accumulation within the global market as contributing to the crisis in global Fordism. Changes in product markets and production strategies have also contributed to this crisis. In conjunction with these arguments that suggest it is inappropriate to discuss production and consumption in terms of Fordism, Watts and Goodman (1994) also suggest that it is inappropriate to apply Fordist and post-Fordist notions to understand the wider changes occurring within agriculture.

However, an investigation into the Australian poultry industry reveals that the industry utilises Fordist strategies in order to maximise efficiency and economic growth. Although it illustrates few characteristics that conform to post-Fordist strategies, it is still largely Fordist in nature. This suggests that some authors may be incorrect in disregarding Fordism as a label to understand modern production regimes and their associated social implications.

Furthermore, and in contrast to Watts and Goodman, integration of poultry production into the wider circuit of capitalist relations by way of processes of appropriationism and substitutionism, support the view that it is appropriate to apply Fordist and post-Fordist notions may be useful in understanding production and consumption norms.

An introduction to the Queensland poultry industry: A case study of Fordist strategies

Analysis of the Queensland poultry industry provides the possibility of highlighting both the Fordist strategies utilised by the industry, as well as the social ramifications associated with this mode of production. In this way it is possible to argue that it is incorrect to de-value the place of Fordist production within modern agriculture.

Concentration and intensification of production

Just as assembly-line production maintained Fordism within industrial production throughout the 1950s and 1960s in car factories and other consumer goods industries via economies of scale, modern poultry production utilises assembly lines and economies of scale in order to maximise production efficiency. As a consequence, industrial poultry production has become dominated by few large farms. Within poultry production, smaller farms are marginalised while larger farms, with access to large quantities of capital maintain, and may in fact increase, productivity. In this way, the nature of Fordist production discriminates against smaller farmers.

Within the Queensland poultry industry, production is undertaken by some 96 farms (Larkin, 1991). These farms are generally comprised of three or four large sheds, each about 1,500m². Birds are contained within these sheds at an average density of about 16 birds/m² (Hamilton, 1994). Poultry production undertaken on these farms is considered to be highly concentrated and intensive, facilitating the production of large numbers of birds for slaughter. As a consequence of the intensive nature of production (something characteristic of Fordism) birds often suffer numerous disorders associated with such over-crowding, including stress, boredom, increased occurance of aggressive behaviour, cannibalism, and related health problems (Singer, 1990).

With the concentration of production within a few large farms, two major companies dominate poultry processing within Queensland, Inghams Enterprises and Australian Poultry Limited (APL). Between them they process 95 percent of the poultry grown in Queensland (Hamilton, 1994). The presence of only two major processing companies within the Queensland poultry industry effectively grants them oligopolistic power over growers, further centralising and concentrating operations. Poultry farmers have little freedom to choose between processing companies, allowing companies to dictate conditions to growers.

171

Appropriationism: methods of production

In conjunction with the centralisation of its operations, the modern poultry industry has rapidly increased production efficiency as a result of the adoption of mechanical, technological and chemical appropriationist strategies throughout the growing stage of poultry production. This is also characteristic of Fordist production. The factory-floor production of the Model-T Ford illustrates this, with reliance placed upon the development of labour-displacing technologies and specialised machinery in order to increase production efficiency (Allen, 1992).

Throughout poultry production, appropriations have been adopeted continuously by growers, including automated feeding and water equipment, as well as climate control mechanisms, to further increase production efficiency. This has been adopted in order to maintain competitiveness in an increasingly competitive global market and has facilitated the Fordist mass production of poultry products. The adoption of these appropriationist strategies has also been required in order to produce poultry to specifications in terms of both quantity and quality, outlined by growers under contracts, the regime under which the majority of poultry is produced. A consequence of the mechanisation of farm activities and increased use of appropriationist strategies has been significant labour displacement. This has occurred as the previous labour intensity associated with the poultry industry is replaced by capital intensive production (Queensland Poultry Growers Association, 1992: 9). At the same time, employment within the processing sector has increased, as poultry has become an increasingly value added commodity. In 1980, 127,700 people were employed in the poultry processing industry. This figure increased by 60 percent, up to 209,300 by 1992 (Hetrick, 1994: 31). These figures indicate the shift in employment away from primary production and towards processing and value adding. In conjunction with labour displacement, farmers are experiencing both increased debt as a result of the adoption of appropriations, and as a further consequence increased stress and illness (Hamilton, 1994).

As a result of the adoption of capital intensive methods of production, modern poultry growing takes place under strictly controlled growing conditions. Technologies are adopted to control shed environments which maintain the climatic conditions which will provide for maximum production efficiency. The use of drugs and antibiotics during the growing stage of poultry production has also facilitated increased production (Milne, 1989). The use of vaccines has reduced the loss of poultry due to disease, leading to increased production efficiency (Fairbrother, 1988). The application of breed selection techniques has also resulted in other production improvements, including a reduction in the time between day-old chicks and their maturation to a marketable age (Fairbrother, 1988). Breed selection techniques have also led to improvements in the feed conversion ratio. The adoption of appropriationist strategies by poultry growers illustrates attmepts to increase the rate of production, and consequently, the speed of the assembly line.

As a consequence of the adoption of appropriationist strategies, capitalist interests have further penetrated the production process through ownership of adopted innovations. This has enabled off-farm interests to increase control over farmers and the production process, enabling the growing of standardised, uniform, poultry of particular quality - characteristic of Fordist production.

Vertical integration of production

In conjunction with the adoption of appropriationist strategies throughout production, changes in the structure of poultry production has also facilitated increased off-farm control. The modern poultry industry has emerged as a complex, highly integrated, system of production (Rabobank, 1993). Inputs into the poultry farming process, combined with poultry growing, processing and retailing have become linked into a vertically integrated structure of production and consumption. The ownership of these different stages of production are commonly dominated by one large agribusiness. Such a regime of production ensures production of standardised commodities, characteristic of Fordism.

The output side of the poultry production process is largely dominated by wholesale and retail outlets, including fast food and supermarket chains (Queensland Poultry Growers Association, 1992). These retail outlets demand specialised inputs in order to supply standardised poultry for mass consumption. In order to guarantee the supply of standardised inputs, these wholesale and retail outlets have increasingly gained control over other stages of the production process, including processing, poultry growing, and as industries supplying inputs into the production process. These inputs include machinery, disease control techniques, technological innovations, genetic improvements, improved feed technology, feed, medicine and veterinary services (including growth hormones), and day old chicks (Queensland Poultry Growers Association, 1992). Processing companies may supply these inputs in order to ensure the supply of standardised poultry products to retail outlets. Within Queensland, processing companies supply day old chicks, medication and feed to growers (Hamilton, 1994). Integration of the retail and processing sectors into the inputs side of poultry production has meant that processors may control the primary breeding of chickens, while growers supply housing, shedding, labour and management until chickens reach slaughter weight.

In order to ensure the production of standardised poultry products, the vertically integrated structure of production has redirected control and decision making away from growers and towards off-farm capitalist interests. This increased dominance by off-farm interests has been reported as leading to increased pressure on farmers, increased stress and illness, as well as a reduction in control and decision making (Burch *et al.*, 1992).

The contract arrangement

Contract arrangements are the dominant method of organisation within the poultry industry. Contracts ensure the supply of standardised poultry products to processing and retail outlets. These arrangements further reduce the role of farmers as decision makers within the production process (Burch *et al.*, 1992). Requirements placed upon growers by processors throughout the contract arrangement in order to produce a standardised product include breed specifications, specifications for feeding, and temperature regimes (Hamilton, 1994). Present breed specifications include farming birds which produce a large amount of breast tissue, combined with characteristics that will increase the rate of feed conversion (Queensland Poultry Growers Association, 1992). This breed selection is undertaken in order to increase production efficiency. Processing companies also dictate feeding times, including type and quantity of feed and water to be utilised (Hamilton, 1994). The density of birds to be housed within poultry sheds is also stipulated by processors within the contract.

Breed and feeding specifications laid out by processors also occur alongside specifications of growing conditions in which poultry must be produced. The sheds in which chickens grow are humidity controlled, with built-in fogging systems, heaters and artificial lighting (Hamilton, 1994). Numerous farmers have undertaken farming with the use of artificial lighting in order to increase the rate of production. Lights are kept on in sheds for up to 22 hours a day, in order to encourage birds to feed longer, thus reducing the time required for birds to reach the weight stipulated within the contract arrangement (Hamilton, 1994). Technology adopted in the growing stage results in the complete artificial control over the shed environment.

These characteristics of poultry-growing production highlight the capitalist imperative that drives poultry production, rather than concern for animal welfare issues. The adoption of breed selection techniques has led to numerous adverse implications for birds. The volume of flesh on birds has grown more quickly than bones and joints, leading to skeletal disorders (Singer, 1990). Transgenic (genetically engineered) birds also suffer from certain ailments, including infertility, lethargy, and poor coordination (Singer, 1990). Birds also suffer enormous adverse effects from the totally artificial environment that is created in order to maximise production efficiency. There is evidence that increased lighting utilised by poultry farmers to increase the rate of growing time also results in increased stress upon birds (reported in Singer, 1990). In conjunction, the increased use of drugs and antibiotics also has significant adverse effects upon poultry including skeletal disorders, arthritis, as well as problems in feeding (see Singer, 1990).

The future of poultry production

The case of the Australian poultry industry highlights the integration that has occurred between agriculture and the broader industrial economy, resulting in the dominance of capitalist relations throughout modern farming. As a consequence, terminology such as Fordism and post-Fordism, utilised to understand the changes occurring throughout industrial production processes, have applicability when attempting to understand the changes occurring within the poultry industry. Furthermore, by looking at industrial accumulation and production processes, it is possible to gain a greater understanding of the nature of agricultural production. We will now turn to consider the characteristics of Fordism and post-Fordism presented in Table 1, so as to compare characteristics of modern poultry production.

Characteristics of modern poultry production highlighted within this chapter include intensive factory production (resulting in increased production) with reliance upon fewer farmers. This centralisation of operations and intensive production aligns poultry production with notions of a Fordist regime of accumulation. The mass production that occurs as a consequence of this regime of accumulation is also a Fordist concept.

The dominant mode of production that exists within the poultry industry illustrates an assembly line operation, a mode of Fordist production. Furthermore, appropriations have been adopted at specific points along the assembly line. This adoption of appropriations by poultry farmers has led to the effective integration of farmers within the wider Fordist industrial relations of accumulation, both through the consumption of mass produced inputs (machinery and petrochemical inputs), as well as in the production of a standardised product. The de-skilling associated with increased reliance upon off-farm inputs is also characteristic of Fordism, which is reliant upon a mass workforce of non-specialised 'factory' labour.

Although poultry production exhibits certain Fordist characteristics, consumption trends in the future may alter this pattern, affecting production, consumption and distribution patterns. The rise of green consumerism, for example, as well as increased demands for healthy and nutritious foods may affect the future of poultry production and consumption patterns. As a consequence, we may see a move towards post-Fordist poultry production. In order to provide the emerging new green consumer, production may become more localised; in order to retain freshness, goods may become highly differentiated; and, in order to cater for individual needs, and commodities may be increasingly produced for specific markets. The move towards post-Fordism within agricultural production may already be evident in certain industries, including organic foods and tropical fruits.

Conclusion

This analysis of the Australian poultry industry highlights the Fordist tendencies prevalent throughout the production process. By considering the nature of Fordism and post-Fordism, it is indicated that Australian poultry production has characteristics that align it with a Fordist mode of production and consumption, although future consumption trends may alter this. Furthermore, the adoption of appropriationist strategies within poultry production has served as a mechanism to integrate poultry production within the framework of capitalist production. This, in conjunction with other characteristics of modern poultry production, including concentration and intensification of production, vertical integration and the contract arrangement, justify the use of Fordist terminology in understanding changes that are occurring within the industry. By utilising Fordism it is also possible to identify the social implications and associated animal welfare issues that arise from the intensive nature of production. This analysis of the Australian poultry industry supports claims by Marsden (1992) and Kim and Curry (1993) that there is validity in applying interpretations of wider industrial capitalism in order to understand agriculture. This case study highlights the fact that it might be imprudent to dismiss as conceptually bankrupt (as Watts and Goodman suggest) terms such as Fordism and post-Fordism, particularly when they are not yet fully explored or understood as concepts that may be applied to agriculture.

References

Aglietta, M. (1979) *Theory of Capitalist Regulation: The US Experience*, London, NLB.

Allen, J. (1992) Fordism and Modern Industry, in Allen, J., Braham, P. and Lewis, P. *Political Economy and Economic Forms of Modernity*, Cambridge, Polity Press.

Berlan, J. (1991) The Historical Roots of the Present Agricultural Crisis, in Friedland, W.H. *et al.*, *Towards A New Political Economy of Agriculture*, Boulder, Westview Press.

Burch, D., Rickson, R. and Annels, R. (1992) The Growth of Agribusiness: Environmental and Social Implications of Contract Farming, in Lawrence, G., Vanclay, F. and Furze, B. (eds) in *Agriculture, Environment and Society*, South Melbourne, Macmillan.

Buttel, F. (1993) Environmentalisation and Greening: Origins, Processes and Implications, in Harper, S. *The Greening of Rural Policy*, London, Belhaven Press.

Clunies-Ross, T. and Hildyard, N. (1992) *The Politics of Industrial Agriculture*, London, Earthscan.

Fairbrother, J. (1988) The Poultry Industry - Technology's Child Two Decades On, *Food Australia*: 456-462.

Fairbrother, J. (1987) Trends in Poultry Consumption, *Food Technology In Australia* 39 5: 191-193.

Friedmann, H. (1991) Changes in the International Division of Labour: Agri-food Complexes and Export Agriculture, in Friedland, W. *et al.*, (eds) *Towards A New Political Economy of Agriculture*, Boulder, Westview Press.

Goodman, D. (1991) Some Recent Tendencies in the Industrial Reorganisation of the Agri-Food System, in Friedland, W. *et al.*, (eds) *Towards A New Political Economy of Agriculture*, Boulder, Westview Press

Goodman, D., Sorj, B. and Wilkinson, J. (1987) *From Farming To Biotechnology*, Oxford, Basil Blackwell.

Hamilton, P. (1994) *Verbal Correspondence*, Queensland Chicken Growers Association.

Jessop, B. (1990) Regulation Theories in Retrospect and Prospect, *Economy and Society* 19, 2: 153-216.

Kenney, M. Lobao, L. Curry, J. and Goe, R. (1989) Midwestern Agriculture in US Fordism. From the New Deal to Economic Restructuring, *Sociologia Ruralis* 29, 2: 131-148.

Kim, C. and Curry, J. (1993) Fordism, Flexible Specialisation and Agri-Industrial Restructuring, *Sociologia Ruralis* 33, 1: 61-80.

Larkin, T. and Associates, (1991) *The Australian Poultry Industry*, Canberra.

Lipietz, A. (1987) *Mirages and Miracles: The Crisis In Global Fordism*, London, New Left Review.

Marsden, T. (1992) Exploring a Rural Sociology For The Fordist Transition, *Sociologia Ruralis* 32: 209-230.

Mathews, J. (1992) New Production Systems: A Response to Critics and a Re-evaluation, *Journal of Australian Political Economy* 30: 91-125.

Milne, N. *et al.*, (1989) *A New Life: The History of The Poultry Industry in Queensland*, Brisbane, Queensland Department of Primary Industries.

Piore, M. and Sabel, C. (1984) *The Second Industrial Divide: Possibilities For Prosperity*, New York, Basic Books.

Queensland Poultry Growers Association, (1992) *The Success Story*, Queensland, unpublished document.

Rabobank, (1988) *The World Poultry Market. Agribusiness Research*, Nederland, J.A.G. Verheijen/R. Kok.

Singer, P. and Mason, J. (1990) *Animal Factories*, New York, Harmony Books.

Watts, M. and Goodman, D. (1994) Reconfiguring the Rural or Fording the Divide? Capitalist Restructuring and the Global Agro-Food System *Journal of Peasant Studies* 22, 1: 1-49.

Chapter 14

The Australian sugar industry and commodity systems analysis

Linda Hungerford

Introduction

The 'economic crisis' of the 1970s precipitated significant restructuring of the global economy. Changes wrought by the deregulation of national economies and the transnationalisation of capital has meant that agriculture, like practically every other field of economic endeavour, is increasingly shaped by the dictates of international economic rationalism rather than local market forces. As a consequence agricultural industry is being restructured.

Since the early 1980s the resultant social-structural changes which have occurred within agriculture and the growing economic difficulties associated with rural living have been the focus of considerable sociological research. Generally such studies have been concentrated at either the macro level or the micro level. That is, they have been confined to either the processes of globalisation of agricultural production, or they have focussed on the results of globalisation on specific local industries and the communities that support them. In order to gain a full understanding of agricultural restructuring processes, however, it is necessary to analyse all of the relationships that exist between the beginning and the end of any given agricultural production process.

This paper looks at how Commodity Systems Analysis, a technique developed in the US by William Friedland, may be used as a framework for an examination of change and restructuring within the sugar industry. The paper is but part of a much larger piece of research, the primary purpose of which is to ascertain some of the possible consequences of restructuring (both national and international) for the sugar industry in Australia generally, and the Bundaberg region specifically. The research will do this by seeking answers to a number of questions about the industry:

- How important is sugar to the Australian economy and what is its future as a major trade commodity?

- How will new sugar developments, such as that which is being established in Thailand, impact on the Australian industry?
- Will the purchase of the Bundaberg Sugar Company (and possibly other Australian sugar companies and cooperatives) by multinationals like Tate and Lyle significantly affect the overall development of the Australian industry?
- What regulatory changes are taking places within national and international sugar industries?
- How might such changes impact on the structure of the Australian sugar industry and the regions in which sugar production is a major part of the local economy?
- Will the restructuring that is now taking place within the Australian sugar industry be sufficient to meet the challenge presented by restructuring within the global sugar industry?

Commodity systems analysis: an overview

Commodity Systems Analysis was developed during the course of a series of commodity studies conducted by William Friedland and his associates. These studies were primarily concerned with tomato and lettuce production and were undertaken in the 1970s and early 1980s (see Friedland, *et al.,* 1972; 1974; 1975; and Friedland, 1981; 1984). Friedland's most recent study (as yet unpublished) investigates grape and wine production in California.

The Commodity Systems approach was selected because it facilitates the examination of specific agricultural production processes, such as the production of sugar, in their entirety. It provides both a theoretical and methodological framework for research. Theoretically, it is anchored in neo-Marxism; methodologically it draws on historical, institutional, quantitative and qualitative analysis which is used to examine five aspects of the 'commodity chain'. The five foci are: production practices, grower organisation, labour as a factor in production, scientific production and application, and marketing and distribution systems (Friedland, 1984: 222). While acknowledging that there is no single, specific methodological procedure associated with these research foci, it is contended that they encompass the major aspects of, and significant points of interaction within the broader economy, of commodity systems or chains. The following brief explanation of the five major foci as identified by Friedland and his associates, demonstrates the validity of this claim.

Production practices: This refers to the techniques of production including the characteristics of given commodities in terms of biology, problems, diseases control process, and so on. Analysis of the way in which production is organised and the problems confronted during the production cycle provide a baseline for the delineation of the social organisation of the commodity system (Friedland, 1984: 225). It is also necessary to consider the impacts of farming practices on the natural environment.

Grower organisation, and organisations: The key player within the agricultural production cycle is the grower or farmer: without the grower there is no production. In order to understand a particular commodity system therefore, an analysis of the ways in which growers are socially organised (be it in terms of family or corporate structures) is vital.

Another topic for research is the nature, composition, and functions of grower organisations. The forms such organisations take can be manifold, however, Friedland suggests that are four major types: production research (such as plant breeding and cultivation technology), advertising and marketing, politics, and labour relations (Friedland, 1981: 17). Some of these organisations may be private associations with voluntary memberships, while other take a public form and because of marketing order legislation, are supported by the force of law (Friedland, 1984: 224). Where organisations are supported by legislation the role of government if a further consideration.

Labour as a factor of production: Traditionally most farmers have, by necessity, been engaged in both management and labouring activities. With the development of monocultural specialisation and industrial agriculture, however, these activities have become more differentiated between sets of actors (Friedland, 1984: 235). Such differentiation has changed the nature of working and social relationships within specific agricultural industries as well between such industries and other industries. While varying patterns can exist within a given agricultural industry it is probable that patterns specific to that industry will emerge.

Science production and application: In a time of ever increasing international competition between commodity producing countries and regions, research and development units play an important role in maintaining the economic viability of specific commodities. Further, R&D units are frequently an integral part of the production process in that such units are the providers of new advice and information pertaining to the process. Among the issues to be examined within the context of science production and application are relationships between commodity organisation R&D units, funding sources, and patron-client relations between private producers and public research and development units.

Marketing and distribution: Marketing and distribution can be described as the end point of a production process and as such it is a vital part of any commodity chain analysis. The nature of the marketing and distribution mechanisms adopted by commodity producers may vary significantly from the very informal device of selling from roadside stalls, to tightly structured and highly regulated models of the kind found in the sugar industry.

Commodity systems analysis: strengths and weaknesses

Each of the five foci identified by Friedland can, in themselves, be used as the basis for separate research projects in which clearly delineated parts of industries are investigated. For example, much of Friedland's own work has concentrated on one of the identified foci, namely, labour as a factor of production. Alternatively, as in this research, all five can be incorporated to provide a comprehensive analysis of all aspects of a specific agricultural industry. In so doing the entire agricultural process, from soil preparation, through harvesting, marketing and distribution, labour relations, financial and conservation issues, and the role of the state, and the linkages between each of these factors may be observed and the impacts or influences each may have on others can be assessed. For example, where the research project is primarily concerned with restructuring which is necessitated by changes to regulatory mechanism within a given agricultural industry, the role of the state is integral to the analysis. The commodity systems analysis framework facilitates the incorporation of the role of the state at each stage of the production, marketing and distribution process.

Friedland's commodity systems approach makes the assumption that the state is one of the most important players in agricultural activity. For example, in his seminal piece *Manufacturing Green Gold: Capital, Labor and Technology in the Lettuce Industry*, Friedland (1981:5) claimed that 'implicit in the analysis of any production process is the role of the state'. He went on to say that the state has consistently played a significant role in agricultural development, and while he was referring to American agriculture, it is fair to suggest that the same would be true, to a greater or lesser degree, in practically every other nation in the world, including Australia. In a highly regulated industry such as sugar the role of the state is particularly influential and as such CSA methodology is a convenient tool for analysis. It allows the researcher to look at the ways in which legislative changes effect various parts of the production, marketing and distribution cycle, while at the same time enabling the influence of a multiplicity of other variables, such as drought, price and the environment, to be considered.

While the role of the state has long been recognised as a significant area of interest when researching agricultural production, critics of the approach (see Bonanno, *et al.,* 1995:31) argue that the increasingly global nature of food systems calls its usefulness into question. Rather than nation-states controlling the trading system, it is TNC trade (that is, companies selling to other companies) that is viewed as the most significant form of trade. In this construction, the role of the nation state is to 'balance accumulation requirements with legitimation demands' (Bonanno, 1995:31). It is the contention of this research that the utility of the commodity systems approach is not merely confined to its incorporation of the role of the state as a medium for analysis. Rather it is the concept of the commodity chain or system, and hence the commodity as the unit of analysis, that is of value.

Despite its utility for projects such as investigations of the effects of government deregulation on agriculture, CSA is not suitable for many other kinds of rural or agricultural sociological research since by choosing the crop or commodity as the unit of analysis, many other units of analysis are overlooked. For example, the concept of community is not addressed, and while some companies may by used to illustrate particular phenomena, individual firms are not examined in any great detail either. Further, the farm as a unit of analysis is given scant, if any, attention (Friedland, 1981:12). The sheer size of a research project which attempts to cover an entire commodity chain may also be considered a drawback.

Commodity systems analysis and the sugar industry

Friedland's approach can be used to demonstrate the linkages between the agricultural production process under examination and the remainder of the political economy. Friedland argues that CSA is particularly appropriate to the study of agricultural systems where 'discrete commodity systems...are conceptually and socially distinct' (Friedland 1984: 223). The sugar industry can be defined in these terms and, while acknowledging that no commodity system in reality stands alone, this research contends that most aspects of the sugar production system can be analysed as parts of singularly identifiable units within a discrete commodity chain.

For the purposes of this research project analysis is confined to the processes involved in the growing of sugar cane through to the production, marketing and distribution of raw sugar. While there are considerable levels of pluriactivity and diversification into other agricultural pursuits by cane growers, consideration of such activities within this study is marginal. Not all aspects of the CSA methodology as delineated by Friedland are to be examined in equal depth. The work begins with the identification of key players and processes in the production cycle of cane sugar.

Key Players	Key Processes
Growers	Cane growing/farm ownership
Growers' organisations	Information and looking after growers' interests
Harvesting Contractors (HCs)	Cane harvesting and delivery to mills
HC organisations	Looking after harvesters interests
Water Resources Commission	Irrigation
Banks/financiers	Capital supply and control
Millers	Crushing and processing to raw sugar stage
Millers' organisations	Looking after millers' interests
Bureau of Sugar Experiment Stations	Research and development
Queensland Government	Regulation, marketing and distribution
Australian Government	Regulation and legislation

Having identified the key players and processes they perform it is a relatively simple matter to allocate them to one of the five foci delineated in Friedland's model (into the categories described below).

Production practices: As noted above production practices refers to the techniques of production. In the case of cane sugar there are two distinct yet intimated related sets of production practices which have to be taken into consideration. The first set of practices relate to the growing of sugar cane while the second set of practices are concerned with the milling process which turns sugar cane into raw cane sugar. Both sets of practices must be considered because, unlike most other commodities which may undergo further processing before sale, sugar cane cannot be sold (except in very small quantities in places such as Papua New Guinea and Fiji) unless it is processed. The interactions and relationships between growers and miller constitute a major part of the social organisation of the sugar industry.

An examination of the production practices pertaining to the growing of sugar needs to include discussion of the nature of the sugar cane plant in terms of its biology, agronomical requirements, water and/or irrigation demands, and problems such as insect infestations and diseases. It should also consider capital investment needs, cultivation techniques and the ways in which they might impact on the natural environment.

While production practices relating to the actual milling process are quite distinct from those of the growing process, many of the problems which affect growers also impact on millers. For example, adverse weather conditions will cause problems for both for farmers who are waiting for their cane to be harvested and for the mills which are anxious to crush it. Farmers cannot re-plant or prepare for the next seasons crop while this seasons crop remains standing in the field, nor can mills operate is plant at maximum levels of efficiency. Similarly, strikes and breakdowns in the mills will impact upon the efficiency of the cane farmers.

Grower/miller organisation, and grower/miller organisations: The Australian sugar industry is what Friedland has described as 'organisationally dense' (pers comm, July, 1994). By this he means that there are many organisations, a significant number of which are sanctioned by government legislation, directly associated with the industry. At the apex of the sugar organisational structure is the Queensland Sugar Corporation (QSC). The QSC was formed under the Sugar Industry Act (1991), when it absorbed the previously existing marketing responsibilities of the Sugar Board (1923-1991) and the production and Regulation responsibilities of the Central Sugar Cane Prices Board (1915-1991). An ancillary arm of the QSC is the Sugar Industry Policy Council which was created to ensure direct industry input into the development of strategic policy for the Corporation (Queensland Sugar Corporation, 1991:42).

Canegrowers' is the main body or organisation representing the interests of cane farmers. Although establish by State Government legislation, however, it is fully accountable to, funded and controlled by, cane growers. It has a three level structure which is comprised of local area committees, district executives and a policy making State council. The other organisation which purports to represent the interests of cane farmers is the Australian Cane Farmers' Association (ACFA). ACFA is a voluntary and independent association which was established in 1987.

The mills have their own representative body called the Australian Sugar Milling Council (ASMC). The ASMC was established in 1988 and its voluntary membership is comprised of the owners of all Australian raw sugar mills. Between the growing and milling processes sugar cane has to be harvested, and harvesting contractors have their own representative body known as the Mechanical Cane Harvesters' Association.

While consideration of the industry's compulsory and voluntary organisations is important, the most essential element of this portion of the research is discussion of the social organisation, actions and interactions of growers and - because of the intimacy of the link between them - millers. Friedland's approach emphasises the importance of the growers because they 'are the major formative element of agricultural production' (Friedland, 1981:15) Friedland acknowledges that they are not the only shapers of the production process, and that the character of agricultural production is determined by the interaction among the various factors that constitute the labour process, however, he argues that they must be the 'beginning point' for analyses of agricultural production systems.

Labour as a factor of production: The organisation of labour as a factor of production is a critical element in the analysis of any agricultural production system. The dual role of farmers as both capitalists (owners of farms) and workers (on their own and sometimes other people's farms) is particularly complex. Friedland argues that with the development of monocultural specialisation these activities have become more differentiated between sets of actors (Friedland, 1984:235), however, in the sugar industry such differentiation is becoming increasingly 'fuzzy'. In the past most cane growers would have employed at least one or two permanent labourers throughout the year. During harvesting and planting times additional casual labour was engaged. More than a decade of difficult economic times however, has meant that for all except a few very large growers, permanent on-site labour is a luxury they have had to dispense with. The work previously undertaken by hired help is now the responsibility of the farm family; additional labour is only recruited and maintained when it is absolutely essential. Analysis of labour relations in this context is therefore problematic.

Labour relations within the milling sector are more easily differentiated, and therefore more readily analysed in terms of existing sociological and/or economic theory. As Friedland (1981:19) notes however, labor 'is not simply a quiescent factor to be organised passively'. In the sugar industry as in all other industries, labour relations are dynamic; they are part of a process which is continually adjusted and developed through the interaction of growers, millers and workers. Because of its importance to the production process, an understanding of the nature of these relationships is crucial to the analysis of the sugar as a commodity system.

Scientific production and application: The oldest and arguably most important scientific body pertaining to the sugar industry is the Bureau of Sugar Experiment Stations (BSES) which was established in 1900. The BSES undertakes research into soils and agronomy, agricultural engineering, cane breeding, biotechnology, entomology and pathology. BSES staff provide technical advice to canegrowers and millers alike (Queensland Sugar Corporation, 1991:48). There are numerous other organisations which provide scientific and technical advise to the industry including the Sugar Research and Development Corporation, the Sugar Research Institute, CSR Limited, CSIRO, and several universities. While there is some government funding provided to these organisations, significant portions of their operational budgets are met by levies which are borne by growers and millers.

As noted above an in-depth examination of these institutions is beyond the parameters of this study, however, because scientific knowledge and its application is and always has been an integral part of the sugar production process, some discussion of the nature of the relationships between science, growers, millers and government will enhance our overall understanding of the sugar industry.

Marketing and distribution: Because all sugar produced in Queensland is compulsorily acquired by the Queensland government (which then undertakes to market the product on behalf of the industry) this part of the research is mainly interested in the role of the state. It is also, however, at this point that the research endeavours to 'connect the global with the local'. Nearly 85 percent of Queensland's annual raw sugar production is exported, about 30 percent of which is price-protected by long-term contracts. The balance of Australia's export sugar is sold on the world market at prices dictated by global supply and demand. The economic welfare of local producers is in effect therefore, heavily dependent on the global market.

Conclusion

Because the impacts of agricultural and rural restructuring are (or are likely to be) extensive, it is essential that they be carefully monitored. The 'big' players in the game - those with the ears of governments or the resources to make them listen - dominate proceedings and make decisions which impact on thousands, if not millions, of farming units throughout the world. Already, there is evidence to suggest that 'in the context of a world agro-food system characterised by oversupply and unfair trading,' restructuring places 'considerable pressure for adjustment on small-scale capital in agriculture' (Lawrence *et al.*, 1992: 17). While small scale capital may have lost control of the game, it is suggested that it nevertheless continues to play a crucial role in the overall scheme of things. It is therefore, necessary to analyse the relationships that exist between the beginning and the end of any given commodity chain. To echo the words of Sarah Whatmore (1994), studies that 'reconnect the global with the local' are essential to a full understanding of the restructuring process. Within this context studies which include the 'local level' have an important role to play.

These sentiments are as relevant to the sugar industry as they are to any other agricultural industry. This study links change within the global sugar industry to change within the Australian context, with particular reference to the sugar industry located in the Bundaberg region. Since the early 1980s the Australian sugar industry has had to contend with a variety of restructuring processes and changes to the conduct of the global sugar industry. These have included market shifts, competition from new sugar industries such as that which is developing in Thailand, competition from other kinds of sweeteners such as High Fructose Corn Syrup, a prolonged period of low prices, escalating production costs, and the most significant restructuring of the its regulatory mechanisms since the industry began.

There is a growing concern among growers that further deregulation will adversely impact on their continued economic viability. One of their greatest fears is that the existing 'single desk' selling mechanism will be abolished (Baldwin, pers comm, 1995). There is a believe that if this happens, the Australian sugar industry will be fragmented and marginalised to the point where it is no longer regarded as a serious producer in the global sugar industry. The effects of restructuring of the sugar industry at the global and national levels will ultimately be felt at the local level and as such it has the potential to change forever, the regional economies which are largely dependent on the production of sugar. The conduct of the restructuring process is, therefore, vitally important to all concerned. It is hoped that by applying Friedland's Commodity Systems Analysis technique to the sugar industry a useful understanding of the restructuring processes that are taking place within it may emerge.

References

Baldwin, N. (1995) Chair, Canegrowers Bundaberg District.

Bonanno, A., Busch, L, Friedland, W., Gouveia, L., and Mingione, E. (eds) (1995) *From Columbus to ConAgra*, Kansas, University of Kansas Press.

Friedland W., and Nellcon, D. (1972) Changing Perspectives on the Organisation of Migrant Farm Workers in the Eastern United States, *Social Problems* 19, 4: 509-521

Friedland W. and Thomas, R. (1974) Paradoxes of Agricultural Unionism in California, *Society* 11 (May/June): 54-62

Friedland W. and Barton, A. (1975) Destalking the Wily Tomato: A Case Study in Social Consequences in California Agricultural Research, Research Monograph No. 15, Davis, College of Agriculture and Environmental Studies, University of California

Friedland W. (1981) *Manufacturing Green Gold: Capital, Labor, and Technology in the Lettuce Industry*, New York, Cambridge University Press.

Friedland W. (1984) Commodity Systems Analysis: An Approach to the Sociology of Agriculture, *Research in Rural Sociology and Development*, 1: 221-236.

Friedland, W. (pers comm, September, 1994).

Lawrence G, Vanclay F. and Furze B. (eds) (1992) *Agriculture, Environment and Society:Contemporary Issues for Australia*, Sydney, Macmillan.

Queensland Sugar Corporation (1991) Sugarnotes, Brisbane, Queensland Sugar Corporation.

Whatmore, S. (1994) Global Agro-food Complexes and the Refashioning of Rural Europe, in Thrift, N. and Amin, A. (eds) (1994) *Holding Down the Global*, London, Oxford University Press.

Chapter 15

Not so sweet: Rural restructuring and its community impact - the Mackay sugar district, Queensland

Rae Passfield, Geoffrey Lawrence and Jim McAllister

Introduction: Changes affecting sugar farmers in Mackay

It was the 1870s when sugar became a major crop produced in Australia's tropical and sub-tropical north. Some 95 percent of Australia's sugar output is derived from Queensland. The vast majority of Australian sugar farms (some 5,600 growers at the beginning of the 1990s) are in Queensland - something which has provided an economic basis for the expansion of numerous sugar milling cities along the Queensland coastline. In 1989/90, 27 mills produced some 3.6 million tonnes of sugar, the vast bulk of which (83 percent) was exported (see Sugar Industry Working Party, 1990).

Like their counterparts abroad, Australian sugar producers experienced a commodity price boom in the 1974/5 period associated with increasing imports from developing countries. The response of Australian growers was to expand production. Not surprisingly, this was also the response of Australia's competitors, including both European and US producers, who increased the volume of sugar entering the world market. This occurred at a time during which the World Bank's investments in Third World sugar production led to decreasing imports by these developing nations. In conjunction with this, the advent of alternative (High Fructose Corn Syrup) sweeteners further reduced demand for Third World sugar within the developed nations. The results of these changes in the global export economy was 'massive oversupply' and a catastrophic 'price collapse' in the mid 1980s (see Sugar Industry Working Party, 1990).

In Australia, the effect of the international price decline saw growers produce ever larger volumes - as an attempt to offset falling incomes (Sugar Industry Working Party, 1990; Van Hilst and Connell, 1994). Projections of volumes and prices indicate that sugar production is to increase from 4.40 million tonnes in 1994/5 to 5.13 million tonnes in 1998/9. During the same period, real average returns from sugar sales are expected to drop from $338 per tonne to $261 per tonne. Significantly, and despite industry-sponsored research, there has been no improvement in the estimated sugar content (Commercial Cane Sugar or CCS content) of cane - indeed, it is acknowledged that there has been a decline in yield since the 1970s (Sugar Industry Working Party, 1990: v and 38).

As a result of financial (cost-price) pressures, producers and millers have been forced to find means of increasing the efficiency of their operations and to seek to identify and exploit new marketing opportunities. Growers have utilised new varieties of sugarcane, and have applied an array of chemicals as well as purchasing new machinery in attempts to increase production efficiencies. Millers have also sought ways of increasing the efficiency of milling operations by closing non-viable mills, purchasing better rolling stock, altering locomotive movements, upgrading refining capacity, improving labour efficiencies in mill operations and increasing the throughput of cane - one example of which has been the introduction, in regions such as Mackay, of continuous crushing. One reason for its introduction was to shorten the period of the crush, thereby avoiding the wet weather which occurs towards the end of the season.

Continuous crushing means that the mills which once closed for weekend maintenance and repair are now operating around the clock during the 22-26 week cane cutting season. Mill workers and growers in the Mackay region (as in some other regions) received incentives for assisting in the new 24 hours per day schedule developed by the mills. For the workers, overtime payments were a direct economic incentive: for the growers, having bins arrive, and leave, at more convenient times has been economically beneficial. The sugar content of the crop (and therefore the price achieved) is maximised by more efficient bin delivery to/from the mills. As a further step toward grower/mill efficiencies, growers are being told by millers that they will need to consider pooling operations (to make the effective 'unit' of production much larger than at present) and that they will need to consider 'extended hours of harvesting'. The concern of some growers is that, just as continuous cropping is an around the clock activity, so too will be harvesting - with all this means for work and family schedules.

There has been a significant amount of grower-related stress in the Mackay cane growing industry in the early 1990s (see Gray, Lawrence and Dunn, 1993). Many growers and industry representatives have recognised that cost-price pressures are forcing farm amalgamation, which is endorsed by the industry (see Sugar Industry Working Party, 1990: iv). Yet, well over half of district producers (estimated to be about 63 percent of canegrowers) are 'landlocked' and unable to increase the size of their holdings. Many are older persons who have no formal educational qualifications, but who have had the ability to combine hard work during the cutting/crushing season with recreation during the 'slack'. This 'lifestyle', undermined by global economic forces, is something which the growers wish to preserve. Many complain about the severity and extent of changes occurring in the industry and often believe the mills to be the main culprit in 'forcing' change upon the growers (see discussion below).

During the early 1990s when the survey of Mackay growers was undertaken, weather conditions - associated with the drought - were very unfavourable, something which would have helped to explain the sorts of negative responses provided by growers (see Gray, Lawrence and Dunn, 1993: 49). In that survey, half of all Mackay growers sampled revealed farm cash income levels below negative $20 000. The normal strategies adopted by these growers in an effort to overcome their debt/low income problem was to reduce costs (24 percent), buy or sell land (19 percent), take off-farm employment (19 percent) and postpone capital purchases (18 percent). Compared with southern producers in other industries, for producers in Central Queensland the stakes were high in relation to material possessions. Many felt that they might easily lose their properties if conditions did not improve (see Gray, Lawrence and Dunn, 1993).

On top of the problems associated with the conditions of production within the sugar industry, producers were facing another 'problem'. The Pioneer Valley in the Mackay district is a picturesque location with a mountain backdrop and within close proximity to the large coastal city of Mackay. Many urban workers had been taking advantage of the cheaper rents available within the valley, living in dwellings on or near the cane fields and commuting to Mackay for work. Unlike the mill workers who readily understood the importance of cane growing, harvesting and milling for their own livelihoods, the new residents appear interested in a 'rural' lifestyle - but not one associated with the noise of harvesters and cane bins, the 'burn off' or the chemicals used to control insects and weeds. There has been, in other words, growing confrontation between those who associate rural space with production and those who see it as a place of 'consumption'.

Agricultural restructuring and its effects on rural communities

There is now quite an extensive literature on agricultural/rural restructuring (see Marsden, Lowe and Whatmore, 1990; Fitchen, 1991; Marsden, *et al.*, 1993). It is recognised, for example: that rural spaces are being increasingly commoditised because of the penetration of new forms of capital; that the globalisation of agriculture (including the presence of new competitors and the operations of transnational agri-business firms) and the move by capitalist states to deregulate agriculture and to reduce, where possible, the degree of commodity underwriting has produced significant effects on farms; and that the combinaion of the above has, both directly and indirectly, affected rural communities (see Lawrence, 1987; Marsden, Lowe and Whatmore, 1990; Gray, Lawrence and Dunn, 1993; Campbell, 1995; McMichael, 1994).

The 'political economy of agriculture' literature (see Buttel, Larson and Gillespie, 1990; Goodman and Redclift, 1991; Le Heron, 1993; Bonanno *et al.*, 1994; and Lawrence, this volume) has recently concentrated on the impact upon rural production of the globalisation of the food industry and the place of the 'family farm' within the changing structure of capitalism. What is highlighted here is the

> redistribution of productive activities and investments across the globe (and the) increased concentration of the control of financial resources and research capabilities, which remain firmly in the hands of a relatively small number of transnational corporations and advanced nations (Bonanno *et al.*, 1994: 1).

It is posited that transnational capital has been able to bypass the 'barriers' of the nation state and engage with rural spaces in ways not possible under state controlled (or state sponsored) rural production. Particular locations are favoured for global 'sourcing' by corporations and a new international division of labour emerges in which the corporation is advantaged by coordinating production through time and across space:

> the globalisation of chicken production is well underway, with the production of eggs in one location, the raising of chickens in another, the slaughter in a third, the deboning of the meat...in yet another, and finally, the shipment of chicken meat into different markets (Bonanno, *et al.*, 1994: 10).

There has also been a globalisation of consumption. Niche markets are created by transnational capital and consumers have been targeted for certain sorts of products, marketed carefully to appeal to particular 'styles'.

So-called post modern tendencies have also altered, in a fundamental way, what is occurring in rural spaces. According to writers such as Lash and Urry (1994: 193) we are living within post industrial spaces which produce post industrial commodities - largely products of the knowledge/service industries and which are 'heavily semiotic'. The wealth of rural regions would seem now to be based as much (or more) on the 'consumption' of those areas by those involved in tourism, recreation, retirement or 'lifestyle' pursuits than on the production of undifferentiated primary products (Lash and Urry, 1994; Lawrence, 1995). We appear to have moved from a world where identity is linked to location within the class structure and clearly defined work relations, to a world of the 'aesthetic consumer' whose preferences for education, leisure and foods is associated with the accumulation of 'cultural capital' (see Lash and Urry, 1994: 54-59).

So, not only are we seeing new meanings attached to rural areas (Mormont, 1990; Marsden *et al.*, 1993) as those who have the economic and social power to define what it is they want decide on the images they wish to preserve/develop.but we are also seeing agricultural industries coming within a new, global, framework in which consumer preferences for clean foods, sustainable production systems, and animal welfare are dictating the shape of production at the local level. McMichael (1994) has gone further in arguing that agro-food systems may no longer be best thought of in terms of industry 'types' (the 'wheat industry', or the 'sheep industry' or the 'sugar industry' for example). He suggests it is becoming impossible to understand those industries independently of the (post modern) forces which are fashioning change within them. Thus, for example, it is as important to understand the political power of new social movements whose voters can decide whether certain activities will take place within rural space, as it is to understand the economics of production. Similarly, the growth of certain forms of organic and 'low chemical input' farming can only be readily understood in terms of the rise of so-called 'green consumers' and their concerns for food security (McMichael, 1994: 279; Lawrence, 1995).

Finally, in an economy which is being socially-spatially transformed as a direct result of post modern forces and the pursuit of post industrial production forms - and all in the context of a nation state exhibiting a reduced ability to control capital flow - the region, rather than the nation state, has an increased significance in the post modern era (see Lash and Urry, 1994). With production becoming spatially disconnected, regions which have the ability to attract capital and those 'knowledge workers' associated with new types of accumulation, will be advantaged. Rural spaces will come to be inhabited by those who can, through global computer networks, locate in climatically-suitable (or other preferred) regions. The choice of these new workers to define rural spaces in their own terms is likely to influence the ways development occurs in regional Australia. In this regard, Goodman and Redclift (1991: 86) have insightfully remarked:

> while modern urban society has elevated 'rural' values to the ideological level, the society from which they are supposed to emanate has passed away. In this sense the passing of rural society might be seen as a *sine qua non* for the development of the modern food system.

Methodology

When researching in a rural community it is important to develop a methodology which not only provides insights into the problem being investigated, but which finds acceptance in that community. For the purpose of this study it was decided that focus group discussion would be used as a first step in understanding community-based attitudes to changes in the district. Focus groups are useful in studies such as this as they allow people who have different experiences of the phenomena being examined to discuss these ideas in a semi-formal manner and debate the ideas with others who have an interest in the outcomes.

In this study groups of both men and women were brought together. Those selected to participate in the focus groups included cane growers (and their spouses), residents of the small cane growing communities, harvester operators and small business operators. Major issues raised within the focus groups included:

- Social life of the community
- Family life
- Noise
- Road safety
- Expectations of business
- Dirt and dust

Semi-structured interviews were also conducted with a number of key individuals from the rural communities being studied. These included teachers, police officers, small business operators and cane industry personnel. In the next phase of the study, questionnaires will be developed incorporating the issues which have been raised by the focus groups. Growers and community members will be randomly sampled. It is envisaged this sample will involve approximately 20 percent of residents. Standard demographic information will also be obtained. This paper discusses the responses to date from focus groups and from individual semi structured interviews.

Findings

> The importance of the family seems to be taking a back seat to everything these days.

> During the crushing everything stops - you don't plan weddings, have babies or die in that five months.

These are two of the comments made within the focus groups when discussing the impact on small rural communities of the changes to the processes within the sugar industry. It would seem that, for many people, community in all its aspects is being restructured by the technological and process changes within the sugar industry, and by other developments. It was agreed that continuous crushing coupled with extended hours of cane harvesting had caused what is seen to be a deterioration in both family and community life in these small close-knit communities of the Pioneer Valley. Research to date indicates that people feel they are losing control - not only over their work environment but also over family and community life.

The 'crushing' - the time during which the sugar cane is harvested and processed - appears to be becoming an all encompassing issue in the community. In future seasons, mills may introduce extended harvesting, which will mean an extension of the time harvesters work. As a consequence, harvesting may be extended from the current 4.00 am to 8.00 pm to (perhaps) 2.00 am to 10.00 pm. Some growers believe that, once this change is made, there will be moves to a 24 hour harvest. Many believe that they will become 'shift workers'. One of the major purposes of this change however, will be to provide a continuous flow of freshly harvested cane to the mill. This is seen to be of benefit to farmers because the shorter the time lapse between harvest and processing, the higher CCS yield.

These changing expectations upon sugar farmers in regard to time spent harvesting seems to impact upon all forms of business, forcing significant change within the small rural communities studied. In relation to continuous crushing, and to the pressures on producers to increase the day-length of cutting, small business operators indicated that there was now an expectation that their business would operate longer hours: growers and harvesters still wanted to collect their milk and papers on the way home from work even though that may now be 10.00 pm. In conjunction with these changes, publicans indicate that 'there is no system or pattern of drinking hours like in the slack'. Like the small store owners, they are finding male patrons drifting in after work from 10.00 am to closing time with no clearly defined 'rush hour'. The area also supports some small engineering service operators who maintain machinery. These people are finding they are being called out at all hours, and, therefore, need to assess their ability to continue as a small family business. As one of these men said 'the amount of work is still the same, the mills just want it day and night.'

The structural changes occurring within this rural community that have been identified throughout this study include changes to the long term institutions in the community. Examples of this include sporting, school and other community activities. One farmer made the statement that:

> there is no sport in the Valley any more. You never can be sure when you will be able to play.

> In the Pioneer Valley extended harvest has killed sport. There is no one to play anymore - particularly team sport. There is no touch football or cricket. It's even impossible to play bowls. I'm off Sunday but nobody else is!

This opinion was reinforced by most of those involved in the study. The bowls club is closing, cricket is a thing of the past and even school sports days and fetes are no longer supported as they once were. There is even some concern that organisations such as the Country Women's Association will no longer function in some of the smaller areas. The reason given for this is that extra strain is being placed on the family because of the new 'intensity' of work in the crushing season.

Another community issue raised which was identified as important was related to the impact these changes were having on schooling. School teachers involved in the study raised several relevant issues which have been supported by other respondents. Some comments have included :

> During the crushing there is a noticeable lack of participation in school functions. We don't put anything on once the crushing starts anymore.

> A lot of high school students help out on the farm after school.

> They come to school exhausted after driving tractors till late at night.

> There are students 'home alone' at night in the crushing. Both parents are working on the farm.

Concern was expressed as to the probability of health problems arising for these young people. Exhaustion and stress is quite commonly seen amongst students. Teachers spoke of students 'having to let school work slip because they were relied on to work on the farm'. Other areas of community life which were seen to be no longer effectively occurring included those which traditionally rely on volunteer participation (particularly in rural areas). These included such services as the library, meals on wheels and even the bush fire brigade.

The changes which are occurring seem also to be manifest in a gender role shift. Although traditional rural ideology supports and is supported by a patriarchal structure, it has been indicated that women are playing an increasing role in the functioning of the farm. Women's participation both in terms of being partners in the family farm, as well as undertaking practical work have increased significantly. Women indicated that they are not only fulfilling the traditional nurturing role for the family and supporting their partner, they are also operating machinery, running errands and generally doing whatever is necessary around the farm. One woman reported:

> My typical day starts after I make breakfast, cut lunches and get the children off to school. Then I go down the paddock and drive haulout until it is time to come home and prepare dinner.

Margaret Alston speaks of women as the 'invisible farmers'. Women's role is changing from the performance of peripheral tasks such as running errands (to pick up spare parts or other requirements) to the more practical tasks involved in the day to day farm work.

> The on-farm work of women has, in fact, been shown to be very significant in Britain, USA and Australia with the drift from the land of hired male workers (Alston, 1990: 22).

Alston suggests, further, that this input of women's labour may mean the difference between the success or failure of the family farm. This view seems to be supported by the people interviewed to date. Both men and women have indicated the high cost of employing workers, not only on the farm but also for harvesting. The costs of employing harvesting contractors is one of the reasons women have become more actively involved in the day to day field work of the industry. It has also been suggested that increased hours of harvesting will exacerbate this problem as many workers are not available or not willing to work before 4.00 am or after 8.00 pm.

In addition to the changes experienced in small rural communities as a direct consequence of alterations in the nature of the sugar industry, urban migration is also contributing to significant changes within these rural locations. Urban drift is a phenomenon which is becoming very relevant to farmers and harvester operators in the Pioneer Valley region. People are moving from large urban areas to the 'quiet' of a country area. These people are not only moving in to settle in the small community centres, it is common for them to purchase small acreages to settle on. This drift means changing expectations of the surrounding area. A few years ago those living in this area were all, in some way, attached to the sugar industry - they worked for the mill or on a farm, or if they worked in the community their employer was still dependent on the industry for their livelihood - they 'understood' the industry and its production needs. This has changed:

> now, you know, there's people moving in from Melbourne and they don't wanna listen to a rattly bin at 6 o'clock on Sunday morning, no way in the world.

This was the comment of a farmer when discussing some of the issues relating to extended harvesting. It is viewed as important as there seems to be a feeling that residents don't really understand or support the industry as they have in the past. Community-based focus groups and interviews indicated that issues such as dirt, dust and noise were important issues for them in the crushing. However, these concerns seem to be based on aesthetic and personal concerns rather than interest in supporting the industry. There appear to be two distinct areas of concern that became apparent from the responses in regard to crushing. First, those who live near or next to a tram line which carries harvested cane to the mills. These people identify noise as a major problem. The other group are those living in close proximity to the cane fields. For this group concerns include dirt, lights, noise and extra traffic. (Some people, of course, live near the fields *and* the tram lines!)

Common concerns expressed include the following

> The cane trains make so much noise we can't even hear the TV.

> They start harvesting at 4.00 in the morning over the road. My nine year old wakes up with nightmares from the noise of irrigators, harvesters and tractors.

> We only notice problems when there is late harvesting close to
> home. Then we have to put up with noise, lights, extra traffic and
> the dust.

Dust has been identified by many as a real problem. There are different forms of dirt and dust related to the crushing season. Dust from the cane fields is stirred up by the machinery being operated. This settles in layers, covering with a fine brown coating everything upon which it falls. 'Black snow', caused by burnt trash from cane fires, also poses a significant dust problem. This not only permeates the home, car, washing and so on, but is also very difficult to get rid of once it settles.

Road safety has also been identified as a community concern. This is particularly so as hours over which harvesting is conducted lengthen. There is not only the issue of extra traffic on the road but also that haulout tractors travel slowly on main roads which have a speed limit of 100 km/h. They complain of the greater danger at night as tractor and truck lights are often covered in dirt and therefore cannot easily be seen, particularly when these vehicles turn suddenly into fields or sidings.

Farm families have identified a major issue for them as the 'lack of family life' for about 22 weeks a year. Both men and women saw this as a real problem. A common comment is that children do not see their father from July to November each year. These families also thought the decrease in social activities was significant to them as a family. One farm worker said:

> It is like I'm not alive for that part of the year. When the season
> ends I have to learn to be a husband and father again.

There seems to be some feelings that the mills should take some responsibility for the changes that are occurring. Those working in the industry indicated that there could, perhaps, be more organisation by the mills, particularly in the area of bin drops and collection. It is thought that mills favour harvesters who are willing to harvest early in the morning. Such harvesters acquire their full quota of bins in one drop, something desired by most, but provided by the mills to the most favoured growers/harvesters. Others indicated that those who harvested later in the day often have to wait up to two hours for a second drop of bins after lunch. One problem with this was having workers paid while being idle in the middle of the day, then having to pay overtime to those labourers for work during the night hours (where this is required to complete the set quota).

Farmers, harvester operators and workers have indicated that the mill hierarchy seem to make decisions which may be against the interests of those growing and cutting the cane. In many ways they feel they have no control over the way they work or even the hours in which they work. As the majority of the mills in the Mackay area are Co-operative mills this is, indeed, an interesting state of affairs!

Discussion

A large number of both farm and non-farm rural families in the upper Pioneer Valley have lived and worked in the area all their lives and, in some instances, for two or three generations. Today, the area seems to be experiencing a period of rapid change in several areas. Changes in sugar production are leading to new 'tensions' associated with alterations to family and community life. The advent of the new rural dweller is changing the profile of the local community. Whereas ten years ago, everyone living in the area had some relationship to the industry, it is now becoming a popular 'new' settlement area with some residents having no direct relationship to sugar production. In fact, many appear antagonistic to what they perceive to be unacceptable farm practices. Prospects for more direct conflict are obvious.

Overall, those interviewed to date recognise the importance of the sugar industry to the Mackay region. Some do, however, have concerns but don't think they can change things:

> We don't really think we have a choice with extended harvest. We need to support the farmers.

> The amount we are willing to accept to allow extended hours is limited. What is more important - dollars, bins or family? Why do it if it is not necessary?

> We realise that the township we live in would not exist without the sugar industry but we would not really be willing to accept much more of an extension of harvesting hours.

One respondent summed up what many were saying when she stated:

> I realise the importance of the sugar industry but I feel family life should not be jeopardised. The important things should be living standards, quality of life and family commitments.

The sugar industry in the upper Pioneer Valley has experienced many changes. The industry has changed since the post War period, where previously the farmer had total control of the crop through to harvest, and furthermore where harvest was performed by teams of cane cutters who harvested the crop by hand. These cutters, along with all other farm workers, were employed by the farmer and worked from 'sun up to sun down'. Now, as the industry responds to changes in the agricultural economy, harvester operators have become increasingly responsible for the harvest. This often includes the employment of not only the harvester operator, but also haulout drivers. Some farmers have very little or no control over the harvest of the crop - including the time during which that harvest will be done.

The changes occurring in the industry have also involved some rationalisation of sugar mills. This has had implications in all areas of the industry. In the upper Pioneer Valley one mill out of two has been closed. The immediate impact of this has been that a town whose population was fully employed suddenly became a community of unemployed people living an hours' drive from the nearest large centre which could provide opportunities for work or education.

This is not to suggest that people are not responding to such change. Another aspect of restructuring is that new industries are beginning to emerge. One of these is a mango processing plant which now exports its products globally. Another has been the opening of a cedar (wood) museum. It appears, in examining change, that technological and process changes in the sugar industry in the Pioneer Valley is having quite important impacts upon communities. People are responding to change, but change is not being 'controlled' by them: they appear to be reacting/adapting to technological changes which are stimulated by conditions in the world marketplace. In this sense, this study provides a brief analysis of the impact of the 'global' upon the 'local'.

Conclusion

Agricultural restructuring is forcing increasing work changes on growers and their families. Changes wrought by cost-price pressures are impacting upon the relationship between growers and mill, and within the farm family. Women, it would seem from this preliminary analysis, are being required to undertake increasing amounts of on-farm labour as a cost-cutting measure. Growers perceive - and their families perceive - that their lifestyle and community interaction has been affected negatively.

What might be termed post modern tendencies within the wider economy are also impacting upon this rural community. New types of residents are appearing who are seeking to define the valley in terms of their own preferences and priorities. This is placing a different sort of pressure on farmers. Furthermore, the subjection of the sugar industry to international and local forces requires that farmers organise their work in a manner which suits the mills. This is becoming increasingly difficult for farmers within a post modernising Australian world of 'bush gentrification'. As a consequence, farmers are unable to deal effectively with the economic realities of cost-price pressures, the community responsibilities/desires for locally-based social interaction, and the demands of the 'new' residents for clean air and noiseless nights.

Further research is aimed at establishing the extent to which agricultural restructuring and the 'post modern' tendency for people to use rural space for consumption is undermining - or indeed enhancing - notions of 'community' in a cane growing district.

References

Alston, M. (1990) Farm Women and Work, in Alston, M. (ed.) *Rural Women, Key PapersNumber 1*, Wagga Wagga, Centre for Rural Social Research.

Bonanno, A., Busch, L., Friedland, W., Gouveia, L. and Mingione, E. (1994) *From Columbus to ConAgra: the Globalization of Agriculture and Food*, Kansas, University Press of Kansas.

Buttel, F., Larson, O. and Gillespie, G. (1990) *The Sociology of Agriculture*, New York, Greenwood.

Campbell, H. (1995) *Regulation and Crisis in New Zealand Agriculture*, Unpublished Doctoral Thesis, Wagga Wagga, Charles Sturt University.

Fitchen, K. (1991) *Endangered Spaces, Enduring Places: Change, Identity and Survival in Rural America*, Boulder, Westview.

Goodman, D. and Redclift, M. (1991) *Refashioning Nature: Food, Ecology and Culture*, London, Routledge and Kegan Paul.

Gray, I., Lawrence, G. and Dunn, T. (1993) *Coping with Change: Australian Farmers in the 1990s*, Wagga Wagga, Centre for Rural Social Research.

Lawrence, G. (1987) *Capitalism and the Countryside: the Rural Crisis in Australia*, Sydney, Pluto.

Lawrence, G. (1995) *Futures for Rural Australia: From Agricultural Productivism to Community Sustainability*, Rockhampton, Rural Social and Economic Research Centre.

Lash, S. and Urry, J. (1994) *Economies of Signs and Space*, London, Sage.

Le Heron, R. (1993) *Globalized Agriculture*, Oxford, Pergamon.

Marsden, T., Lowe, P. and Whatmore, S. (1990) *Rural Restructuring: Global Processes and Their Responses*, London, David Fulton.

Marsden, T., Murdoch, J., Lowe, P., Munton, R. and Flynn, A. (1993) *Constructing the Countryside*, London, UCL Press.

Mormont, M. (1990) Who is Rural? or, How to be Rural: Towards a Sociology of the Rural, in Marsden, T., Lowe, P. and Whatmore, S. *Rural Restructuring; Global Processes and Their Responses*, London, David Fulton: 21-44.

McMichael, P. (ed.) (1994) *The Global Restructuring of Agro-food Systems*, Ithaca, Cornell University Press.

Share, P. and Lawrence, G. (1990) Fear and Loathing in Wagga Wagga: Cultural Representations of the Rural and Possible Policy Implications, *Culture and Policy* 1, 2.

Sugar Industry Working Party (1990) *Report of the Sugar Industry Working Party*, Brisbane, Department of Primary Industries.

Van Hilst, R. and Connell, P. (1994) Developments in the World Sugar Market, in *Outlook 94, Agriculture*, Canberra, ABARE: 105-114.

Chapter 16

University students learning at a distance in rural and metropolitan settings: Focus group research

Ken Purnell and Eve Cuskelly

Introduction

Learning at a distance is an important way for a number of rural people to undertake their university studies. For various reasons (eg. family and work commitments) a number of people who live in larger urban areas also study in the distance mode. This chapter examines aspects of the main issues identified by students studying and learning in the distance mode in rural and non-rural settings. The institution providing the distance education service is Central Queensland University (CQU) which has students enrolled in various undergraduate and postgraduate courses throughout Australia and in a number of overseas locations. Most of the students studying at a distance with the University reside in the state of Queensland. The main campus of the University is located at Rockhampton, with branch campuses at Bundaberg, Emerald, Gladstone and Mackay. Distance education is conducted chiefly through the main campus at Rockhampton with some additional support (eg. lectures and/or tutorials) offered in selected units at some branch campuses. Focus group sessions were held in selected areas throughout Queensland to identify key issues facing distance education students at CQU. The researchers selected six sites in which to interview small groups of students - Rockhampton, Brisbane, Bundaberg, Cairns, Emerald and Longreach. Specific issues were identified and discussed in detail and then prioritised by the students involved in each focus group. These issues are examined after a review of literature related to the study. A number of differences are discussed which show the inequality of experiences of students studying in rural settings compared to their counterparts in larger urban areas.

Kemp (1986: 1) defined student support as 'those institutionally provided or facilitated aids to external students, which collectively constitute the total learning environment in which external students function'. Distance education students, with their diverse levels of experience and support (from family, work and community) and different learning preferences, have a correspondingly diverse range of level and type of support needed. Some students choose to study via distance education because that is their preferred study mode: such students typically demonstrate particular personal characteristics such as a need for autonomy and independence, self-confidence, flexibility and a capacity to deal with uncertain situations (Peters, 1992: 241). For many students, however, the decision to study at a distance is forced upon them by factors such as physical location (eg. in a rural setting away from a university campus), work and/or family commitments (ATAX Evaluation Committee, 1994). The time demands (juggling work, family and study commitments), financial costs and the study materials themselves are causes of anxiety which may affect these students' studies and their choices of how they will study (Jegede and Kirkwood, 1994).

The literature suggests that support services for distance education students are required to:

- maintain or increase student motivation
- promote effective study skills
- generate a feeling of 'belonging' to the providing institution, by providing contact with lecturers and other students for both social and academic purposes
- provide guidance through the study materials
- provide access to resources
- provide answers to administrative queries (See Ramaiah and Srinivasacharyulu, 1991; Dillon *et al.,* 1992; Peters, 1992; Bernt and Bugbee, 1993; Carmichael, 1995).

While all students require some form of support at one time or another, for rural students some aspects of support are especially critical; for example, providing contact with lecturers and other students and providing access to resources. Students' needs for support are currently met through organised activities such as teletutorials or residential schools, student-initiated individual contact and library services.

Educational technology is being used increasingly to provide greater opportunities for communications for distance education students between themselves and staff and other students, and for access to information as well as for the delivery of some study materials. Computer mediated communication, for example, offers distance education students the opportunity to develop higher order skills such as problem-solving, through student-student interaction and group work, as well as greater access to lecturers (see Davies and Wells, 1991; Gunawardena, 1991).

Focus group research

A series of focus group sessions were held by the researchers at Brisbane, Bundaberg, Cairns, Emerald, Rockhampton and Longreach. Social scientists often use focus group discussions where little is known about the phenomenon being investigated, but where the sharing of knowledge might provide 'cues' to other participants to debate particular ideas and suggestions (see Morgan, 1993; Krueger, 1994). Our literature review revealed that, while there had been considerable discussion about some elements of distance education in Australia, very little was known, for example, about students' views on the use of new technology, their concerns about learning in the distance education mode, and their suggestions for improvement in delivery. Focus groups can be useful vehicles for the exploration of the bases of differences of opinion about a select number of issues. They are especially useful in circumstances where it is desired to explore group attitudes rather than simply to aggregate the responses of individuals (as might occur in the analysis of data derived from randomly distributed questionnaires).

The focus group method has been shown to be advantageous where people have varying ideas and can, in a semi-formal manner, debate/discuss those ideas with others. The canvassing of different ideas provides opportunities for the focus group facilitator to list concerns and opinions. These can be summarised and then turned back to the group for comment and prioritisation. It is important in such research not to impose ideas upon the group; what arises out of discussion must be the product of the group and not of the researcher. However, that does not mean that the researcher has a passive role in the proceedings. As Frey and Fontana (1993) have argued, where people who do not know each other are asked to meet in semi-formal settings (such as occurred in this research where selected students were asked to visit a specific location) it is appropriate for the researcher to take an active role in guiding discussions and keeping participants to the point. Similarly, in such circumstances, it is usual for the researcher to have at her/his disposal a series of questions, together with a series of prompts or 'probes' (see Krueger, 1994) which are designed to ensure that there is general focus on the topic/s selected for discussion. Prompts may or may not be used - depending on the extent to which participants address the issues under discussion.

The research was not being used in an exploratory way or as a pretest for a larger, quantitative study. Rather, it was employed phenomenologically - that is, to understand the shared meanings (and differences in meaning) between distance education students and to report these differences in reasonable time and on a limited budget (see Morgan and Krueger, 1993) to a group of senior academics who would be discussing, and making recommendations about, ways to improve distance education delivery at CQU. Because follow up interviews with students were not to be held, it was decided to conduct the focus groups over a fairly long period of two hours. It was felt that most of the important issues would be revealed in this time, and that there would be sufficient time for interaction/discussion and for the prioritisation of issues. Participants were informed that the outcomes of this research were likely to be crucial to the future delivery of distance education at CQU.

In an effort to canvass wide opinion it was decided to organise the groups in a somewhat random manner names were chosen from lists which provided student details. No student was selected because she or he was known to the researchers. Each group comprised between five and eight persons (see Krueger, 1994). There was a balance between men and women, between younger and older students, those enrolled in different Faculties, between undergraduates and postgraduates, as well as those who were just beginning, and those just completing, their studies. It was considered important to have a spatial dimension to the study - to canvass the views of those living in cities (capital and regional), large coastal centres, smaller (inland) towns and isolated regions. The locations chosen were Brisbane, Bundaberg (two groups), Cairns, Emerald, Longreach, and Rockhampton. (In the Bundaberg region, a group of post graduates and another of undergraduates were selected.)

Following the study, audio tapes of the sessions were transcribed and analysed. The research team evaluated groups' prioritisation of the issues and results were written up under each of the headings which had emerged from the focus group sessions. There was no disagreement among the researchers as to what prioritisation should be accorded the items discussed in the sessions. However, to obtain clarification about several issues raised, face-to-face discussions were held with key stakeholders at CQU. What follows is a summary of the views of students. The comments from the focus groups, we believe, are broadly representative of the body of distance education students. We do not have, of course, any basis for suggesting statistical validity.

Selection of participants

All distance education students at CQU are assigned to a study centre at the time of their first enrolment. Students are assigned to the centre nearest their home address if they do not nominate a centre themselves. Having determined where the focus group sessions were to be conducted, lists of distance students assigned to each of those centres were obtained from the CQU Student Records system. As the numbers for the Longreach centre were low, a list of students at the Barcaldine centre was also obtained. Separate lists for Bundaberg postgraduate and undergraduate list were also used. A target of 10 students was set for each focus group. In order to reach this target it was felt that about 20 students would initially need to be identified. The number of students at each centre was consequently divided by 20 to obtain 'n' for each centre. Every 'nth' student on each centre's list was then highlighted. Adjustments were then made to achieve the desired representation by selecting students above or below the one initially highlighted as required. Consideration also had to be given to the actual location of the students at the Longreach centre, for example, has students assigned to it from as far away as Winton. The identified students were then contacted by telephone. Due to difficulties in reaching some students and others declining/being unable to attend, further students were selected primarily to meet the desired representation. In some centres this representation could not be met due to the number of students and their course of study; for example, in Longreach all students attending were undergraduates, with the majority being enrolled in Faculty of Education courses.

Students who agreed to participate were mailed a confirmation letter, giving details of the focus group session - its purpose, location and time. Students' freedom to withdraw from the study at any time and the confidentiality of all responses were also stressed. At the sessions students were informed further about the study, were told of its importance to the university, of their own anonymity, and how they could obtain copies of the final report of the study. At the sessions all students participating signed a letter indicating that they understood the implications of their involvement. At the outset, the study had received approval from the ethics committee of CQU.

Results and discussion

The focus group sessions held throughout Queensland identified key issues facing distance education students at CQU. In each of the focus group sessions discussions led to the identification of key issues which were subsequently written on a white board and, following more discussion, were prioritised by the group. While specific results varied among the groups, common themes emerged (the priorities for Brisbane and Longreach focus groups are given in the Appendix). The main issues were clearly concerned with five interrelated areas: student contact with lecturers, assignments, flexibility, study materials and educational technology. These will be examined by identifying providing quotes from students involved in the focus groups and then a summary and discussion of the main issues identified. At the outset of this discussion it should be noted that none of the participants in the study intended to give up her or his studies. The data collected clearly showed most of the students who participated in the study greatly appreciated the quality of service and highly praised the support that they had received. They did not intend to give up their studies but were keen to discuss issues which they had found during their studies. In other words, they were supportive of distance education but were prepared to give suggestions for improvement. All student comments are shown, below, in italics.

Student contact with lecturers
I think I'm getting the level of support I need.
The voicemail has made a big difference.
I had a teleconference where the lecturer actually gave us his home phone number and he has actually rung me at home to see how I was going with an assignment even though I hadn't contacted him ... I do appreciate his call

She has even given her home number at certain hours and (the lecturers I have) do return calls - so everything's worked out.

One advantage of having e-mail is that unlike an answering machine it will sit there until it gets answered basically

I've had the opportunity to come to a few Saturday sessions with the (course) which I've found quite helpful.

The attitude of most lecturers is beyond reproach. I mean most of them are committed and that comes through I think. I think it's just resource constraints tend to give you the problems you have. But one thing I think causes dramas is that on-campus students have the luxury (of) tutorials. External students don't.

The videos are great because you see their faces and you get to know their personality and mannerisms ... you know a face to the name.

The essence of external studies is that there's only a certain percentage of your course that you really perhaps need an explanation on or you need clarification ... So it's just those subjects that would allow you to clarify some difficult points here I think it needs more action.

She rang an answering machine on Monday and got a reply on the Wednesday or the Thursday of that week. If we can only do it (study) after hours you're completely at a loss for all those days because one subject leads onto the other and until I crack this bit and find out what I'm doing I can't go any further and a day phone number is nearly useless. You do take time off work and sit down and ring up, but you're not actually studying then and you sort of lose track of where you're going.

Personally, I've found it hard to get hold of a lecturer.

I don't really have a problem with seeing the lecturer. I'm just happy to plod along on my own.

My phone bill from the time I started (studying) jumped from $180 to $500 and that's just from ringing the university and I mean it is an STD.

I sent a fax last week about something and the lecturer didn't get it till yesterday. So that's a week, a whole six days more you know.

I was a bit disappointed that the fax I sent I never got a reply.

Where I live we only get two mail services a week.

I think ... face to face is better.

If I had the option I'd go face to face.

I mean sometimes you have some very burning little questions and you can't necessarily get hold of lecturers. It's quite handy to be able to phone up another student and say 'and did you have a problem with this?'.

(Receiving a phone call) actually makes you feel like you're part of the subject. Just to have them call up and say 'hello, this is so and so, and are you enjoying the subject and how's it going, are you understanding the material?' Now they don't have to say much and you really feel that they've actually (helped).

This year ... I haven't got any tutors. I feel a bit more isolated than I did last year.

With that I didn't tick mine because I didn't really want people ringing me up. I'm a fairly solitary person especially when I'm studying and because my timelines are so tight the last thing I perceive that I wanted was someone

ringing me up and saying 'hey can you explain this to me in fifteen words or less' type thing. So I find I'm fairly selfish in terms of wanting to talk to other students and things. I don't see that it's part of my study.
Once I'd made contact with the lecturer I found it very easy to ring him up. It's hard to get a hold of him but to go out and see him I found that he gave me a lot of support.

Summary of what improvements students would like

1 Greater access to lecturers, especially after normal working hours.
2 Clear unit information - clarification of content, technical terms and work tasks.
3 Personal contact - contact initiated by the lecturer, plus face-to-face contact.

While the students participating in the study expressed differing study patterns and degrees of independence in their studies, and consequently varying levels of need for support services, almost all indicated the need at some point to contact their lecturer or tutor. Students required this contact mainly to clarify content, technical terms and work tasks. The fact that most students needed to contact lecturers outside normal working hours meant that many encountered difficulties in this respect, in terms of time delays or non-response, which added to existing feelings of isolation and often frustration. For many students there was also the feeling of not wanting to 'bother' academic staff with a minor problem, and for some a hesitancy to approach a staff member with whom they had had no previous contact. This latter feeling appeared to be less evident in the more experienced students who had been studying for longer and made contacts with other lecturers.

These feelings would seem to be an expression of the 'social distance' identified by Ramaiah and Srinivasacharyulu (1991). Students stated that they found it easier to approach a staff member, or another student, whom they had already met or talked to, for example during a teletutorial. A number of students felt that academic staff should initiate individual telephone contact early in the semester: students who had experienced this felt that the personal approach had increased their motivation and sense of 'belonging' in that subject. Local visits by their lecturer or tutor would also be greatly appreciated. Kember (1989) has stated that the quality and quantity of personal contact between students and staff influences the academic integration of the students. This contact may be face-to-face or via another medium, such as the telephone.

Assignments

The best markers that I've ever had - the best feedback ... they're the ones who say you've done this well, and you did that well. And they start out with the positives. And then they say, but if you had done this or you had left pages 8 to 9 or if you had structured your argument more tightly - if you had done this or had done that you would have got a better mark. Now that's the sort of stuff you really need.

They have a hotline that you can use and I've tried them a couple of times.

They have a marking criteria - they just don't tell us what it is.

We've all played that game of writing an assignment and then wondering was that what the lecturer really wanted waiting three or four agonising weeks to come and see whether you were on the right track.

To be able to get instant feedback is one of the major issues

Different lecturers mark different ways. Some are really picky on grammatical errors. Some are really picky on content. Some are picky on different things. . . You really don't have a clue what this guy's looking for. So I just think that's unfair.

He put down the good points of her assignmen ... but she has no idea why she only got a P - if there's all these good points, why didn't she get a C or a D?

They sent us out the criteria of what they - how they were going to mark your assignment - what they expected, which was excellent.

I'm currently sitting- or going to sit for an exam in four weeks time and I don't have any idea of how the examination is to be formed. I don't know whether it's short answer or essays or whether I've got to get up and tap dance on the table. I've got no idea.

Summary of what improvements students would like

1 Marking criteria - state criteria and standards.
2 Quality of feedback - constructive feedback in accordance with the marking criteria (generally at least half a page on a major assignment) and in particular to know what they have to do to improve the quality of their assignments. Exemplars.
3 Improved timing and turnaround time.

Assignment requirements, turnaround time and feedback were major sources of concern and frustration for the students in this study. Much of the contact with academic staff centred upon obtaining clear criteria and standards for assignments, and understanding what it was the lecturer required in terms not only of content, but also of format, referencing, length and other aspects of essay and assignment writing and presentation. Students were confused and frustrated when different requirements existed but were not clearly and explicitly stated (for example with respect to referencing) between different units within the same discipline, or when lecturers worked with materials which they had not authored or assembled. Distance education students felt particularly disadvantaged in comparison with on-campus students in relation to knowledge about assignment requirements.

Assignments which were returned too late for comments to be incorporated in the work for subsequent submissions, or with limited, unconstructive, comments were frequently mentioned as a major concern by the students. Students who had experienced the use of assignment criteria sheets were more satisfied with their assignment feedback in those subjects, and their use was seen by all students as a means of improving feedback.

The tactics adopted in Rekkedal's study (1985, cited in Peters, 1992) to decrease student attrition rates (the provision of more detailed introductions - including photographs - to the lecturers/tutors, increased tutor-initiated contact with the students, correcting and returning assignments to students promptly and with 'model' answers) would appear to be providing many of the support systems which the students involved in this study would most appreciate.

Flexibility

That's why I wanted to do it (study) this way (externally) so that I had that flexibility.
You're not committed to a time frame. You fit it in with your lifestyle.
I would like to see some of the units that are offered over my break times.
It's hard to get stuff done because there's no one to look after the bloody kids and you're trying to do it at 10 o'clock at night, you're falling asleep. It doesn't work.
It really is difficult to be an external student with kids.
(I wish) they (would) provide an education program for the other half or something, you know. And the kids?
I would like to see some of the units that are offered over my break times.
(A third semester) - I think it would be a good idea.
My major concern is the requirement that you have to do residential schools ...
(Attending residential schools) is very expensive.
I had to stop studying externally when I had a child.
I get up at 4 am (to study).
Then the grasshoppers and insects were so bad you couldn't have the lights on at night (to study) (Longreach).
Me going to the Open Learning Centre is difficult because for the simple reason I have two small children and I have a husband who is not at home. What do I do with the kids? Do I take them and let them run riot?
If teleconferences were real options as an alternative (to residential schools) most people would prefer the teleconferences for a variety of reasons, but one being the lesser amount of time you have to commit to it. Because time you travel is time you're not studying or spending quality time with your family
And the advantages (of portable study materials) - that's like a library book - so you don't all have to turn up at the same time.

Summary of what improvements students would like

1 Time and location - distance education provides flexibility many students needed ... Flexibility to be enhanced.
2 Study materials - preferably portable to be able to be taken and used anywhere.

3 Residential schools - not compulsory.
4 Third semester - continue or commence studies.

With the many competing demands on their time, the students participating in this study felt that flexibility was a critical factor in successfully completing their studies. This flexibility was needed in the area of assignment submission (where there were extenuating circumstances which made submission on the set date impossible) and also in the setting of topics to suit students' particular circumstances (for example, access to resources). Further, the possibility of a third semester, whereby students could elect to study during all three or during the most convenient two semesters, was attractive to a number of students. The students also wanted to receive their materials as early as possible, before the official start of the semester, so that study could begin early, to compensate for later periods when other commitments might interfere with planned study times.

Study materials

When I first started in 1992 there were so many questions that I was having problems with and I can honestly say that now they are producing the handbooks in (name of Faculty) that are addressing a lot of the concerns that I had.

Even at the level I'm doing they are really good (library). They went to great lengths to help me find the material that I wanted.

I think the handouts at the beginning of the course and at the beginning of the semesters is my only link with the university in a lot of instances and it helps me get motivated through the beginning of the course. So I read everything from cover to cover.

Yes, the best subjects are the ones where your study guide matches your text book and matches your resource material. It all follows through and when you get to your assignment you know exactly what they're on about, you know, and it's all just beautiful and clear.

I would say self-sufficient study materials (is the most important thing for distance students).

(Study) material never arrives on time.

More books in the library. More please.

You can't get textbooks out now anyway ... they're putting the textbooks on use in the library only.

If you're external and study in Brisbane, you've got about five libraries you can go to. It's not a hassle. If you're external and you study here (Longreach) (and) I imagine if you go west it's even worse - suddenly your resource capabilities diminish quite substantially ... Whilst you can get the books out from Rocky, you've still got to pay for them to go back. So that's a cost incurred for a provincial student, that a city student doesn't have.

I noticed a big difference when I moved from Brisbane to here (Longreach), just in terms of how I was doing my assignments because I wasn't able to resource what I was resourcing in Brisbane ... But it suddenly hit me that you are truly external when you go west.

I do get a lot of useless information from the university, especially when all you want is the notes and the books.

It was six weeks into the semester before I got all my books. And that wasn't my fault.

I don't like to go through a lot of pointless researching and reading.

(My best unit) was practical, relevant to my teaching.

I also think you end up a better learner. You learn better externally because you have to. You come out with a far superior product because you have to think for yourself but gee, it's tough.

I would say self-sufficient study materials (is the most important thing for distance students).

Now it's 13 units in 13 weeks. Each unit on average would involve reading three chapters of a text book - some of them are up to six. We've got three assignments, and an exam, all in 13 weeks. It's just incredible.

You always go short on the references and they always write not enough references and then you talk to other people and they say, well, what do they expect from the country areas? You live in the country and you haven't got the facilities of the big city.

But it's not only books. It's journals and things like that. I mean we can't go and look through the journals.

Summary of what improvements students would like

1 Delivery - the earlier the materials are delivered, the better.
2 Quantity and content - comprehensive but no extraneous materials.
3 Practical relevance.
4 No mismatches between study materials, textbook(s) and lecturer expectations.
5 Access to additional resources - books and journals.

The students participating in this study were generally happy with their study materials. Some concerns were expressed over materials where study guides and textbooks did not 'match', through the use of a newer edition, or through a change of text. Students were also unhappy when requested to buy textbooks which were rarely used. The quantity of materials to be covered in some subjects was a further area of concern. The students in this study felt disadvantaged in comparison with on-campus students in a number of areas. It was felt that on-campus students received content far more succinctly in lectures, compared with the reading required of distance students to cover the same content. This was particularly felt when extensive resource materials were included in the study package, with little or no guidance as to what was directly relevant or important.

The distance students also felt disadvantaged at the other end of the spectrum, where their study materials were sufficient only to generate the lower passing grades, additional resources being required in order to obtain the highest grades. The students felt that their materials should be self-sufficient so that the need to look for additional resources was minimised. Some means of prioritising resource materials was also considered desirable.

The link between the students' work and their studies was reflected in their attitudes towards subject content, with most expressing the view that materials which they found directly relevant and having practical application to their work were 'easier' to study. In terms of maintaining motivation - where motivation was linked directly to perceived relevance - students preferred practical to theoretical subject content.

One participant, who had already withdrawn from her studies at the time of the interview, said that she had experienced difficulties because she was not working and found it difficult to see the appropriateness of, or the likely application of, the content. For other students, having weathered the initial difficulties of distance study, the fact that they had already committed so much time and effort provided a major motivation for continuing - this effort could not be easily dismissed and 'wasted'. Rashid's *et al.,* (1994) contention that new distance education students in particular had special needs was supported in this study.

Educational technology

(Some lecturers) sat around the table and taped a cassette to talk (the unit and) it was 'hi, how are you? We hope you're going to enjoy it?' and all that sort of nice stuff - join the crowd ... And you have that cassette. You could listen to it over and over and nobody ever asked for it back ... Now that's a very cheap way of getting to 200 students.

CD Rom was the best thing I've seen since sliced bread. I mean it was wonderful - the ability to access material overseas in just slipping a disc.

Computer based learning (is) ... my only other source of learning apart from the Study Guide and text books - there's no residential schools or teletutes or anything like that this semester. And I found that very good - I mean to just learn - it is particularly good for (name of unit) and you can have that and you can be assessed and quietly delete the file when you fail and go back and try again. But it's very user friendly. It's very good.

I feel that I haven't got the necessary links. I've applied to get the 'slip' for the modem and I'm hoping to get onto that (so) I can establish a web of people that I can talk to further afield

A lot of people (will not use other communication technologies) because of the lack of knowledge of how to use them, so unless it's really needed, they won't use it.

I haven't been involved in it (videoconferencing), no. Because the line doesn't come out here ... But I know that Mackay gets it and I know that the lecturer can do (things at) Mackay that he can't do with us out here. And we just find that frustrating. It's got to be better than the telephone.

Telephones can be rather intimidating and you don't tend to open up as much ... as you would to a person face to face.

I look at this email and think what the hell's that. No. Sorry, I'll just stick to the telephone and the field that I sort of know.

I think it would be really good if we could get World Wide Web ... you know that you can actually access information.

Study is a financial burden. If you fix that on to the rest of your family - with the time - that's a burden, yes, the cost of textbooks, travel, all the rest of it - it means that it's affecting things that maybe should go to your family. Now for instance, I'm not going out and borrow $3,000 to set myself up with a computer.

I love technology. I do like it and I can hardly wait to get on and test it out.

Summary of what improvements students would like

1   Greater interaction with materials - supplements to the standard print materials are desirable.
2   Better communication - little experience with new communications technologies but most students were interested in using them in their learning.

The use of educational technology may be divided into two categories: to supplement the traditional print materials, and to provide additional communication channels for distance education students. The students participating in this study expressed little or no experience with educational technologies such as audio graphics, video conferencing and computer mediated communication. This lack of experience made it difficult for them to make informed comment on these technologies and their potential. However, most students were interested in using them in their learning. Which medium to be used was dependent upon the type of material and teaching strategies involved in the unit. Students did, however, express a preference for technologies, like videoconferencing, which came as close as possible to matching face-to-face teaching, confirming the students' desire for real contact with their lecturers and peers. This finding has implications for the expanded use of technology in distance education. Electronic mail and use of the Internet are being widely touted as solutions to the problem of providing greater contact with distance education students. If these are perceived as impersonal by the students, however, they may not be fulfilling their total support needs.

Students wanted supplements to the standard print materials. Videos or audio cassettes introducing the lecturer and providing an overview of the unit and discussing assessment tasks were highly desirable. Where lectures were provided to students on campus the distance education students wanted an audio or video copy of these available. Interestingly, while these technologies may be considered passive (Bowser and Shepherd, 1991) in that they require no input from the student, they can provide the contact that students want, by giving them some exposure to other students and providing a human element for the lecturer.

With respect to technology for communication, teleconferences were very much appreciated as making valuable contributions to learning and assessment task preparation, and for providing contact with the lecturer and other students. The telephone was the most familiar (and thus least threatening) technology for the students, was readily available and was perceived as being relatively low-cost (in comparison, for example, with purchasing computers). Carmichael's (1995) use of voicemail to provide recorded information for distance education students may thus be an appropriate means of providing the social as well as academic contact that distance education students, particularly in rural areas, so strongly want.

Conclusion

Overall, the implications of this research for the provision of distance education is significant. The issues identified in the different focus groups were similar, and across groups there was some consensus as to the priority of a particular issue to that group. It is important to note that the issues identified come from the student participants across the seven geographical areas. The student participants generally had reasonable expectations given what they perceived as various economic and social constraints upon lecturers and upon the university (for example, none suggested 'one on one' lecturer support be provided to students). There were some differences in terms of support students were able to get in metropolitan areas like Brisbane and provincial cities such as Rockhampton compared to rural areas such as Emerald and Longreach. Clearly students who had experiences of both felt that the resources they had access to, for example, in Brisbane were far superior to those available in say Longreach for university studies. The issues faced by distance students especially in rural areas need to be considered in providing distance education resource materials and the types of assignments set.

It should be recognised that the results presented here are those from the distance education students' perspectives in mid 1995. That is, while some students may on occasion raise issues which relate to their own lack of knowledge of what is available (such as a toll free phone number for the Library) or about what is to become available (offering undergraduate programs at regional campuses), these issues are not discounted or dismissed in this study: they are part of the 'reality' for a number of people studying as distance education students.

Student experiences of distance education is an area ripe for further research. A closer examination of the role of educational technologies and differences between geographical areas particularly between metropolitan and rural settings may yield valuable data to improve the quality of teaching and learning in distance education.

Acknowledgments

We wish to thank Professor Geoffrey Lawrence at Central Queensland University for his insightful comments on earlier drafts of this chapter and his substantial contributions to the report on which this chapter is based (Cuskelly, Purnell and Lawrence, 1995). We also wish to thank all those who participated in the focus groups, and to Pam Gale and Paula Miller who transcribed the cassette tapes from each group. Funding for this study was provided by the Chancellery of Central Queensland University and was greatly appreciated. Pro-Vice Chancellor (Academic) Professor Ian Goulter, in particular, is thanked for his encouragement and overall support in relation to this research project.

References

Albrecht, T., Johnson, G. and Walther, J. (1993) Understanding Communication Processes in Focus Groups, in Morgan, D. (ed.) *Successful Focus Groups: Advancing the State of the Art*, California, Sage: 51-64.

ATAX Evaluation Committee. (1994) *Survey of Students Withdrawn and Deferred From Studies*, Report No.3, Rockhampton, Central Queensland University.

Bernt, F. and Bugbee, A. (1993) Study Practices and Attitudes Related to Academic Success in a Distance Learning Programme, *Distance Education* 14, 1: 97-112.

Bowser, D. and Shepherd, D. (1991) Student Perceptions in the Role of Technology in Enhancing the Quality of Management Education at a Distance, *Paper Presented at Quality in Distance Education*, ASPESA Biennial Forum, Bathurst, NSW, 15-19 July.

Carmichael, J. (1995) Voice Mail and Telephone: a New Student Support Strategy in the Teaching of Law by Distance Education, in *Proceedings of the 1995 Annual Conference of the Higher Education and Research Development Society of Australasia* 18: 191-196

Cuskelly, E., Purnell, K. and Lawrence, G. (1995) *Student Experiences of Distance Education at Central Queensland University: Findings from Focus Group Research*, Rockhampton, Rural Social and Economic Research Centre, Central Queensland University.

Davies, L. and Wells, R. (1991) Empowering the Learner Through Computer-Mediated Communication, *American Journal of Distance Education* 5, 1: 15-23.

Dillon, C., Gunawardena, C. and Parker, R. (1992) Learner Support: the Critical Link in Distance Education, *Distance Education* 13, 1: 29-45.

Frey, J. and Fontana, A. (1993) *The Group Interview in Social Research*, in Morgan, D. (ed.) *op cit*: 20-34.

Gunawardena, C. (1991) Collaborative Learning and Group Dynamics in Computer Mediated Communication Networks, *Paper Presented at the*

Second American Symposium on Research and Development in Distance Education, Pennsylvania State University, May: 22-24.

Jegede, O. and Kirkwood, J. (1994) Students' Anxiety in Learning Through Distance Education, *Distance Education* 15, 2: 279-290.

Kember, D. (1989) An Illustration, With Case Studies, of a Linear-process Model of Drop-out from Distance Education', *Distance Education* 10, 2:196-211.

Kemp, J. (1986) Support Services for External Students, *ACDP Working Party on External Studies*, Darling Downs Institute of Advanced Education, Toowoomba.

Knodel, J. (1993*) The Design and Analysis of Focus Group Studies: A Practical Approach,* in Morgan, D. (ed.) *op cit*: 35-50.

Krueger, R. (1994*) Focus Groups: A Practical Guide for Applied Research, Second Edition,* California, Sage.

Morgan, D. (1993) *Successful Focus Groups: Advancing the State of the Art,* California, Sage.

Morgan, D. and Krueger, R. (1993) *When to Use Focus Groups and Why,* in Morgan, D. (ed.) *op cit*: 3-19.

Peters, O. (1992) Some Observations on Dropping Out in Distance Education, *Distance Education* 13, 2: 234-269.

Purnell, K. (In press). Case studies, in Naish, M. and Gerber, R. (eds) *Qualitative Research Methods in Geography*, London, London International Geographical Union.

Ramaiah, P. and Srinivasacharyulu, G. (1991) Face to Face Support Services at APOU: Student Response, *Paper Presented at the 1991 AAOU Annual Conference,* Colombo, Sri Lanka.

Rashid, R., Nordin, R., Sulaiman, S., Ibrahim, A. and Majid, O. (1994) Supporting Students Learning Process and Developing Their Self-directed Learning Skills: Universiti Sans Malaysia Experience' in Evans, T. and Murphy, D. (eds) *RIDE 3: Revised Papers from the Third Research in Distance Education Conference*, Melbourne, Deakin University.

Appendix: Prioritised issues for focus groups at Brisbane and Longreach

<table>
<tr><td valign="top">

BRISBANE

1 Study materials
   Timely delivery
   Assignment feedback
   Assignment clarity/
      requirements definition
   Textbooks: availability/
      appropriateness
   Different author/lecturer and
      resultant conflict of
      ideas/requirements

2 Lecturer contact
   Access for direction/
      clarification/support

3 Student contact
   Support
   Information/resource
      exchange

4 Personal issues
   Time constraints
   Work/family demands

Technology
Materials supplement:
   Computer based learning
   Audio tapes
   Communication
   Audio conferences
Email

</td><td valign="top">

LONGREACH

1 Study materials
   Self sufficient
   Practical and relevant
   Efficient (concentrate on
      essentials)
   Access to lecturers/tutors
      Must have appropriate
      knowledge

2 Resources
   Availability
   Assignments
   Criteria sheets (know what
      lecturer wants)
   Comprehensive feedback
   Flexible 'due dates'

3 Materials delivery

4 Student interaction
   Isolation/distances
   Meetings/study groups
   Teleconferences
   Prior to assignment due dates

5 Costs
   Time Management
   Conflicting demands
   3rd semester
   Residential schools
   Cost
   Time
   Videos of lectures/tutorials
   Get other students' questions/
      perspectives
   Assignment issues

Technology
   Teleconferences
   Videoconferencing
   Audiographics
   Electronic mail

</td></tr>
</table>

Chapter 17

Saline politics - local participation and neo-liberalism in Australian rural environments

Peter Martin

Participatory approaches to sustainable development have gained considerable currency in both western countries and in the Third World. Citizen participation occupies a predominant position in the Brundtland Report, in Agenda 21 and in the revitalised development strategies of the World Bank. In Australian rural environments, local participatory approaches have been promoted by the state as effective and democratic means of 'government' of rural environments (see Martin and Woodhill, 1995; Martin, in press)[1].

'Bottom up' approaches, as they have been termed, have been contrasted with 'top-down' approaches which have constituted the core of development practice, and aim to regulate and manage development through the state apparatus. However, many scholars and practitioners alike are ambivalent about participatory approaches as a basis for sustainable development, especially when initiated by the state. While there is general agreement that sustainable development requires local participation and people taking control of their own environments, there is also a recognition that some forms of devolution and decentralisation do not have the capacity to address the wide spatial and temporal dimensions of environmental problems (Lockie, 1994; Martin and Woodhill, 1995). More specifically, development programs based on local participation are being questioned in terms of their efficacy given the increasing globalisation of capital and the fragmentation and decentralisation of state institutional and regulatory capability (Swyngedouw, 1989).

This latter point has particular relevance for public good issues, such as environmental quality. The rise of neo-liberalist reforms in the West has been supported by democratising rhetoric which has emphasised notions of 'freedom to choose' through reduced state intervention. Post-structuralist theorists talk of neo-liberalism as a 'de-governmentalisation of the state' (Rose, 1993: 296) where state deliberation focuses on mechanisms that enhance self-regulation of individuals rather than considering the substantive social issues facing societies.

These tendencies have also been described as a move from public to private forms of regulation (Flynn and Marsden, 1995). While the political and social nature of citizen participation in sustainable development seems to contrast with the neo-liberalist agenda to depoliticise government, some have suggested that particular forms of institutionalised participation might enhance legitimation of the state (Lockie, 1994; Martin *et al*, 1992) and provide the vehicle for the development of economically rational subjects (Martin, in press). These arguments suggest that forms of citizen participation and related participatory discourses might enable the project of neo-liberalist reform rather than provide sites of resistance. In terms of the current debates in regulation theory regarding the stability and reproducibility of neo-liberalism (see Tickell and Peck, 1995), forms of participation might provide an important component of a new 'mode of social regulation'.

These broader and more abstract theoretical debates have practical and political significance for development practice in Australia. In an environment of increasing social concern with the quality of rural environments and a declining rural sector, 'participatory' rural development policies are being promoted by the Federal government within a policy framework of market deregulation, a withdrawal of rural services and a rationalisation of the public service. One result of this is the decline in permanent extension and development staff in state agencies and an increase in contractual and flexible staffing and 'outsourcing' of 'projects' to consultants. Practitioners are being asked to orient their practice towards 'facilitation' of community participation within a 'project' environment. What are the implications of these changes for Australian rural development and, more specifically, for the quality of rural environments? In relation to the preceding theoretical discussion, do these participatory programs stabilise and enable neo-liberalism or do they provide opportunities for resistance and political action?

This paper addresses these questions by relating two projects concerned with the government of dryland salinity in the Hunter Valley, NSW. Previous analysis has reviewed policy development at the national level and points to how development practice is shaped (see Martin and Woodhill, 1995) but does not indicate the conditions under which practice is constrained or enabled and how this 'agency' might challenge neo-liberal ideology and practices. To understand the implications of the constellation of neo-liberalist reforms and participatory development policy, requires a sensitivity to context and an elaboration of the complexities of practice. My approach then is to elaborate in some detail my experiences, observations and reflections from my participation in the government of a particular environmental problem (salinity) within the Hunter Valley, NSW, and to link this with the broader policy and political environment. Following this detailed elaboration, I will draw some conclusions about the implications of neo-liberalism for rural environmental and development practice and the opportunities for an improved strategic practice.

The aim of the first project was to clarify the extent and intensity of dryland salinity and to provide a report to the Hunter Catchment Management Trust (HCMT) with recommendations for action (see Martin and Lockie, 1991;

Martin and Lockie, 1993). The recommendations catalysed the second project which involved the collaborative development of a strategic approach to salinity in the Hunter with the HCMT, Government agencies and community groups. My involvement in these projects from 1990 to 1993, allowed considerable insights into the construction and politicisation of rural environmental issues in relationship to the intersection of participatory policies and neo-liberalist reforms.

Background salinity concern and action

The story of salinity in the Hunter Valley begins 260 million years ago with the formation of Permian coal-bearing sediments during alternating marine and continental environments. Salts accumulated both within these marine sediments and in coal seam aquifers. This time is significant for the Hunter. The formation of coal seams has been the basis for the industrial wealth of the region. Flow on industries such as electricity production, steel production and aluminium smelters have produced considerable wealth for the Valley. The primary accumulation of salts during the Permian period, however, has predisposed the region to extensive salinisation.

The central region of the Hunter Valley catchment has large areas of Permian sediments relatively close to the surface. They are known to contain considerable amounts of salts. In other areas of the catchment these strata are overlaid by more recent formations such as carboniferous sequences in the north-east of the basin, Triassic sediments in the southern sections and tertiary basalt's in the north-west. On and adjacent to the Hunter floodplain, unconsolidated sediments of recent origin (Quaternary) dominate. Although Permian sediments dominate the central and upper central catchment, these formations occur to a variable extent throughout the western and northern catchment.

Preliminary work in the Hunter Valley in 1988 found that many people did not perceive dryland salinity as a major issue, and those that did, thought that it was limited to a small area (Hunter Valley Project Group, 1989). The professional staff on the Hunter Catchment Management Trust believed that 'dryland salinity is localised around the Singleton area and is a fairly low priority for the catchment as a whole'. Four officers of the Department of Agriculture and Fisheries and two officers of the Soil Conservation Service indicated that salinity could present a problem in the future. However, other information such as the land degradation survey of NSW and the soil erosion mapping of the Hunter Valley suggested that salinity was more widespread than originally thought, especially in the central Hunter. Even so, the present and future extent of salinity and its significance in terms of environmental damage was difficult to establish from these surveys. By 1990, the time my work on the salinity issue began, there had been no attempts by any government agency to assess either the extent of the current problem or the possible future threat of dryland salinity in the Hunter Valley.

An examination of local (Hunter) newspaper cuttings on environmental problems over the last 20 years revealed the existence of historical concerns with salinity which corresponded to times of drought in the region. In times of low flow, irrigators experienced rising salt levels in the Hunter and its tributaries often resulting in stunted growth or death of crops. Further, during these flow regimes, mine water discharge created large pulses of saline water through the river system. These problems seem to have little direct functional relationship to dryland salinity,[2] however, the general concern created by these problems often renewed interest in dryland salinity. At various times, inter-departmental committees have been set up by the Trust to look at salinity in general (including dryland) but these committees have had a limited life, especially after the breaking of a drought. General concerns have led to forums and conferences on water supply and quality, and several research projects from the Commonwealth Scientific Industrial Research Organisation (CSIRO) have attempted to assess the general salinity threat in the valley and the hydrogeological basis for salinity (see Baker and Williams, 1980; Kellet *et al*, 1989). Notwithstanding the infrequent and limited action on salinity in the past, several vocal community groups (comprised mainly of irrigation farmers) have been formed in the Hunter to express concerns about mining problems, especially in relation to salinity.

Discussions in the Hunter indicated that actions that have arisen out of a concern for dryland salinity in the past seemed to have centred primarily on the local scale with actions such as fencing, small-scale structural works and tree planting. There is little information regarding the number of works completed but only a small proportion of the sites identified as salinised have actually been treated. There was a general lack of knowledge regarding the appropriate treatment of salinised areas in the Hunter and that local knowledge that existed was not co-ordinated effectively.

Raised attention and local response

In attempting to clarify the extent and potential threat of salinity in the Hunter, I drew on a number of secondary data sources and interviews with state officials and farmers. Interestingly, when this work commenced, many people in the Valley had already began to express interest and concern about the problem. Salinity was becoming a more widely known issue. NSW State Government funding was becoming available for community groups for treatment and demonstration works on dryland salinity. In a neighbouring catchment, the Liverpool Plains, some of the most fertile cropping soils in Australia were threatened by rising water tables. The Department of Water Resources hydrologist in the Hunter claimed that many large groundwater seeps that had been dormant for hundreds of years were beginning to flow throughout NSW.

The mobilisation and shaping of attention towards salinity in the Hunter was a complex matter. From the perspective of local people experiencing these problems, attention was shaped from the local level. Earlier accounts of dryland salinity in the Hunter, indicated concerns well before state agencies became interested. However, in most cases the symptoms of salinity were thought to be due to poor fertility even though many noticed increased salty water and occasional stock deaths from drinking the water. Contact was often made with relevant state agencies to obtain advice on the problems but the experts had little to offer in diagnoses or remedial action. That is until Salt Action funds became available in 1990-1991. State agency interest in salinity grew immensely.

Mostly, however, this interest remained local. The influx of funds for salinity work was directed to local problem sites. Much of the money available was tagged for local community action groups - to be known as Salt Action groups - and state officers in the catchment were busy trying to find appropriate sites for disbursement of the monies. This required the formation of a community group with a substantial interest/concern with salinity, as well as a site which had demonstration potential. This usually meant that projects needed to be carried out close to roads where 'action' could be seen by passing traffic. Applications for funds were submitted by state officials in consultation with a small number of farmers often before a substantial group had evolved. Within these applications were substantial funds for state agency works such as local surveys and conservation works (dams, contour banks and drains).

At the local level then, the state had a marked presence, not in an authoritarian relationship with local people, but as collaborators in local problems. This is not to say that problems did not occasionally occur in relationships between local people and state officers. However, the increasing rationalisation of state agencies and the direction of funds towards local communities provided a powerful incentive for local co-operation by state officers. From the perspective of local people, state involvement was needed for technical advice and assessment of community plans and projects to guarantee funding.

The project sites identified throughout the Hunter Valley were made in a vacuum of information on the regional dynamics, extent and intensity of salinity on a catchment scale (see Martin and Lockie, 1993). The raised concern about salinity did not emerge from some ongoing review and monitoring of the health of the catchment. There seemed little interest in this from either the TCM group (HCMT) or the Soil Conservation Service at the time. Local Salt Action applications were tied to approval by the HCMT but there was little information and knowledge available to establish the importance of these projects on a catchment level. Approval by the TCM group was a formality and simply related to criteria regarding demonstration and community group, the latter of which was highly suspect in some cases. The sites submitted for funding were identified by District Soil Conservation officers who happened to know about particular salinity outbreaks.

Patterns of salinity action

The salinity action in the Hunter exhibits a particular spatial and institutional pattern which:

- is characterised by as absence of regional planning and monitoring,
- is focused on clearly degraded *local* rural sites. Preference is often given to sites adjacent to main thoroughfares through the catchment. These sites of development are also limited temporally, that is, they are constituted as 'projects', and
- is characterised by close working relationships between state officers and farmers and facilitated by the regional TCM (HCMT) group.

This pattern not just limited to the Hunter Valley in NSW. In other parts of Australia, there has been a distinct lack of strategic planning and monitoring of salinity and other rural environmental problems (see Martin and Woodhill, 1995). Throughout Australia, community-based 'Landcare' programs have been developed in the absence of National, State and regional monitoring programs (see Dovers, 1995: 144). The 'Dryland Salinity R&D National Review' sums up the common features throughout Australia which relate back to the problems identified in the Hunter. The Review found that there was little emphasis on mapping and elaboration on dryland salinity processes, a neglect of socio-economic aspects, and a lack of monitoring and evaluation of project impact (Policy Development Planning Australia Pty Ltd, 1992: 2-3).

In the context of sustainable development, Dovers (1995: 143) lists a host of environmental issues such as land degradation, water resources, biodiversity and climate change as lacking in information and monitoring programs. He states that 'better information, although universally called for, may not really be desired by some decision-makers' and that there might be some use 'in clouding understanding'. It is implicit in many of the variants of crisis theory (Habermas, 1975), that state intervention through monitoring and planning can politicise issues and 'interfere' with the normal operation of the market.

The local focus of environmental action in the Hunter and Australia more generally, reflects the outcome of a number of social and political forces. On the one hand, there has been increased social concern with the degradation of rural environments, reflected in the joint development of the National Land Management Program by Australian Conservation Foundation and the National Farmers' Federation (see Toyne and Farley, 1989) and a host of parliamentary inquiries into related matters. However, parallel with this politicisation of the environment, has been the development of neo-liberal rural policy which has been intent on deregulating economic markets, restructuring the state along corporate lines, and reducing budget outlays. Politicising rural environments and increased levels of state intervention threaten these neo-liberalist political projects by increasing the risk of greater demands for government expenditure, direct state action and for re-regulating agricultural production. Local participatory approaches, such as Landcare and Salt-Action, in the absence of broader monitoring and planning, can be seen as 'crisis management strategies' (see Offe, 1984) that depoliticise rural environments whilst maintaining relatively low levels of government expenditure and intervention (see also Lockie, 1994). Rural environmental action is, in effect, limited in time and space, which allows for flexibility of state funding and intervention.

These arguments suggest a level of compatibility between participatory approaches to sustainable development and neo-liberalist reforms and ideology. However, as I elaborate in the next section, this pattern of intervention results in a 'reactive' form of government which can have a number of unintended and unexpected outcomes.

Back to the Hunter Valley, I submitted my research report to the regional Total Catchment Management group of the Hunter Catchment Management Trust (HCMT). The report elucidated the extent of salinity, deficiencies of current approaches and the need for a strategic planning and monitoring program. The report was also sent in draft form to the NSW Soil Conservation Service which is primarily responsible for the management of dryland salinity in the Valley. They 'coincidentally' proposed many of the recommendations from the report at the following HCMT meeting. Many of these recommendations were carried and a salinity task force was established. The following section outlines the progress on salinity in the Valley since that time (mid-1991) until the end of 1992. Here, I aim to show both the limitations of 'participatory' approaches at the catchment level but also how opportunities can be created for a broader co-ordinative practice that provides sites of resistance against neo-liberalism. I then offer an analysis of how these opportunities come about in terms of the intersection of neo-liberalist reforms and participatory policy.

The 'strategic' government of salinity

I concluded in my report that while there was a number of community groups engaged in salinity work, there was a lack of understanding and action at the regional TCM level. In the Hunter, and elsewhere, the problem of dryland salinity was treated as a local problem.

In 1989, at the time of my initial work in the Hunter, dryland salinity was thought to be 'localised around the Singleton area and a fairly low priority for the catchment as a whole', with Government estimates of only 1,000 ha being affected. By the end of 1992, salinity was described as a 'most important issue requiring resolution, with dryland salinity affecting 50,000 ha of land at a cost of $880,000 pa. with capitalised value of losses calculated at $22.6 million. How did this 50 fold increase come about and what factors propelled salinity into the Hunter Valley's catchment 'consciousness'?

The Salinity Task Force had a difficult birth and a temporary existence in the Hunter Valley. The resolution for its formation was passed by the Trust in mid-1991 but the first meeting did not occur until July, 1992. Representation was initially from 11 organisations but was extended to 12 at the next meeting.

All up, 16 people from four state agencies, two universities, two state corporations, two community groups, one industry association and from the Trust constituted the group. My participation within the group came about through my previous work on salinity; however, I was the only non-catchment resident within the group and was not a 'stakeholder' in the sense usually applied in TCM jargon. My interests in participating in the group were to help develop regional monitoring networks in relation to catchment-wide learning strategies. Further, I was interested in the ability of the 'stakeholders' to develop group strategies at the regional level and hoped to play a role in facilitating this process.

The initial meeting set the ground rules for the group and participants outlined their concerns and/ or activities in regard to salinity in the Hunter Valley. Not all organisations were represented at this meeting. Notable in their absence were agencies and organisations that were seen as major salinity 'polluters' and their regulators, such as NSW Coal Association, Pacific Power, Department of Mineral Resources and Environmental Protection Agency. The ensuing discussion, however, yielded a host of activities from the different agencies and made clear to the participants that much of this work was uncoordinated and fragmented across the Valley. One of the major outcomes for the meeting was for this group to merge into the recently formed 'water quality' group to form the Hunter Water Quality Task Group. Many of the participants were on both groups and it was seen as more efficient, in terms of participants time, to merge. There was some concern that dryland salinity would be marginalised, however, it was guaranteed that it would remain a predominant issue. For a number of reasons it did decline in importance, at least in the short term.

The merging of the two groups reflected a number of forces that were impacting in the Valley. Firstly, state agencies had little time to spend at meetings and some were somewhat cynical about their benefits. Subsequent meetings were to substantiate this to a degree. Notwithstanding the claims of efficiency of integrated and participatory approaches, TCM and Landcare were stretching state agency resources at a time of cut-backs and restructuring. The participatory policies of the state had encouraged much greater awareness of environmental problems and subsequently a greater need for state technical support. At the same time, state agencies could not afford to be unrepresented at catchment meetings. For state agencies, these fora offered opportunities for influence and for supplementary resources that often flowed from group decisions. These opportunities were to be heightened at a later stage when 'salinity hit the headlines' in the media. The Trust was understaffed and did not have the resources to cope with a myriad of TCM task groups. The decision to merge was therefore partly due to the need for efficiency of resource use under conditions of higher demand and, in the case of state agencies, declining resources. The need to participate was also related to these factors.

In the background, issues of water quality were of particular significance at the national level. Importantly, these issues did not emerge from state monitoring programs but through 'environmental crises' such as blue-green algae in the Murray-Darling basin. On 2 December, 1991, the Premier declared a state of emergency and the army was called in to install water treatment works. Rain began to fall by 14 December, and the algae was flushed from the river. The state of emergency ended on 24 December. In the period of two months, direct agricultural damage was estimated at $1.3m. Other indirect costs were not able to be established and the natural environment of the Darling River sustained significant damage (Blue-Green Algae, May 1992: 3).

It was these events and the raised concern with water quality issues in the press that first oriented group attention towards water quality in the Hunter. Algal blooms were occurring in the main water storages of the Hunter and lack of rain had resulted in elevated river salinity levels. Farmers were occasionally experiencing toxic effects of saline water irrigated on pastures and crops. Both these issues were receiving media attention. Dryland salinity was only partly related to river salinity, but, more importantly, did not have the political clout of water quality issues. Further meetings were to see dryland salinity marginalised as an issue.

The increasing media prominence of river salinity issues in the Hunter prompted full attendance at the following meeting. Local media focus on saline discharges from mines stimulated attendance of the Coal Association and its regulators. The meeting, however, was plagued with sectarian arguments that addressed a diversity of issues under the broad banner of water quality. With such a wide diversity of issues and participants, little agreement was reached regarding the role of the group. The number of participants, representing a diversity of organisational interests, mitigated against a productive group process. Nevertheless, there were some broad outcomes from the meeting such as agreement about the group as a forum for debate on water quality issues, and the need to develop water quality standards for the Hunter catchment. The latter need was enthusiastically supported by all except the mining and power generation representatives. Similarly, the group agreed in principle for the need for a water quality co-ordinator position to be established within the Hunter but could not agree to funding arrangements, agency links or what specific activities this co-ordinator would engage in.

It is interesting to reflect on group process in terms of the aims of TCM as working for the 'good of the catchment' determined through 'consensual processes between stakeholders'. The aims of TCM policy suggest that processes are oriented towards, what Habermas might call, 'generalisable interests' (see Martin, 1991). However, my experience of the first two meetings suggested that, as representatives of various organisations embedded in particular 'systemic' webs of interaction (profit and power), this goal seemed unobtainable. Neo-liberal reforms of the NSW public service have put significant pressure on state agencies. For example, there is significant competition for funding between state agencies, and these pressures are often not conducive to co-operative activity. Further, the restructuring of CaLM and NSW Agriculture towards more cost-effective corporatised structures, threatened a number of state agency positions in the Hunter. Many participants from state agencies needed to promote the agency line and orientation to the problem. This, along with the profit orientation of mining and power generation representatives, created a stalemate situation in the group which was characterised by a diversity of views, with little overlap or potential for substantive agreement except around broad statements such as the 'need for debate'.

The Trust, charged with the responsibility to facilitate TCM processes and derive substantive outcomes for the catchment, found this situation increasingly frustrating and suggested that if the Hunter region could not formulate its own water quality policy and standards, then it could be imposed from the outside. This was to become an important threat that, when bolstered by widespread media attention, would eventually create a form of 'communicative solidarity' within the group and initiate substantial action.

The communicative transformation of the task group

On Wednesday, 23 September 1992, I made my way towards the Joint Coal Board Building in Singleton in anticipation of another frustrating meeting. The previous two hours on the Putty road from Windsor to Singleton gave me plenty of time to review my role in the group. What was I contributing to TCM and the salinity issue? In some ways, the past two meetings had increased my cynicism of 'community and government working together'. With all the best intentions of the Trust and the many individuals in the group, the lack of enabling structures in 'higher' levels of government seemed to suggest that TCM was merely a legitimation strategy for the state. The emphasis on the efficiency of state agencies had focused competition within the state and had left many state officials involved directly in TCM in an uncertain and insecure career position.

With these thoughts in the background, I entered the building to find an Australian Broadcasting Corporation (ABC) production crew in the foyer. Somewhat surprised, I asked the Chairperson of the TCM group what the situation was. 'The '7.30 report' is doing a story on river salinity and they want to get some shots of us in action'. And action they got. Under the glare of camera lights, the Hunter Water Quality Task Force had its most productive meeting, discussing numerous issues with a number of state agencies agreeing to collaborative projects. Aspects of water quality in the draft strategic plan of the Trust were discussed and a summary list of water quality issues in the Valley was agreed to.

The appearance of the electronic media was not a surprise to many in the group. In early September, the Minewatch committee, a community group concerned with mining activities, released monitoring data that showed high levels of salt in the Hunter and its tributaries and continual dry weather 'uncovered' highly visible salt-scalding in dry stream beds. This, in conjunction with a release of a report on mine water management in the Hunter and a draft Federal government report on 'Water Quality Management in the Rural Environment', stimulated national media attention to the issue.

The increased attention towards river salinity and the apparent urgency for its resolution focused the Trust, and subsequently the Hunter Water Quality Task Group, towards a 'communicative' solution. One of the most significant outcomes of the Task Group, coincidentally captured on film, was for a catchment workshop to:

> involve all participants in developing solutions to the problems of salinity - it is not about pointing the finger at others. We are looking to produce strategies, both short-term and long-term, to take to departmental senior executives, politicians etc., so that funds can be sought to implement specific works and measures.

The broadcast of the '7.30 Report' gained spectacular government attention with 'ministerials' stimulating a chain reaction down the bureaucracy. Media attention had focused on the coal mine releases and their effect on irrigation farming in the Valley. Mining companies made the point that they could not afford not to release saline water into the Hunter while irrigation farmers and concerned catchment residents were expecting tighter forms of state regulation. At this time, of course, dryland salinity disappeared from the agenda. The government was caught in what seemed like a no-win situation. Coal mining in the Hunter valley creates significant state revenue and employment. On the other hand, the Hunter Valley contained some marginal State seats.

Opportunities and threats

The politicisation of river salinity represented both a threat and opportunity for the Trust, state agencies and individual state officials in the Hunter. The Trust was keen to establish itself as the co-ordinating resource management agency in the Hunter. Professional Officers of the Trust thought that too much publicity would reflect on the capacity of the Trust to carry out its role, and a government in panic might take the debate out of the Hunter and impose outside solutions. The opportunity for the Trust was to develop a form of catchment solidarity through the 'communicative' processes stimulated through politicisation of the issues, and to orient this support for prestige and for claims for greater resources to manage the salinity issue.

Importantly, it was not just the Trust which recognised this opportunity. With the catchment workshop approaching, state officials in the Hunter found themselves the centre of attention with Ministers and senior bureaucrats. State agency directors in the Hunter received urgent requests for 'salinity strategies' and 'situation updates'. For those in uncertain career conditions, this attention provided opportunities for demonstrating their significance to the particular agency. It was becoming increasingly clear from the local press and state agency officials that the salinity problems could not be addressed without a substantial co-ordination and monitoring effort, and that this was hampered by a lack of funds for catchment management. A combination of this and requests for status reports, resulted in a further politicisation of salinity issues. In the case of CaLM, the agency responsible for dryland salinity, previous fragmented information was hastily integrated and used to highlight the now *extensive* nature of dryland salinity to both senior bureaucrats, politicians and the Hunter public. At the workshop, which was first oriented towards dealing with river salinity from mines, CaLM set up a large display publicising the extent of dryland salinity in the Hunter Valley. Notwithstanding the tentative (biophysical) link between dryland salinity and river salinity, the politicisation of salinity in the TCM discourse 'whole systems approaches' resulted in the issue expanding again, and placing dryland salinity firmly on the political agenda. In the subsequent workshop, dryland salinity was given a predominant place.

The 'communicative catchment' workshop and its outcomes

The workshop process, which I helped facilitate, was based upon strategic planning. The (brief) objective of this process was to firstly come to a common understanding of the issue, identify constraints (problem identification), and identify possible solutions and subsequent action plans. The common understanding or *salinity situation goal* was 'To minimise and reduce, where possible, the impact of salinity through promoting sustainable land and water management practices. One of the tendencies of strategic planning at this stage is the development of statements of such a 'generalisable' nature, that everyone must agree. Nevertheless, this statement could be seen to encapsulate a 'generalisable interest' in the catchment and did orient participants towards this interest rather than 'particular' interests. Minewatch and coal mining representatives, who were clearly antagonistic in the earlier session, now engaged in constructive dialogue in small working groups helped by a sense of solidarity created through the agreement on the salinity situation goal.

The outcomes of the workshop were considerable. Firstly, and rather predictably, the mining conflict was resolved, at least in the short term, through improved co-ordination and contact between agencies, miners and irrigators. The short term plan was to time discharges from the Glenbawn dam (Dept. Water Resources) in the upper reaches of the Hunter with mine water releases lower down and to provide a monitoring service (EPA) for the irrigation farmers. One might ask why these fairly straight-forward solutions required a catchment workshop? However, mobilisation towards this partial resolution required politicisation and conflict *and* an open 'communicative' forum for a solution to be legitimated. This is an essential outcome of participatory policies where principles of legitimation are based on more 'communicative' grounds. While this outcome further involved the state in subsidising the social costs of private capital in coal mining, other outcomes promised to keep salinity on the political boil whilst urging the state to take a more supportive role in catchment management.

The factors seen to be obstructing the achievement of the 'generalisable interest' embodied in the 'salinity situation goal' are outlined as follows:

Lack of co-ordination: 'best overcome by devising a co-ordination plan. This would entail the appointment of a co-ordinator to work with the Water Quality Task Group. It would involve considerable co-ordination groups such as landcare, farming and mining'.

Entrenched attitudes: 'a public awareness campaign using the media to bring public pressure to bear and change attitude'.

Limited resources: 'Politicians should be lobbied to make them aware of the gravity of the salinity/water quality situation to obtain more funds to apply a *meaningful* effort in the problem resolutions. The workshop recognised the limited nature of the monitoring effort to date and the lack of co-ordination of diverse and individual monitoring exercises'.

Inadequate communications: 'There needs to be a regular publication of salinity status in a form that is well understood'.

Lack of water goals: 'there is a need to establish a clear range of water quality goals which address the needs of key participants. Much *diplomacy* and compromise is needed here but the duty must not be shirked'.

Economic sustainability: 'the ability of industries which affect, or are affected by water quality, to sustain economic production must be taken into account in options for strategically planning the salinity control program'.

These findings, legitimated by the participatory nature of the process, were presented as a 'situation report' to a meeting of NSW Departmental Heads on 23 November, 1992 with preliminary costings of $900,000 to support the communicatively agreed actions of the Hunter catchment. Most of these actions were eventually funded.

In the first paragraph of the 'situation report' it was stated that the results of a survey showed that 'water quality/salinity was identified and accepted as the most significant environmental issue in the Hunter. Salinity, promoted and politicised by related water quality issues, had emerged from a low priority to the top of the list in two years.

The rather tortured route of 'communicative' TCM processes resulted in the instigation of a number of broader co-ordinative mechanisms and forms of social integration across the Valley. The evolution of the salinity issue over a relatively short period of time created forms of catchment solidarity, social learning (cultural reproduction) and significantly improved the chances of effective catchment care. New mechanisms, that resulted from a 'differentiation' out from communicative processes, have been developed, for example rules regarding water quality that institutionalised 'communicatively' determined agreements about the environment (water quality standards). These new mechanisms and the new levels of 'social integration' throughout the valley, hold the potential for greater public scrutiny of water quality and salinity and therefore an enhanced *accountability* of catchment residents and state agencies to their quality. In terms of dryland salinity, significant resources were allocated to monitoring and broader regional planning which is significant in terms of the almost total lack of monitoring and co-ordination up until 1992. As is argued later, these outcomes are related to contradictions that emerge from the intersection of participatory practice with the neo-liberalist policy.

I argue that these outcomes are positive developments in the Hunter Valley towards a democratising environmental practice. Of course, this need not have been the case, and much of the 'transformative' practice occurred because of the capacity of a number of actors to identify opportunities and convergence of interests. Persons operating in practice, such as the Trust officers, state agencies, and myself become bound up in events that, to a certain extent, defy what Bourdieu (1992) calls 'theoretical reason'. However, this is no way diminishes the import of theory and reflection. As I show in the following section, patterns emerge from reflection on the government of salinity in the Hunter which tie together the contradictions in participatory approaches within neo-liberalist policy frameworks. Identification of these contradictions provides some guidance for a progressive political practice for sustainable development practitioners in Australia.

Reflections on practice

The positive outcomes identified from this case indicate that forms of interaction that approach communicative processes are possible within the web of systemic imperatives that bear down on farmers, community and state officials. In the Hunter, these processes were encouraged by a number of complex factors.

Firstly, the visibility of rural environmental problems outside the catchment maintained a background sensitivity that was easily mobilised. The 'blue-green' algae crisis had only recently subsided and the Federal government had set up an Blue-Green Algae task force and released a discussion paper on water quality in rural environments. The EPA had reaffirmed the need for state water quality standards and there was a salinity crisis in the adjacent catchment (Liverpool Plains). All these elements, while separated spatially and in some cases conceptually from issues in the Hunter, provided a tension that can easily 'ignite' regional issues.

This background tension is exacerbated by a reactionary and unpredictable environmental politics. The hesitancy of the state to monitor the quality of rural environments means that state action is either localised or dependent on the obvious manifestation of crisis situations, such as the salinisation of the Liverpool Plains or the death of irrigated crops by saline water in the Hunter. In most cases, state action is *projectised*, that is, it is limited spatially and temporally and, because of the absence of monitoring, is *reactive* to politicised crises. To add to this instability, the rationalisation of the public sector and fiscal constraint has altered the nature of *relationships* within the state and between the state and rural people. State governments are reducing permanent extension staff and replacing them with temporary 'project' officers at the local level. As I demonstrated in the Hunter Valley, security of employment for these project officers is dependent on maintaining environmental issues on the 'political boil'. This vertical fragmentation of the state is also accompanied by communicative coalitions between rural people and local state officers who both have similar interests in demonstrating the significance of *their* local environmental problems. On a broader scale, these project officers become part of community projects and add weight and legitimacy to demands that might arise out of these fora.

From this, it is apparent that the very forces that depoliticise rural environments can also create the conditions for their re-politicisation. This unstable background, can mitigate against the fragmentation of rural environmental action. In the Hunter, while some local salinity work was underway, the thematisation of salinity on a regional scale was *catalysed* by my research document which threatened to highlight the ineptitude of a particular state agency, within the circumstances of state agency competition and funding uncertainty. Within the heightened public awareness of salinity, this agency immediately started to take action by suggesting a 'communicative' approach. This dynamic of a 'catalyst', creating a threat and transformation into a more or less communicative approach was apparent throughout the evolution of the salinity issue. These apparent threats, however, also opened up opportunities for communicative processes to satisfy both local particular interests and more 'generalisable' interests of the catchment. If one examines the 'practice' of the Trust officers, it was their ability to identify these opportunities within their own constraints that contributed to a generalisable benefit and a strengthening of power, autonomy and the resource base for catchment management in the Hunter.

Why do these threats lead to communicative processes? A clue to this comes from type of discourse which supports state-initiated participatory programs. Parts of the state, aim to spread the political burden through defining rural environmental problems as problems of community, and therefore for community to solve. The communicative processes of Landcare and TCM provide an avenue for spreading political risk for particular state agents. These particular agents, rather than ignoring the issue, highlight it, and through the legitimating mechanisms of TCM, propose communicative solutions. Because the community 'owns' the problem, the threat to the particular agency or agent becomes less significant. As the proposal for the communicative workshop in the Hunter stated: '(The aim is to) involve all participants in developing solutions to the problems of salinity - it is not about pointing the finger at others!' Ironically, 'not pointing the finger at others' helped strengthen the particular resource agencies and the Trust.

While participatory programs and their supporting rhetoric provides particular routes for the resolution of political conflict, the outcomes of these communicative forums take on a level of legitimacy that is difficult for governments to ignore. The catchcry of TCM, ie 'Community and Government Working Together', is powerful political discourse which tends to tie the state to the outcome of participatory processes. At the level of TCM, regional 'communicative' groupings and processes, while 'disempowered' through lack of state support, can mobilise attention to issues, and stimulate the formation of broader participatory processes. These processes can develop powerful demands for broader forms of regional government that can enhance the transparency of social life, protect generalisable interests and communicative processes, and institute 'mechanisms' for integrating action over social time-space.

Conclusion

The discourse and emerging practice of sustainable rural development in Australia is one of community ownership and responsibility, legitimated by rhetorical phrases such as 'Community and Government Working Together'. However, the local orientation of participation in state-initiated rural environmental programs suggests a highly fragmented approach to sustainable development. Combined with the deregulation of economic markets and cutbacks in permanent extension and development staff, rural environments are constituted 'privatised' and 'particularised' spaces. As other studies have pointed out, self-help and participatory approaches to sustainable development are important but should be only part of an integrated approach which includes monitoring and deliberative planning activities (see McLauglin, 1987; Sandercock, 1986).

It has been argued previously that this form of sustainable development aims to enhance self-regulatory capacity of rural subjects and to form disciplining arenas where the calculating rural subject is constituted (see Martin, in press) and depoliticise issues by shifting attention away from the (formal) political sphere (see Crook *et al*, 1993: 105 and Martin and Woodhill, 1995: 174). In terms of the neo-liberalist orientation to governance in Australia, participatory programs are relatively inexpensive and can legitimate a non-interventionist role of the state. As a prominent economic rationalist Landcare policy adviser argued, in commenting on increased calls for Landcare support from government:

> The message is that Landcare will fail unless the Government provides much more money for implementation. However, this argument presents a paradox. The strength of the Landcare initiative is its community basis and 'self-help' origins. If this is so, why should further progress be dependent on increased Government support? (Taylor , 1994: 105)

But as the example of salinity government points out, the overriding concern for the efficiency of the state apparatus and the consequent 'reactive' form of state action results in an even greater 'paradox'. This political 'porosity' of local participation and the potential for repoliticisation is, ironically, fuelled by contradictions in neo-liberalism. The rationalisation of the public sector has increased competition within the state and places many state officials in insecure career situations. As I have mentioned earlier, state funding is either for short-term contracts for state officials working with local people, or at the regional level, is directed towards limited term *projects*. Ironically, in the absence of monitoring and co-ordination, *project* funding becomes more dependent on political mobilisation around a particular environmental problem rather than a 'rational' appraisal. State withdrawal and lack of concern with environmental monitoring will not make the problems go away. As in the case of salinity in the Hunter, problems continue to extend and intensify until, after a number of unpredictable events and a growing community consciousness of environmental issues, they explode in the media, helped along by a technically and politically competent green movement. In the meantime, private economic production, ecological values and public goods have been affected.

What does this mean, then, for strategic practice? I do not conclude from this analysis that the contradictions of neo-liberalism need simply to be left alone for improved rural environments to appear in history. What the case of 'salinity government' demonstrated was the importance of agency and the practical knowledge of people bound up in practice. Within these chaotic and contradictory circumstances outlined above, development practitioners were able to 'make a difference'. In the Hunter, more regional approaches to dryland salinity were catalysed by my report which highlighted the extent of the problem and was perceived to challenge the competence of the Soil Conservation Service. Within the participatory rhetoric of state policy, the Regional Director of Soil Conservation Service was able to initiate a 'communicative' approach that minimised blame on the agency and defined dryland salinity as a community-owned problem. A salinity task group was initiated, but was ineffective until salinity was politicised through increased media attention. Trust officers were able to take advantage of increased concern with water quality and a convergence of interest between local state officials and themselves to reinvigorate collective action within the task group and initiated a catchment 'communicative' workshop. The outcomes of this workshop have resulted in the development of water quality standards and salinity monitoring and mapping activities and an overall more focused approach to the government of salinity.

The communitarian orientation of state rural development policy is limited in its capacity to sustain rural environments and, ironically, in its capacity to sustain rural communities. As Beilin and Ewing (1994: 125) suggest, 'whilst Landcare calls for increased community participation, that 'community' is rapidly being lost.' Hence, the sustainable development of rural Australia needs to go beyond a local, communitarian practice and engage in activities that demand complementary state activity that enhances and stabilises local practice. A focus on developing coalitions with local state officers, developing contacts within other regional developments and forging closer alliances with other interest groups such as parts of the environmental movement, might provide a basis for a wider and more inclusive practice that highlights and addresses the extent of rural environmental degradation and the particular political-economic conditions to which they are related.

These forms of practice indicate that sustainable rural development be eminently *political*, not just in the sense of participating in local groups as emphasised in the state participatory policy, but in developing an understanding of the range of diverse interests in rural environments and ways in which these interests can be articulated in broader communicative fora. It means identifying opportunities and convergences of interest within the apparent chaos of practice. Importantly, the involvement of practitioners in developing broader, and more deliberative institutions for environmental governance will be the most potent form of resistance to neo-liberalism. These institutions, formed on the interface of the state and civil society, have the potential to provide a more democratic *and* rational form of rural environmental governance.

Notes

1   I use the term government as 'modes of action, more or less considered and calculated, which were destined to act upon the possibilities of action of other people' (Foucault, 1982:208). In terms of the notion of disciplining power, government can also refer to self-regulation or 'government of the self'.
2   Increased river salinity in low flow conditions is attributed to the greater proportion of (saline) groundwater contribution to surface flow. During times of drought, flow maintenance from major storage's in the Hunter is reduced. The problem of dryland salinity, however, is basically a problem of relocation of salts from locations of benign environmental impact - usually at depth, to surface areas where biota are exposed to the toxic affects. In dryland salinity, this movement of salts occurs through the upward movement of groundwater towards the root zone of plants. It is thought that large scale removal of trees subsequently reduces the amount of groundwater removed through evapotranspiration, thereby, shifting the hydrological balance towards increased groundwater levels.

References

Baker, G. and Williams, B. (1980) *Sources of Salinity in the Upper Hunter Valley: An Electromagnetic Investigation.*, Canberra, CSIRO, Division of Land Use Research.
Beilin, R., and Ewing, S. (1994) Landcare: What's Missing, in Defenderfer, D. (ed.) *Proceedings of the 1994 National Landcare Conference - Landcare in*

the Balance Vol I, Hobart, Tasmanian Department of Primary Industry and Fisheries.

Bourdieu, P. (1992) *The Logic of Practice*, London, Polity Press.

Crook, S., Pakulski, J. and Waters, M. (1993) *Postmodernization: Change in Advanced Society*, London, Sage.

Dovers, S. (1995) Information, Sustainability and Policy, *Australian Journal of Environmental Management* 2: 142-156.

Emery, K. (1989a) *The Hunter Valley Erosion Survey - 1983-1985: Catchment Management Unit Summaries*, Sydney, Soil Conservation Service of NSW.

Emery, K. (1989b) *The Hunter Valley Erosion Survey - 1983-85: Maps*, Sydney, Soil Conservation Service of NSW.

Emery, K. (1989c) *The Hunter Valley Erosion Survey - 1983-85: Program Proposals for the Integrated Management of Soil Erosion and Related Land Degradation Issues Within the Hunter River Catchment*, Sydney, Summary document for the Hunter Valley Erosion Survey, Soil Conservation Service of NSW.

Flynn, A., and T. Marsden. (1995) Guest Editorial, *Environment and Planning A* 27: 1180-1192.

Foucault, M. (1983) Afterword: The Subject and Power, in Deyfus, H. and Rabinow, P. (ed.) *Michel Foucault: Beyond Structuralism and Hermeneutics*, Chicago, University of Chicago Press.

Habermas, J. (1975) *Legitimation Crisis*, Boston, Beacon Press.

Hunter Valley Project Group (1989) *Rapid Rural Appraisal Report on Natural Resource Management in the Hunter Valley Catchment Area Undertaken in August, 1988*, Faculty of Agriculture, Hawkesbury Agricultural College.

Kellett, J., Williams, B., and Ward, J. (1989) *Hydrogeochemistry of the Upper Hunter River Valley, New South Wales.*, BMR Bulletin 221, Canberra, Australian Government Publishing Service.

Lockie, S. (1994) Farmers and the State: Local Knowledge and Self Help in Rural Environmental Management, *Regional Journal of Social Issues* 28: 24-36.

Martin, P. (1991) Environmental Care in Agricultural Catchments: Towards the Communicative Catchment, *Environmental Management* 15: 773-783.

Martin, P. (1995) The Constitution of Power in Landcare: A Post-structuralist Perspective with Modernist Undertones, *Rural Society* 5 (in press).

Martin, P., and Lockie, S. (1991) *Dryland Salinity in the Hunter Valley*, unpublished research report, Landcare and Environment Program, University of Western Sydney-Hawkesbury, Centre for Extension and Rural Development.

Martin, P. and Woodhill, J. (1995) Landcare in the Balance: Government Roles and Policy Issues in Sustaining Rural Environments, *Australian Journal of Environmental Management* 2: 173-183.

Martin, P., Tarr, S. , and Lockie, S. (1992) Participatory Environmental Practice in NSW: Policy and Practice, in G. Lawrence, F. Vanclay, and B. Furze (ed.) *Agriculture, Environment and Society: Contemporary Issues for Australia*, Melbourne, Macmillan.

McLaughlin, B. (1987) Rural Policy into the 1990's - Self Help or Self Deception, *Journal of Rural Studies* 3: 361-364.

NSW Salt Action Task Force (1991) *Salt Action - the Salinity Control Strategy for New South Wales*, Sydney, NSW Department of Conservation and Land Management.

NSW Soil Conservation Service (1988) *Land Degradation Survey of NSW*, Sydney, NSW Soil Conservation Service.

Offe, C. (1984) Ungovernability: On the Renaissance of Conservative Theories of Crisis, in Habermas, J. (ed.) *Observations on 'The Spiritual Situation of the Age': Contemporary German Perspectives*, Massachusetts, MIT Press.

Policy Development Planning Pty Ltd (1992) *Dryland Salinity R&D: A Review of Efforts and Recommendations for the Future*, Canberra.

Rose, N. (1993) Government, Authority and Expertise in Advanced Liberalism, *Economy and Society* 22: 238-299.

Stewart, D., and McColl, G. (1994) The Resource Assessment Commission: an Inside Assessment, *Australian Journal of Environmental Management* 1: 12.

Swyngedouw, E. (1989) The Heart of the Place: The Resurrection of Locality in an Age of Hyperspace, *Geografiska Annaler* 71: 31-42.

Taylor, G. (1994) The Landcare Partnership - Where to From Here, in Defenderfer, D. (ed.) *Proceedings of the 1994 National Landcare Conference - Landcare in the Balance Vol II*, Hobart, Tasmanian Department of Primary Industry and Fisheries.

Taylor, S. (1991) *Dryland Salinity: Introductory Extension Notes*, Sydney, NSW Department of Conservation and Land Management.

Tickell, A., and Peck, J. (1995) Social Regulation after Fordism: regulation theory, neo-liberalism and the global local nexus, *Economy and Society* 24: 357-386.

Toyne, P., and Farley, R. (1989) A National Land Management Program, *Australian Journal of Soil and Water Conservation* 2: 6-9.

Williams, B., Baker, G., Laut, P. and Cook, B. (1981) Sources of Salinity: Present and Potential Problems, in *Proceedings of the Conference 'When Will the Hunter Dry Up? Water Availability and Salinity Problems'*, Singleton, Australian Institute of Agricultural Science.

Woodhill, J. 1991, *Landcare - Who Cares? Current Issues and Future Directions for Landcare in NSW.*, Landcare and Environment Program, Hawkesbury, Centre for Rural Development, University of Western Sydney.

Chapter 18

Does the Landcare model have a place in rural community development?

Patrick Morrisey

Introduction

Landcare has emerged within Australia during the 1990s as an attempt to alleviate environmental issues facing rural communities. This model is proving successful in parts of rural Australia at addressing ecological concerns by involving many more sections of rural communities in natural resource management decision making. However, as Landcare becomes adopted as a model for change in many rural communities, it is necessary to undertake a critical assessment of the success of the movement at representing rural social concerns as well as addressing environmental issues.

The Landcare model offers the potential for a self-help community based approach for addressing these ecological and social issues that face rural communities. Such a model also aims to recognise the contributions of rural residents within political decision making. Although recent federal and state government policies support such regional initiatives, State approaches traditionally follow a top down approach, with reliance upon 'expert knowledge' within final decision making. The Landcare model offers an alternative from this method of decision making, by recognising the contributions of rural residents. Consequently, the focus of this chapter is upon both the success of Landcare at addressing environmental issues, as well as the contributions of Landcare as a model for including the local rural community within community development.

Landcare in Australia

Landcare arose in Victoria throughout the 1980s through the formation of local community groups, and has since further evolved to include more rural communities and Landcare groups throughout Australia, making the 1990s the so-called 'Decade of Landcare'. Landcare groups involve voluntary groups of people, mainly comprised of land users in rural areas, whose primary objectives have been to tackle land degradation and develop more sustainable land management practices. The word Landcare has now been adopted by many agency, industry, academic and community initiatives and means much more than voluntary community groups.

The Landcare model has been claimed as a success by many politicians, governments, rural industries and community members. That over 2,000 Landcare Groups have formed in the last five years, with approximately 30 percent of farmers throughout Australia members, is provided as proof of this success. Yet the distribution of farmers involved in Landcare across Australia is not even. For example, observation of more than 200 Landcare Groups in Queensland suggests a more sober and critical evaluation of Landcare is needed. In many regions less than 5 percent of farmer/graziers are members of Landcare Groups.

Although Landcare is not adopted evenly by farmers throughout Australia, common problems faced by agricultural producers as a consequence of global agri-food restructuring indicates that the adoption of such a model may alleviate some of these problems. Problems faced by farmers as a consequence of current restructuring have included increased global competition and the cost price squeeze, leading to a reduction in the number of farms in many rural areas. Decreases in rural population have had significant effects on the availability of amenities and services for rural communities. Share *et al.,* (1993) claim that in relation to wealth distribution and the availability of social services, those living in communities of under 10,000 face considerable disadvantage, while those in towns with populations below 5,000 face extreme disadvantage. Could the Landcare model help to address issues of community decline and social disadvantage? To answer this question it is necessary to look at the broader issues facing rural communities, and the ability of communities to facilitate a Landcare group.

Constraints to the community Landcare model, such as leadership, equity in decision making, and power struggles within communities are issues that must be considered when considering the ability of communities to adopt the Landcare model. The pool from which a community can draw leaders who can orchestrate unity within such mixed communities differs between traditional agricultural rural areas participating in contract arrangements, to the strong growth communities along the east coast.

Policy constraints to rural community development in Australia

In conjunction with the variety of experiences within communities, the lack of an appropriate policy framework from which to work may also serve to constrain the effectiveness of a Landcare model for community development. It can be debated as to whether Australia needs a coherent, explicit and comprehensive, community-orientated rural development policy or not (Sher and Sher, 1994). If the priority issue is purely ecological restoration of the rural landscape, then policies that support changes in land use, such as further rationalisation of farming on marginal rural land may address this. If maintaining or increasing rural populations is given a higher priority, then a different mix of policies would be needed. Where there is more conflict over land use, the emphasis shifts from rural development to managing growth. State policies do not clearly deal with this issue.

Sher and Sher's (1994) critique of Australia's policy direction for rural Australia calls for - as a starting point, - 'an explicit, powerful, and comprehensive policy, rather than continuing to rely on its odd amalgam of industry policies'. They argue that Australia's present policy position illustrates a clear bias towards urban issues. In addition, Sher and Sher suggest that contemporary policy also fails to recognise the diversity located in rural areas. Why Australian rural policy makers have chosen to rely on industrial and social policies as opposed to specific rural policies, seems to be associated with a belief that having a *rural* policy would lead policy makers and the broader community to assume rural Australia is catered for, rather than trying to make all existing policies appropriate to both urban and rural people (DPIE, pers comm).

Rather than a uniform policy, rural Australia has experienced government intervention in a variety of forms, including industry support policies and subsidies, government supplied incomes for individuals, and social policies and programs. Sher and Sher (1994) argue that an example of the inequalities within current policies affecting rural communities is seen in Australia's Rural Adjustment Scheme (RAS), which has been designed to respond pragmatically to those hardest hit by Australia's continuing rural crisis. Many are not farmers, but small businesspeople - and are not included in RAS support schemes. Sher and Sher (1994) also point out the peculiar blindness and injustice of government policies and programs based on the misconception that assisting the nation's rural population can be accomplished solely by aiding Australia's farmers. This is especially so when no more than 17 percent of rural Australians are farmers.

According to Campbell (1995), political decision making within Australia, particularly when related to environmental issues, is heavily directed by the political clout of (neo-classical) economists. Such a perspective utilises limited evaluative tools and simplistic prescriptions. Consequently, if Australia is to adopt a successful rural policy, there is a need for a new vision or visions. Rural dwellers and others need to fully understand the federal government's choice of industrial and social policies as opposed to an all encompassing coherent rural development policy. They need to determine for themselves which policy direction will assist them in achieving their visions for rural Australia.

It must be noted that the former Labor government's support for regional development initiatives did not necessarily advantage smaller rural communities. At a state level, as agents of federal government policies, and with their own similar choice for industrial and social rather than specific comprehensive rural polices, specific support for rural community development type policies are at best, *ad hoc* arrangements. For example, while both federal and state governments have programs, such as future search, rural partnership and agribusiness support (which assist in the development of new initiatives and industries) funding and support is still extremely small in comparison to those given to other production-related and conservation-related programs. However, the extent to which some sections of rural communities can access public resources by integrating more entrepreneurial type activities into these existing programs is an issue for the research, to be discussed later.

Action research as a method to achieve rural community development

Action research is the methodological approach adopted within this study in order to contribute towards rural community development. This approach is not new, and using it as a vehicle for change in communities has been both used and documented for some decades. According to Dick (1995) action research is a cyclic process directed at achieving two sets of outcomes: *action* in the form of change and *research* in the form of understanding. It is often participative and should always be critically reflective. Some action research pursues action as a first priority, while others emphasise the research component. At its best, both action and research should enhance each other.

Action research aims not only to discover facts, but also to help in altering certain conditions experienced by the community as unsatisfactory. The relevance for community development is not so much the theoretical orientation or the research technique, but the peculiar relationship between research and action within an on-going community that is relevant (see Voth in Blakely, 1979).

Some principles for action research (see Voth, 1979; 1989) have been listed as follows:

1 The problem for research should stem from a recognised community need rather than (an) hypothesis generated from the personal interest of the research specialist.
2 For maximum effectiveness, those who are expected to implement the recommendations should participate in the study process.
3 Action research in community planning implies teamwork among researchers, other professionals, technicians, and lay citizenry.
4 The motivations for action research effect the nature of the research as well as its utilisation.
5 An action research project should result in recommendations for actions or social change.

According to Voth (in Blakely, 1979) significant elements of the community are intimately involved in the research process, and the research is performed to inform and enlighten the community and to stimulate some kind of action program on the part of the community.

241

Voth emphasises that action research is about a relationship between a community/organisation and sponsored community development practitioners with the community/organisation defining the problems and acting on the information provided by the research. Theoretically this sounds possible, however in practice it is difficult to achieve without a mixed representative group becoming political in nature.

Some authors make distinctions between what is and what is not action research, describing the 'self-study' style of community development as action research, since research is one of the many techniques used - together with public meetings, use of media, and various kinds of committees - in achieving community development. On the other hand, impact evaluation is not necessarily action research, since it attempts to stand outside the community development process in order to observe, analyse, and evaluate that process.

Some authors, like Wadsworth (1993), strongly advocate *participatory* action research, while others claim that action research is *collective* self-reflective inquiry and that the approach is only action research when it is *collaborative*. Dick (1995) sees participation and action research as separate methodological tools. While the two methods can be used together, participation is not an essential element of action research. The methodology for this research entails a number of aspects that make it participatory. It draws from principles inherent in participation and democratic theory which promote concepts such as self-government being better than good government. Lewin highlights the importance of group and individuals actions being subject to critical reflection, which then prepares the way for the next phase of planning. Lewin recognises the need for action plans to be flexible and responsive to the real world. Wadsworth (1993) suggests such critical reflection should include the historical, political, cultural, economic and geographic issues.

Wadsworth states that such research may change shape and focus over time (and sometimes quite unexpectedly) as participants focus and refocus their understandings. As Dick (1995) argues, each cycle of critical reflection continually focuses the questions which lead to pursuing a deeper understanding. These are crucial parts of the methodology and ample flexibility is designed into the research process for this to occur. This allows a freedom that more rigid methodologies do not allow. As Wadsworth (1993) remarks, change does not happen at the end - it happens throughout.

These perspectives on action research and their application to community development have been documented since the 1940s. Yet, it would seem nearly 50 years later, very little action research is used to achieve rural community development in Australia. Practitioners apply action research methods to welfare and health issues, corporate and government consultancies in urban settings, others may apply action research principles within their work with rural individuals, groups and sections of communities. Little is documented about applying such methodologies to complex rural issues, including issues that combine delicate internal community issues with macro-structural issues. It is within this area, that my research is based. The main aim in the research is to determine whether the Landcare group model of rural community development

(RCD) could or should include a broader range of social, economic and ecological issues. Hopefully, this focus will contribute to a better understanding of the enabling and constraining factors for rural communities to develop sustainably.

Research methodology

My strategy for answering the question above includes a number of aspects. Data will come form various sources. The literature on rural community development will be a source of 'data'. This will be used as a basis for comparison with the field work. Field work in the form of an action research project which engages three rural communities in a process towards RCD will then occur - providing other sources of data. A variety of mechanisms to facilitate critical review will provide different methods to interpret data. Convergent interviewing is another source of data. As part of the critical reflection process, data from these interviews are being fed back to the interviewees for clarification and discussion. These different forms of data collection, literature review, convergent interviews, focus groups, and semi structured interviews, provide opportunity to triangulate the data.

Each new action cycle gives another opportunity to challenge the data and interpretations of the previous cycle. This way rigour is built into process - the more cycles and the more challenges, the more assurance that the results are valid (Dick, 1995).

The aim of this action research is to assist parts of three communities in achieving specific RCD objectives and provide a forum to trial this methodology. In turn, this should increase understanding about its effectiveness, its possible use elsewhere, and contribute to theory development. Another aspect entails providing recommendations to the sponsors of the project, federal and state primary industries departments.

There are three co-researchers, one in each of the three areas. Within the research, participation is occurring along a continuum from informants to co-researcher. Each of the three co-researchers is essentially at a different point along this continuum. Therefore, part of the process involves a continual redefining of the role they would prefer to take along this continuum.

Critical reflection phases are built into the research process. As principle researcher, I use a number of techniques to assist the reference groups reflect on their actions. I continuously reflect on my actions including the appropriateness of the methodology and on what is happening in the research. Writing a personal journal also aids in critical reflection. This way evaluation is done as part of each action research cycle. This contributes to theory development in addition to the writing of the project assessment.

A critical part of the project methodology, consistent with action research principles, is to set up a process where by the co-researchers, can:

1 guide the actual direction of the project. (Deliberately, there are more community members than government personnel in the reference group.)
2 determine what processes will be used to involve their 'community'
3 increase the potential benefit, by harnessing local knowledge, networks and skills of committed rural community development practitioners
4 learn from the other communities involved in the project
5 learn, through the field work, discussion of theory and planned critical reflection, about community development action research
6 Decide at what level they want to participate in the research.

Apart from one or two co-researchers from each community, two members of the reference group are from two state departments with a major rural/industry focus, and the principal researcher. This group is responsible for the overall direction of the project. They are appropriate participants as they can, in some ways, enable or prevent the desired change at a community level. Action research and group process techniques are used by the reference group to manage the project and better to understand the opportunities for this type of methodology.

As the critical reference group is the place where roles, responsibilities and rewards are negotiated between researcher and clients, and flexibility in the research is determined by the flexibility in the relationship between researcher and client (Dick, 1995). This forum plays a key role in the research. After one year of the field work, it is appropriate to review many of the processes put in place, the focus of the research and who should be involved.

By deciding how, when, and which activities will take place in each community, the reference group members' intervention ('meddling') becomes a key part of the strategy within the methodology. The action in each community will provide the field work component of the thesis, a forum for issues to be identified and addressed and an opportunity to increase understanding and research findings.

As a reference group of people chosen to speak for a number of larger groups the co-researchers provide indirect consultation. The degree to which the communities they represent can directly participate through their representatives is an important issue to consider within the overall study.

Case study profiles

The research works with two communities which have established Landcare groups, as well as a community which has not formed a group. They are three very different types of rural settlements (communities).

Noosa and District Landcare Group; Sunshine Coast Hinterland, Queensland

This five year old incorporated non-government organisation is based within the rapidly growing Sunshine Coast hinterland. Here, rural community development is mainly concerned with *managing* growth. This area is typical of a number of rural communities around Australia's coastal hinterland and some other rural towns that have attracted a newer breed of rural inhabitants - often previous urban dwellers who have moved to rural areas for perceived quality of life reasons. They bring new resources, skills, capital, time, attitudes, values, and political and other affiliations to bear on local problems. These people can either compete with and in some cases dominate the more traditional values and power structures, or decide to operate as an independent group.

The Noosa Landcare Group is an example of the trend toward group interdependence. It comprises a mixture of people, mainly recently-arrived rural inhabitants. Out of a financial membership of over 300, about 30 are active volunteers. The group has completed many successful projects over their five year history. Throughout this time they have developed credibility and a reputation as being motivated and professional in enacting policy change.

Of particular interest to this research project is the Noosa Landcare group's work on a farm forestry project. One of the main constraints this group has identified to commercial investment in farm forestry has been economic and policy-related. Within this case study growth management, not economic development, is the critical issue. The groups' persistent endeavours to initiate a farm forestry industry validates this. This case studies critical reflection process has helped highlight this for the group's leadership.

The group's various and long standing working relationship with the three levels of government has highlighted to the group each level's special interest in farm forestry. The Commonwealth Government has generally been supportive, especially through funding projects. Its particular interest has been to facilitate the establishment of alternate wood and fibre supplies, while forcing the proponents of the industrial forestry model (those logging native forests) to restructure. Here the Noosa Landcare group's preliminary research, grass roots support and demonstrated successful completion of numerous projects resulted in their being one of five pilot projects across Australia, funded under an interdepartmental federal government project comprising property planning, plantation establishment and labour market components.

The State government, with its constitutional responsibility for land management, has surprisingly been somewhat less than fully supportive of this community group's eagerness to take a lead role in what has always been their domain - that of promoting forestry. The group claims that a close relationship between the State department of forestry and the forestry industry has hindered the investment in farm (community) forestry. Examples include policies of the state to rural rating incentives for farm foresters, the saw milling licensing act, low log royalties, and contracts given to machinery operators with poor regard to farm planning principles - to name a few.

Upper Boyne Landcare Group, Durong South Burnett Region, Queensland

The Durong community staddles the Great Dividing Range, four hours north west of Brisbane. Here, some members of the Upper Boyne Landcare Group are in the Murray-Darling Catchment, whereas others are in the eastern seaboard (the Boyne and Burnett River Catchments). This community is predominantly agriculturally based, with cattle grazing and some grain cropping, with occasional opportunity cropping. The area used to be called the Big Scrub, due to the distinctive soil and vegetation that grows there. Administratively, they form part of the western section of the Wondai Shire. Yet socially they form their own distinct community, being one hour's drive from towns such as Dalby, Chinchilla or Kingaroy.

The sparsely populated area has been in decline for a number of years. Current cattle prices and a prolonged drought have made financial circumstances particularly difficult for those engaged in agriculture: there have been few, alternative, sources of income.

Several public meetings including a search workshop, resulted in a number of landowners (14 out of 16 attending being women) agreeing to pursue an Export Marketing Skills Program with the DPI, as a way of addressing their dissatisfaction with the low returns they receive on their beef. A search workshop identified, in order of priority, beef marketing, access to water, utilising waste timber products, marketing, flowers, herbs and spices, tourism, landscape supplies and aquaculture as potentially new enterprises for the local community. Other enterprises in order of priority were, a plant nursery, sport facilities, grain marketing, wool and kangaroo products. A decision was made by those at the workshop to focus on gaining skills in beef and horticulture marketing. After preliminary research beef marketing was the preferred option. From an state agency perspective this 'project' has been consumed into a broader regional project with other groups of graziers on the Darling Downs.

Also, as part of a push for quality produce, the co-researcher in the district organised a nutrition workshop for local cattle producers, which attracted about 40 people. At the time of writing it does not appear that the others issues identified at the search workshop have been acted upon. A focus on the 'economic' at the expense of social issues may well indicate the degree of urgency which project participants feel at present, which may be preventing them from addressing others issues at this time.

That the State government's response to the community's concern for low meat prices - to develop skills of locals in export marketing - is consistent with its desire to encourage primary producers to compete globally. According to Sher and Sher (1994: 19) this policy direction is based on the judgement:

> that the future will belong to those who are clever, flexible, well-researched strategically-placed, vertically integrated, aggressive and market orientated enough to deliver top quality, competitively priced, value-added primary products to increasingly demanding and disloyal customers around the world.

So far, all local participants in this case study are from within the traditional agricultural section of the community, and they have decided to focus the attention of the project on the economic side of that same primary production.

A number of issues emerge from this. First, there is a small, but growing, separate community not dependent on farming on small acreage in the Durong area which has not been involved in this project to date. Second, while a number of new enterprises in viticulture, tourism, flowers, herb and spices, aquaculture are occurring in the broader South Burnett, lack of time, funding, water, distance from markets, and the volumes of production needed, appear to be retarding these new developments. Third, different people within the group have different needs, have different amounts of access to support services, and to markets and communication facilities.

Finally, a lack of local leadership skills was perceived by the group as a community development issue. This has resulted in endeavours by the State government to investigate the establishment of a short leadership course for group members.

These issues identified make rural community development, with or without the Landcare model, difficult. The action research component of the project at this stage only been in conjunction with the reference group, not the broader community. Here critical reflection is assisting the reference group's understanding and action. Whether that benefit is passed onto the broader community is a matter for further research.

Eidsvold Community, North Burnett Region, Queensland

This case study focuses on the whole of the Eidsvold Shire, some 265 kilometres west of Fraser Island, within the Burnett and Fitzroy Catchments. Eidsvold Shire has traditionally relied upon the pastoral and forestry industries. Like many inland primary industry-focused communities it has experienced steady decline over the past few decades due to terms of trade decline in agriculture. Yet, an unusual recent trend has seen an increase in the town's Aboriginal population - one not linked to primary industry.

The two co-researchers' choice of processes for giving members of this Shire an opportunity to be involved in this project has been through a representative structure (writing letters formally to key interest groups). Over twelve months, this has included working within the community to facilitate meetings with members of Council, the Chamber of Commerce, the timber and grazing industries, the Aboriginal community, the youth group and the Kindergarten Society.

Issues emerging from these discussions include support for the Council's plan for a cattle abattoir, hopes for a Burnett River dam, community desires for a kindergarten, a swimming pool and for new employment opportunities - to name a few. The project has established links with some members of the Ghoondoo Women's Group, through the Eidsvold Kindergarten Association. There is also a large proportion of the indigenous community that are not involved in the project. According to Quixley (1992), it is important for Aboriginal communities and organisations to be given sufficient time to develop a position relating to involvement with projects of the sort initiated here.

Other government-initiated processes currently affecting Eidsvold's interests are (for primary producers) grants available under the Drought Landcare Program; and the forest reserve system process, which may result in the closure of a timber mill. Consultation on tree clearing guidelines is also under way. A series of Regional Economic Development Organisations (REDOs) which were being established around Australia concerned Eidsvold's Mayor. He stated that 'the competing interests of the different regions lumped into a single REDO would be counter productive to equitable decision making'. Of course, now that the Howard government has announced that the REDOs will no longer be funded, such a concern may no longer be warranted.

Conclusion

Preliminary research suggests a variety of RCD models exist in Australia. Structures within rural communities such as Landcare, are demonstrating innovative methods to address current land management issues. As such, Landcare is a form of rural community development. One of Landcare's greatest strengths is its diversity in social make up. Diversity and flexibility in models is critical to any attempt to broaden the Landcare model.

In relation to the needs of young people in rural and remote Australia Quixley (1992), suggests service deliverers, rural communities and policy makers alike would be pleased to be presented with a collection of 'favourite recipes' to improve services. But to suggest that an effective service model in one rural community can be transplanted to another would be as potentially disastrous as wholesale transplantation of urban models to rural communities. The same may be said of the transferring of Landcare (with its emphasis on the environment) to rural communities (which have much wider concerns).

The extent to which broader, dominant, external trends are acknowledged and factored into rural community development processes, like these case studies, also influence communities sustainability.

Regardless of the model and constraints from outside, other issues will continue to influence the sustainability of rural communities. These include the presence of traditionally marginalised groups, processes of political democracy, and 'paradigm gridlock' (see Hyman, 1994) - where people can only see one version of 'reality'.

References

Blakely E. (1979) *Community Development Research*, London, Human Science Press.

Campbell. A. (1995) Landcare - Greenfields for Green Economics, *Inaugural Conference of the Australian and New Zealand Society for Ecological Economics*, Coffs Harbour.

Dick, B. (1995) *You Want to do an Action Research Thesis?* Brisbane, Interchange.

Fitchen J. (1991) *Endangered Spaces, Enduring Places - Change: Identity, and Survival in Rural America,* Boulder, Westview Press.

Hyman, D. (1994) Towards a Quality of Life Paradigm for Sustainable Communities, in McSwan, D. and McShane, R. (eds) *Issues Affecting Rural Communities,* Townsville, Rural Education Research and Development Centre.

Kenny, S. (1994) *Developing Communities for the Future: Community Development in Australia,* Melbourne, Nelson.

Quixley, S. (1992) *Living, Learning and Working: The Experiences of Young People in Rural and Remote Communities in Australia,* Canberra, The National Youth Coalition for Housing.

Share, P., Lawrence, G. and Gray, I. (1993) Rural Australia, in Najman, J. and Western, J.(eds) *A Sociology of Australian Society,* Melbourne, Macmillan.

Sher, J. and Sher, K. (1994) Beyond the Conventional Wisdom: Rural Development as if Australia's Rural People and Communities Really Mattered, *Journal of Research in Rural Education* 10, 1: 2-43.

Voth. D. (1979) Social Action Research in Community Development in Blakely, E. (ed.) (1979) *Community Development Research,* London, Human Science Press.

Voth. D. (1989) Evaluation in Community Development. Christenson, J. and Robinson J. (eds) *Community Development in Perspective,* Ames, Iowa State University Press.

Wadsworth, Y. (1993) *What is Participatory Action Research?* Melbourne, Action Research Issues Association.

Chapter 19

Imperative, challenging and diverse: The contributions that rural based social research can make to the development of sociology and social policy in contemporary Australia

Ruth Liepins

Introduction

As an increasing number of research organisations and projects are operating in rural Australia, it is timely to ask at least one question: What contribution can rural based social research make to the development of sociology and social policy in contemporary Australia? I would argue that our contributions through this type of research are imperative, challenging and diverse. They are imperative particularly at a time of both continuing economic rationalisation and new forms of communication and information technology. Economic policies and communication technologies form major challenges and opportunities for many rural communities but the important social components of rural Australia can be guarded through careful research so that they are not forgotten in the face of economic indicators and surfing on the internet. Likewise, our contributions in social research are challenging and we should strive to ensure this continues since the urban dominance of academic thought and policy development requires vigorous commentary and alternative contributions from the rural community. And finally, our contributions are diverse and we should aim to increase their diversity as the nature of contemporary Australia and the critique of social sciences shows the need for greater attention to the diversity of social groups, experiences and agendas that must be recognised.

To demonstrate the character and importance of rural based social research in Australia this paper is organised in three sections. First, a review is made of the types of organisations that are contributing to rural based social research.

Second, a sample of themes are sketched from the range of research being conducted. This sample demonstrates contributions made to the broader development of sociology and social policy. The third part of this discussion then analyses three specific examples of research. These cases present contrasting methods of research and different contributions to either sociology or social policy.

The range of both contemporary rural research projects and issues for policy and sociology are enormous. This brief review, however, is confined to a selection of topics that are pertinent to undergraduate sociology and rural sociology courses. Specifically, these topics are listed in Table 1.

Table 1
Selected topics of relevance to sociology and rural sociology units:
Australian Society, Rural Sociology and Contemporary Social Issues.

Topics	Degree of attention given in this paper
Australian Society	
the changing role of women	••
Aboriginal Australia	•
reading Australian culture	•
social implications of Australia's integration into the Asia-Pacific region	•
Contemporary Social Issues	
environmental movement	••
feminism	••
criminal justice	•
education	•
Rural Sociology	
rurality	•
rural restructuring in the global system	••
rural social conditions	•
sociology of contemporary agriculture	••
ecological and social sustainability	••

Table based on components of units taught at Central Queensland University 1996.

So, to reiterate, these particular issues are the ones I have selected to demonstrate whilst arguing that rural based social research is imperative, and must continue to be challenging and diverse. In this way I have identified rural based social research with the description De Haan has made of rural sociology:

> (It) is not an autonomous academic affair. The direction it takes, the theories it adopts and the empirical questions it studies are interlinked with the wider political and ideological climate and with concrete economic and social developments (De Haan, 1993: 130)

Part 1: Organisations producing rural based social research

Research organisations constitute part of the 'climate' in which De Haan identifies rural sociology. The following discussion outlines some of the organisations producing Australian rural based social research. This is an important contextual review to make from time to time since the environment in which the research is supported will have both procedural and substantive consequences.

Australian sources of rural based social research are diverse. Table 2 illustrates a sample of the types of organisations that are completing such work. This is not compiled as an exhaustive list, however, the table reminds us of both academic and other sources of rural social research.

Table 2
Organisations contributing to rural based social research:
A sample of Australian sources

Organisation	Selected rural social research interests
Centre for Social Research, Northern Territory University, Darwin	• criminal justice • Aboriginal health • military families
North Australia Research Unit, Australian National University, Darwin	• economic development and social equity, • quality of community life • environmental management and planning
Co-operative Research Centre for the Sustainable Development of Tropical Savannas, based at Northern Territory University, Darwin	• socio-cultural and resource valuation of tropical savannas • social decision making and adoption of sustainable development practices
Rural Social and Economic Research Centre, Central Queensland University, Rockhampton	• community development • agri-food restructuring • rural health and welfare • heritage, culture and environment
Centre for Rural Social Research, Charles Sturt University-Riverina, Wagga Wagga	• rural social conditions • human services delivery • social aspects of agriculture, environment and sustainability • technology transfer
Australian Bureau of Agricultural and Resource Economics, Canberra	• social issues for rural centres, rural families and rural women
Ballarat University Student Association, Ballarat	• access and social contexts for rural students education
Australian Centre, University of Melbourne, Parkville	• multiculturalism and cultural diversity • rural communities and sustainability
Dairy Research and Development Corporation, Glen Iris	• community and regional development during industry adjustment • social aspects of technology transfer

The organisations are listed by geographic location moving north to south. Alongside the university based unit's and centres the example of a cooperative research centre is shown at Darwin[1] which enables the collaboration of a far greater number of researchers and resources.

In contrast to these academic organisations three examples of other sources of rural social research are also included. First, the Australian Bureau of Agricultural and Resource Economics, as a government body, is primarily driven by an economic and industry focus. In 1994, however, the agricultural surveys[2] included a supplementary survey concerning social issues.[3] Second, the Ballarat University Student Association is modelling a form of social research that could be adopted effectively by many rural institutions. The Association has employed a full time researcher, who is a sociologist, and her work involves practical projects which are either of direct relevance to the association or are tendered for by the association.[4] The feature I wish to note from this arrangement is the proactive relationship it provides between the profession of sociology and the students and graduates who may gain research experience in the process (pers. comm. L. Dietrich, 1995). The third example included outside the academic environment is an industry research corporation, in this case, the Dairy Research and Development Corporation. This particular body has recently expanded an interest in community and regional development since reflecting upon the effectiveness of technology transfer and industry adjustment measures (University of Western Sydney 1994, and pers. comm. J. Craven, 1995). Each of these examples relate directly to a community, social or education issue in contemporary sociology units (return to Table 1).

From Table 2 it can be seen that each of these selected organisations is completing work which is in some way relevant to the issues I have chosen to focus upon. For example, the Darwin-based cooperative research centre is investigating social and cultural issues of valuation and decision making for sustainable development. This work is complimentary to the topics of rural restructuring and ecological and social sustainability identified in Table 1. It exemplifies some of the issues in sociology units including Aboriginal Australia, Australian culture, and ecological and social sustainability. Alternatively, the Australian Centre is developing projects on cultural diversity and rural sustainability which also inform sociological issues of Australian culture and community that are of direct relevance to sociology courses.

This first section has provided a brief overview of the type of organisations which are contributing rural based social research. I have confined my comments thus far to examples of work which compliment and inform the sociological issues selected for Table 1.

Part 2: Types of rural based social research

Rural based social research is as diverse as any other field, however at least four themes can be identified in such research, each of which contribute to developments in sociology and social policy developments. Table 3 summarises these issues. It documents the issue followed by an example of relevant rural research and a brief note on some of the sociological and social policy agendas being addressed.

Table 3
Examples of rural based social research and its relevance to broader agendas of sociology and social policy

General Issue	Example of Rural Research	Sociology Agenda/s	Policy Agenda/s
1 Cultural Diversity	Centre for Rural Social Research and Yamin and Associates, (1995) *A Program for Partnership*, Canberra, Office of Multicultural Affairs	• Cultural diversity • Needs analysis	• Human Services Delivery • Rural cultural diversity
2 Environmental Sustainability	A. Curtis, P. Davidson and C. McGowan, 1994 *Women's participation and experience of landcare in north east Victoria*	• Environmental organisation • Gender studies	• Landcare
3 Agricultural Adjustment	R. Stayner, and J. Gow 1992 *A review of the process of farm adjustment in Australia* I. Gray, G. Lawrence and T. Dunn, 1993 *Coping with change*	• Sociology of family farming • Political economy of agriculture	• Rural Adjustment • Rural Community Affairs
4 Rural Identity and Sustainability	M. Maklin, 1994 *Local media and gender relations in a rural community* R. Liepins, forthcoming '*Women of broad vision': The* women in agriculture *movement and its use of environmental discourse to promote rural sustainability*	• Discursive construction of knowledge • Gender relations • Sustainability • Discourses in agricultural politics	• Status and portrayal of women in the media • Rural sustainability • Community affairs and service provision

Cultural diversity

Cultural diversity as the first issue, has become increasingly important in both government policy and the general scope of sociology. See for example works published through *The Australian and New Zealand Journal of Sociology* including Stevens' (1993) work on Cambodian young people in South Australia, and Vasta's (1993) and Goot's (1993) analyses of multiculturalism. Current rural studies that contribute to these general debates include the analysis of needs for aged care investigated by the Centre for Rural Social Research. In this case, social inquiry is illustrating the different demographic and cultural requirements of rural communities with aged persons from non-English speaking backgrounds; that is, social analysis of culturally appropriate services must not assume urban models will be effective (pers. comm. M. Alston, September 1995). Moreover, the report submitted to the Department of

Immigration and Ethnic Affairs is of direct policy importance in its presentation of rural-specific needs analysis for the delivery of aged care services.

Environmental sustainability

Studies of environmentalism and social movements are a second pair of issues that have become increasingly topical in sociology. See for example Crook *et.al.*, (1992) and Burgmann (1993) on environmental movements. Environmental issues have also influenced federal agricultural policy (Australian Agricultural Council, 1991 and the continuing National Landcare Progam) to which rural based social research has much to contribute. The Johnstone Centre of Parks, Recreation and Heritage report (Curtis *et.al.*, 1994) on women and Landcare is an example of rural studies which inform not only the sociology of environmental values but also the gender relations that operate in environmental organisations. Work of this kind is also important at a policy level as Landcare programs are evaluated (see Curtis *et.al.*, 1993). The women and Landcare example is a specific project based report however the broad range of studies now being funded and published[5] suggest that social research should continue to be supported if environmentally sustainable development is to be effectively pursued. Australian studies of this kind can also learn from and contribute to international considerations of agriculture and environment linked policy (eg. Liepins, forthcoming, and Frouws and Tatenhove, 1993).

Agricultural adjustment

Agricultural adjustment is a third issue demonstrating the contribution rural social research can make to sociology and social policy. There is now an extensive literature on agricultural adjustment both in Australia and internationally. The Australian reports by Stayner and Gow (1992) and by Gray, Lawrence and Dunn (1993) are recent examples of this work and compliment the wider economic commentary that sociologists can provide on Australia's place in regional and global economies. A good example of this broader analysis is found in the Trend Report on 'Corporate Power in the Pacific Rim' published last year in *Current Sociology* (Murray, 1995). The importance of studies on the social impact of agricultural adjustment must be further stressed, however, with even greater links made to government researchers and policy makers, since leaders in these areas continue to avoid the *social implications* of their economic terms. The Director of ABARE's continuing predictions of 'severe adjustment pressures' are a case in point (see Fisher, 1995).

Rural identity and sustainability

Contrasting but mutually informing studies of rurality, identity and rural sustainability make up a fourth set of issues I wish to note. International writings on rural discourses (Jones, 1995), sustainability (Gale and Cordray, 1994) and rural policy (Wimberley, 1993) contribute to wider social theory on identity and discourse and general concerns regarding sustainability and policy development. The discursive construction of rural Australia is an underdeveloped area of research although Macklin (1994) for example has provided a media analysis of gender relations in rural community.

In regard to rural sustainability, Wimberley has argued that agricultural policy has been an inadequate substitute for rural policy and this is a point that has been equally demonstrated in Australia by Lawrence and Share (1993). My own research into the W*omen in Agriculture* movement suggests that women wish to extend public and political attention beyond concerns for economic and environmental viability in agriculture to those of rural community sustainability (Liepins, forthcoming). Rural based social research has a strong part to play in arguing for and supporting rural policy. In Queensland the Office of Rural Communities is an obvious policy development partner for researchers working on issues beyond primary industries. In one case, the office has consulted Dr Tony Sorenson on issues of community leadership in regional development (pers. comm. L. Dally, 1995). The recent regular review process which the Office has undergone has recommended a greater research emphasis and this will support not only program and service planning but the Rural Communities Impact Statements that are developed for Cabinet Submissions.

The preceding four themes have attempted to sketch out some of the diversity of rural social research. The projects that are completed within these themes compliment both directions in the wider discipline of sociology, and the immediate policy concerns of various Australian government bodies. The ways these contributions are made will vary according to topic, method and audience of research, and it is these differences which are address in the final part of this paper.

Part 3: Examples of the contribution of rural based social research

To explore the types of contributions made by rural social research I have chosen to discuss three practical examples. In reviewing these projects I will briefly sketch out the background of the research since this often establishes the potential contribution that will be made to either sociology or social policy. Second, I will review the approach to the study and the methodologies used since I wish to demonstrate the appropriateness of a range of approaches; and finally, I will note a selection of implications and contributions the studies make to either or both sociology or social policy.

Example 1: 'Coping with Change: Australian Farmers in the 1990s'

For the first example I wish to return to the report by Gray, Lawrence and Dunn (1993), entitled *Coping with Change: Australian Farmers in the 1990s*. The contextual background of the report is important in showing a model of collaborative or team research within one institution, namely the Charles Sturt Centre for Rural Social Research. It is also important to note that the study was supported by the Rural Industries Research and Development Corporation.

The approach to the study was specified as *applying qualitative and quantitative methods of social science* (Gray et. al., 1993:1) and was primarily developed through an interview and questionnaire process with 245 people from 106 farms drawn from four contrasting areas along the eastern States of Australia. Farmer organisations provided advice in establishing the samples while a number of interviewers were employed to complete the research. Data were collected through the extensive five-part instrument. This predominantly used closed and neatly structured questions to enable a range of statistical analyses to be completed later in the project. These methods were employed to gain a statistically valid profile of the coping strategies of farm people which might then inform future policies and programs concerned with economic and social change in Australian agriculture.

The approach to this project has been interdependent with the implications and consequences of the research. In the current context of federal rural adjustment management the methods of the project have been important for what Asad has called the 'strong language' of statistics which is employed as 'a tool of social intervention' (1994: 76-78). Without the data displayed as they are in this report, the importance of the findings would be lost in many policy arenas.

Following the passage of the report back through the Rural Industries Research and Development Corporation has proved insightful. The implications of the report were recognised by the Corporation and circulated widely to the relevant industry organisations, farmer federations and federal government sections dealing with rural adjustment and agricultural change (pers. comm. K. Hide, 27 September 1995). One such organisation included the Dairy Research and Development Corporation. While the study itself was not vividly remembered, the corporation has noted the wider social and community research environment in which it now operates. An indirect consequence of these circumstances has involved what I earlier noted as the Corporation's recent expansion into studies of community and regional planning which compliment their more traditional technical programs (pers. comm. J. Craven, 28 September 1995).

The New South Wales Farmers' Organisation was a second source of information on the consequences of the *Coping with Change* report. Happily, the report was noted as part of the justification for establishing a Community Affairs and Services Committee. In this way many of the social issues of the report could be addressed and developed into NSW Farmers' policy. The committee was fortuitously established in time to respond to the drought and has now gone on to address some of wider issues of education and appropriate adjustment services which were identified in the report (pers. comm. V. Sinderberry, 1995).

Inquiring about the report through the Department of Primary Industries and Energy was an interesting 'ping pong' activity. Although the study has provided a rigorous and detailed social alternative to statements of *severe adjustment pressures* from the Australian Bureau of Agricultural and Resource Economics, the Rural Policy branch referred me to the Rural Adjustment branch which then referred me back to the Rural Policy branch. The policy branch staff recalled the report and acknowledged that social and cultural factors discussed in the study were important to adjustment decisions, although the Rural Adjustment Scheme has until recently focused on economic considerations (pers. comm. N. Lippert and N. Kirk, 1995). Most importantly perhaps, the Rural Adjustment Scheme staff member stated the importance of the forthcoming review process and I would argue that this provides an opportunity for the ongoing commentary and challenge that social research can provide.

Example 2: 'Women in Agriculture - A Geography of Australian Agricultural Activism'

The second example of rural based social research involves my own research into the W*omen in Agriculture* movement in Australia and its impact on agricultural politics (Liepins, 1996). The context of the research has been shaped in part by the PhD process in which I have participated since, although I wished to develop a community form of participatory action research, I was also influence by the conventional ownership and responsibility of doctoral research.

The approach and methods I adopted in this research have been guided by feminist and poststructural literatures. As such the research was conducted with a commitment to social change and the recognition of women's voices and experiences. It was also conducted from a position that acknowledged the cultural and discursive contexts of agricultural knowledge and research (Kloppenburg, 1991, 1992). Rather than seeking a set of quantifiable 'truths', I was able to establish a reading of selected contexts and activities surrounding three community case studies. These readings were developed from data gained through a combination of surveys, cumulative interviews, participant questionnaires, discourse analysis and participant observation.

The implications of this research are relevant to rural sociology in three ways. First, the work demonstrates the need for theory on the agency and active and multiple identities of rural people. Second, the research suggests a Foucauldian analysis of power (Foucault, 1990) can be appropriate to understanding the webs and practices of agricultural politics. Third, the research values the discursive nature of meanings and arrangements in agriculture. This final point is important for highlighting the relevance of this study to government discourse and social policy.

During and following the fieldwork period I have been able to document the movement's activism in gaining a government review of the legal status of farm women and in agitating for a Rural Women's Unit within the Department of Primary Industries and Energy. Like the movement itself, the impact of this research has been informal and based upon a range of federal, state and community networks in which I am positioned. My early analysis of the movement has been circulated through government and W*omen in Agriculture* networks as well as conventional academic forums. In a more concrete example, and acting as both a researcher and supporter of W*omen in Agriculture,* I have been able to contribute to the organisation of the federally funded National Rural Women's Forum which was conducted to identify policy issues relevant to rural women.

Example 3: Queensland Rural Women's Use of Communications Technologies: Implications for Information and Referral Services and for Networking Organisations

The last example of rural based social research I wish to analyse is a uniquely Queensland project which has had significant implications for State-level policy. This project is entitled *Queensland Rural Women's Use of Communications Technologies: Implications For Information and Referral Services and For Networking Organisations* and it is pertinent to recent literature on the need for a sociology of information (see Balnaves, 1993).

The contextual background of the research shows a link between industry funding and academic inquiry since the team investigators work through the Queensland University of Technology[6] but are supported by a grant from the Telecom fund for social and policy research.

The approach and methods surrounding this study form a different example of feminist and ethnographic work based upon models of Action Research and Action Learning. An important feature of the research arrangements has been the use of a reference group which includes representatives from the Queensland Women's Policy Unit, the Department of Primary Industries and the Office of Rural Communities as well as representatives from the three case studies, these being the State government Women's Infolink, the Rockhampton Women's Health Centre and the Queensland Rural Women's Network (pers. comm. M. Grace, 1995).

The reference group structure of this project has had important policy implications. The Women's Policy Unit has used this research as a basis to support their budget submission for the Women and Information Technology Strategy in the 1995-1996 Women's Policy Package (pers. comm. W. Selby, 1995). The information technology strategy aims to *increase women's access to information, training, consultative processes and leadership roles* (Queensland Government, 1995 iii). It addresses women across Queensland, however it includes a focus on the special needs of women and girls in rural and remote locations.

Conclusion

Through the preceding discussion I have argued the need for rural based social research to temper, and even challenge, the dominance of physical sciences and economics in the determination and support of contemporary rural Australia. In selecting my cases of rural based social research I have demonstrated a range of types and contexts. The examples show the important contributions such research makes to current debates in the discipline: including those concerning cultural diversity, economic adjustment, sustainability, rural identity and power.

I have also shown that there are at least three ways in which we can pursue rural based social research so that appropriate social policy is consequently developed. First, we can respond to tenders, briefs and inquiries by government (the Tropical Savanna Cooperative Research Centre and the work of Tony Sorenson illustrates this). Second, we can support and analyse the voices and strategies of rural populations (the *Coping with Change* report and my own research on W*omen in Agriculture* are examples of this work). Third, we can establish research-policy networks to encourage understanding and enhance informed policy development (the Queensland women and technology project illustrates this process).

Returning to the title of this chapter I have structured the content to show that the issues of community, sustainability, and decision making that we explore in rural based social research are imperative to the viable future of rural Australia. Similarly, as researchers the forms of investigation we choose can ensure that we challenge inequitable assumptions of dominant discourses and the excessive consideration of economic and scientific concerns. Finally, the research we design can demonstrate approaches that appropriately reflect the diversity of gender, class and ethnicity that constitute contemporary Australian society.

Notes

1   The Cooperative research centre for the sustainable development of tropical savannas is formed by the collaboration of: Northern Territory University, The Australian National University, the James Cook University of North Queensland, the Department of Conservation and Land Management (WA), the State of Queensland, the Northern Territory of Australia, the Australian Nature Conservation Agency and the Commonwealth Scientific and Industrial Research Organisation (Documents of Agreement, January 1995).

2   The two major surveys are the Australian agricultural and grazing industries surveys (AAGIS) and the Australian dairy industry survey (ADIS).

3   Principal contact and spouse were asked to select what they perceive as the most important issue affecting, rural centres, rural families and rural women from nine pre-defined categories: health and social services, educational facilities, transport, communication, rural employment opportunities, the performance of farm business and the rural sector, planning for retirement, planning for managerial succession of the property.

4   The successful tender for the evaluation of the Soil and Water Conservation Association of Australia 1995 conference is an example of this process (pers.

comm. L. Dietrich, 1995).
5   Martin *et.al.,* (1992) and Campbell (1992) and the current work of the Rural Social and Economic Research Centre's work in the sugar industry through the Sugar Research Institute and the Cooperative Research Centre for Sustainable Sugar Production.
6   Investigators are Dr Margaret Grace, Dr Leonie Daws and Dr Roy Lundun.

References

Asad, T. (1994) Ethnographic Representation, Statistics and Modern Power, *Social Research* 61, 1: 55-88.

Australian Agricultural Council. Standing Committee on Agriculture. Working Group on Sustainable Agriculture (1991) *Sustainable Agriculture: Report of the Working Group on Sustainable Agriculture,* East Melbourne, CSIRO Australia.

Balnaves, M. (1993) The Sociology of Information *The Australian and New Zealand Journal of Sociology* 29, 1: 93-111.

Burgmann, V. (1993) *Power and Protest: Movements for Change in Australian Society,* St Leonards, Allen and Unwin.

Campbell, A (1992) Farm and Catchment Planning: Tools for Sustainability? in G. Lawrence, F. Vanclay and B. Furze (eds) *Agriculture, Environment and Society: Contemporary Issues for Australia,* Melbourne, Macmillan: 224-232.

Centre for Rural Social Research and Yamin and Associates (1995) *A Program for Partnership,* Canberra: Office of Multicultural Affairs.

Crook, S., Pakulski, J. and Waters, M. (1992) *Postmodernization: Change in Advanced Society,* London, Sage.

Curtis, A, De Lacy, T. and Klomp, N. (1993) Assessing the Effectiveness of Landcare Groups: The Victorian Experience, *Regional Journal of Social Issues* 27: 78-91.

Curtis, A., Davidson, P. and McGowan, C. (1994) *Women's Participation and Experience of Landcare in North East Victoria* Johnstone Centre of Parks, Recreation and Heritage Report No. 4, Albury, Charles Sturt University.

De Haan, H. (1993) Rural Crisis and Rural Research in the Netherlands: Introduction, *Sociologia Ruralis* 33, 2: 127-136.

Fisher, B. (1995) Australian Commodities: Overview, *Australian Commodities* 2, 1: 50-55.

Foucault, M. (1990) *The History of Sexuality: Volume 1 An Introduction,* Harmondsworth, Penguin.

Frouws, J. and van Tatenhove, J. (1993) Agriculture, Environment and the State: The Development of Agro-environmental Policy Making in the Netherlands, *Sociologia Ruralis* 33, 2: 220-239.

Gale, R. and Cordray, S. (1994) Making Sense of Sustainabiltiy: Nine answers to What Should be Sustained? *Rural Sociology* 59, 2: 311-332.

Goot, M. (1993) Multiculturalists, Monoculturalists and the Many in Between: Attitudes to Cultural Diversity and their Correlates, *The Australian and New Zealand Journal of Sociology* 29, 2: 226-253.

Gray, I., Lawrence, G. and Dunn, T. (1993) *Coping with Change: Australian Farmers in the 1990s,* Wagga Wagga, Centre for Rural Social Research.

Jones, O. (1995) Lay Discourses of the Rural: Developments and Implications for Rural Studies, *Journal of Rural Studies* 11:1 35-49.

Kloppenburg, J. (1991) Social Theory and the De/reconstruction of Agricultural Science: Local Knowledge for an Alternative Agriculture, *Rural Sociology* 56 4: 519-548.

Kloppenburg, J. (1992) Science in Agriculture: A reply to Molnar, Duffy, Cummmins and Van Santen and to Flora, *Rural Sociology* 57 1: 98-107.

Lawrence, G. and Share, P. (1993) Rural Australia: Current Problems and Policy Directions, *Regional Journal of Social Issues* No. 27: 3-9.

Liepins, R. (1996) *Women in Agriculture: A Geography of Australian Agricultural Activism*, PhD thesis, University of Melbourne, Department of Geography and Environmental Studies.

Liepins, R. (forthcoming) Women of Broad Vision: The W*omen in Agriculture* Movement and its use of Environmental Discourse to Promote Rural Sustainability, in Whatmore, S., Lowe, P. and Marsden, T. (eds) *Nature's Refuge? Rethinking the Environment in Rural Studies,* London, Wiley.

Macklin, M. (1994) Local Media and Gender Relations in a Rural Community, *Rural Society* 3, 3: 2-7.

Martin, P., Tarr, S. and Lockie, S. (1992) Participatory Environmental Management in New South Wales: Policy and Practice, in Lawrence, G., Vanclay, F. and Furze, B. (eds) *Agriculture, Environment and Society: Contemporary Issues for Australia,* Melbourne, Macmillan: 184-207.

Murray, G. (ed.) (1995) Corporate Power in the Pacific Rim, *Current Sociology* 43: 1.

Queensland Government (1995) *Queensland Women: Enriching our Future: Women's Policy Package 1995-96,* Brisbane, Women's Policy Unit.

Stayner, R. and Gow, J. (1992) *A Review of the Process of Farm Adjustment in Australia,* The Rural Development Centre, Armidale, University of New England.

Stevens, C. (1993) The School to Work Transition: Young Cambodians in South Australia, *The Australian and New Zealand Journal of Sociology* 29, 2: 173-193.

University of Western Sydney, Hawkesbury (1994) *Report to Dairy Research and Development Corporation: Understanding the Dairy Industry: Knowledge, Beliefs and Values,* Hawkesbury, University of Western Sydney.

Vasta, E. (1993) Multiculturalism and Ethnic Identity: the Relationship Between Racism and Resistance, *The Australian and New Zealand Journal of Sociology* 29, 2: 209-225.

Wimberley, R. (1993) Policy Perspectives on Social, Agricultural and Rural Sustainability, *Rural Sociology* 58, 1: 1-29.

Chapter 20

Towards a social construction of drought: A preliminary analysis

Dani Stehlik
Andrea Witcomb
Geoffrey Lawrence
Ian Gray

Introduction

'It is difficult to plan for a drought, because you only know it's a drought when you are in one' (Beef producer, Kunwarara area, Queensland).

While the worst drought in white Australian history (see *Sydney Morning Herald*, 31 December, 1994: 1) will have long term economic and social costs to all Australians, there is little current research and even less literature available on what that experience has been like for many of the farm families who have lived, and are still living, through it. Anecdotal stories and media reports are the main sources of information and provide less than reliable evidence for decision making by key stakeholders. Little is known about the ways in which farmers perceive drought conditions to be emerging. This is despite the fact that the signs of being in drought are often obvious, and the point at which drought is 'declared' is specified technically. What we don't know is the point at which farmers recognise that a long drought is likely. Research needs to be conducted to establish how and when farmers recognise that climatic conditions are not normal and so alter their farm operation and plans for future operations, in response. There is no simple formula for this process. Normal conditions for some farmers may be seen as abnormal for others. Decisions about farming operations and planning are taken in the contexts of farm and community interaction in which the 'signs' are discussed and interpreted. Action arising from those interpretations may be based on local and traditional knowledge as well as on technical data.

The cost to families can be measured not only in loss of stock and depletion of resources, but also in deterioration of family cohesion, loss of community networks and a sense of hopelessness (Daly, 1994). The long term impact of the drought on the consciousness of families and on their relationships with their communities are yet to be considered. One piece of research conducted in 1992 suggested that the stakes were high as people struggled to stay on their farms (Gray, Lawrence and Dunn, 1993) however that research was undertaken without the overarching impact of a major drought.

The Rural Social and Economic Research Centre at Central Queensland University and the Centre for Rural Social Research at Charles Sturt University have commenced a two year research project, funded by the Rural Industries Research and Development Corporation and the Land and Water Resources Research and Development Corporation, to undertake a study of the recent (and still current) drought. This paper will provide a context for the research study and identify its aims and methodology. The project is designed to explore the ways in which drought is socially constructed and how such constructions influence on-farm drought strategies. In addition, the ways in which resource management strategies used by farm families were altered during the recently-experienced drought will be identified. One outcome of the research will be to establish how agricultural (and wider rural community) sustainability can be achieved in times of drought. This study will be undertaken at a time when the consequences of the drought and the decisions farming families have had to take during the drought will be uppermost in their minds, and will give the research clear immediacy and relevance.

Drought and the restructuring of agriculture

The current drought, which has affected broadly the area from the Gulf of Carpentaria in the north, to Gippsland in the south and the Eyre Peninsula to the west, has not been - as far as we are able to discern - investigated by sociologists. Located at the Rural Social and Economic Research Centre in Rockhampton and the Centre for Rural Social Research in Wagga Wagga, researchers are ideally placed to undertake a comparative analysis of the way drought has been 'experienced' in both regions. Historically, drought has not been regarded as part of a normal cycle. It has been viewed as a crisis, as an aberration, a strange quirk of nature. As a result, there is a cultural expectation that farmers and farming families will be 'bailed out' (supported by banks and by governments).

In the present drought, for example, the Federal Government has provided some $276 million in emergency relief and has enabled farmers to take out low interest loans to drought-proof their properties (*Australian*, 9 December 1994: 3). As the current drought has unfolded, Federal Government policy statements, the National Farmers' Federation and various Departments of Agriculture began to develop educational material which asked farmers to be better prepared for drought conditions. The argument used by governments and their agencies has been that droughts can, and should, be managed not only for environmental reasons but also to enable maintenance of farming communities.

A defining moment in this process of 're-education' was the former Labor Prime Ministers' statement that farmers needed to consider the drought as a normal part of their management strategy (see *Australian*, 9 December 1994: 1). Such experiences provide opportunities for a detailed policy analysis to be undertaken which would then inform strategies for the management of future droughts.

The process of change within rural communities can be viewed as a lived experience both communally, familially and individually. Traditionally, in times of natural crisis, communities and families are brought together to face adversity. Traditionally too, 'sympathies are mobilised and individuals and governments show compassion by providing funding' (Lawrence and Killion, 1994: 7). However, a prolonged crisis such as this drought may tend to create a sense of its permanency which, in turn, denies the reality of the individual day-to-day struggle. This can then result in a sense of rejection and perhaps a suspicion of the motives of those who try to provide assistance. Research conducted in the late 1970s and early 1980s found that men have usually discussed farming problems only with other men (Gibbs, 1989). It was argued that this was because 'the pastoral community is little influenced by the mass media and has little contact with urban society, where the status and image of women has undergone its most public change' (Gibbs, 1989: 36). The farming community of the mid-1990s, we would argue, appears to be a much more sophisticated one, connected by electronic media to both the national and international world. Yet the current drought - in the context of export sales slumps and input cost increases (see *Australian*, 21 December 1994: 5) - has had significant 'spillover' effects on local rural communities. It was reported at the end of 1994 that approximately one third of Australia's non-farm businesses in drought-affected areas might be forced to close. In one telephone survey of small business it was revealed that some 25 percent of businesses contacted had put off staff and another 19 percent had reduced the hours and pay of those employed (see *Australian*, 16 November 1994:50).

In times of economic desperation, farm families tend to rely upon their own resources, rather than hiring labour. As James (1989: 7) indicated before the current drought began 'most farms cannot afford to hire labour, even if it were available in sparsely populated localities, yet farming has become more complex'. To what extent, in drought, has the burden of responsibility for the provision of farm labour fallen back onto the family unit? If, as Alston (1995) suggests, women (and children) have become a 'reserve army of labour' on family farms, to what extent have their roles been affected by the drought? Is there an expectation that 'things will return to normal' with the onset of better seasons? Has the decision-making process within the family irrevocably changed? What roles do men and women adopt in drought? How does the intergenerational aspect of the farming culture impact on crucial decisions undertaken in times of great crisis? To what extent is the environment knowingly compromised by producers affected by drought (see Vanclay and Lawrence, 1995)?

As suggested above, the natural crisis being experienced has come, for many farming families, on top of economic difficulties associated with technological change, deregulation, as well as the increased competition associated with the 'globalisation' of agricultural products (Marsden *et al.*, 1993). These have combined to 'force a reduction in the number of rural producers and ... to cause the erosion of the economies of many smaller country towns' (Lawrence, 1990: 103). For example, the recent Industry Commission *Draft Report into Charitable Organisations in Australia*, made the point that the current drought has combined with the recent recession to create a 'scarcity' of resources from the non-government sector in 'difficult economic circumstances' (Industry Commission, 1994: xxvii). When placed alongside comments from the Regional Director of the New England and North West Region of NSW Agriculture, the impact becomes clearer:

> many farm families are in a desperate situation and are unable to find money for day to day necessities such as food and electricity. Those who are identifying themselves through the hotlines are being referred to welfare agencies for assistance. However, the worry is that these people are only the 'tip of the iceberg' (*The Country Web*, 1994: 15).

The nature of Australia's current economic circumstances, the relationship between our agricultural industry and global markets, and the farming family's responses to the 'desperate situation' of drought need to be documented in order to be more appreciated and for explanations to be provided about the decision making in 'survival' times. Yet, the literature specifically related to farm families in natural crisis is limited. Much of the international literature tends to concentrate upon the effect of rural restructuring on the household and the impact of changing economics on farming communities (see for example, Marsden *et al.*, 1990; Flora *et al.*, 1992; Marsden *et al.*, 1993; Bonanno *et al.*, 1994). One pertinent and interesting phenomenon relevant to this study, demonstrated from research in Great Britain, is that

> the close-knit kinship ties traditionally associated with rural areas are more important as a component of English ideologies of rurality - ideologies that inform both policy and research discourses - than as a contemporary feature of rural life (Redclift and Whatmore, 1990: 186).

In other words, what is the impact of 'community' and how relevant is it to strategic planning in times of drought? What determines 'rural' and how does this construction influence understanding of the crisis? (Mormont, 1990). Is there a strong kinship network which sustains people during crises? Has the long term nature of the drought changed perceptions in the wider community and lessened the support available? Finally, to what extent are producers' desires for a sustainable agriculture influenced by drought? These and other questions will assist us to begin to develop a framework of what could be termed the 'Social Construction of Drought'.

We believe that this is an appropriate time, before the memories of the drought are lost, and while some major regions still remain in drought, to identify the social aspects of drought. The way in which we have begun to conceptualise such a construction includes questions about the way in which social relationships evolve, and when people begin to talk about drought as a 'given' - rather than as a possibility. When do producerslook around and 'see' conditions which identify drought? Are some farmers more perceptive than others? From which sources do they obtain information about drought and what to do about it? Is this an issue of leadership, perhaps? Is there someone in the community to whom others turn? Or is there perhaps someone who is left to state the problem for others? Does this tie in with concepts of masculinity? Is there a feeling of inadequacy when farming practices are compared, for example, - 'if my neighbour is managing why can't I'? or, on the other hand, 'if my neighbour is in drought I must be'. Or is it more fundamentally about farm management practices, that is, 'I tend to want everything out of my property and am prepared to push it to its limits', or 'my neighbour is weaker and less competitive, therefore s/he may manage longer than I can with less'. What are the issues of masculinity and femininity in this construction? How much actual decision making takes place in the family home as opposed to out in the field? How are decisions taken about family-related (as opposed to farm†-related) matters, such as education, social life, keeping social networks going, and so on. What importance does the notion of 'coping' have in this construction? Do men and women cope differently?

The social construction of drought is a process which is carried on across generations. Farm people learn the symbols of drought and how to interpret them. Those interpretations become meanings which are made available to others across time and space. Development of theory for the social construction of drought needs to accommodate cultural ideas and their transmission and it must do so in a way which can itself be interpreted and applied by farm people. It is their cultural construction as much as it is a meteorological phenomenon and it is for them that the theory is to be applied in research.

Such theory-building needs to be based on conceptualisation of the process of cultural construction. One possible basis for theory-building comes from a mechanism for transmission of ideas about drought: the telling of stories. As argued by Ericson and Shearing (1991) and applied to farmers by Phillips (ongoing), stories are a repository of historical experience and a means of transmitting ideas. Advice about the nature of drought and the interpretation of its indicators (symbols) may be transmitted by way of stories. Many such stories are emerging currently in the press as drought is thought to be breaking in southern Queensland.

Stories also offer opportunities for researchers to use locally-constructed concepts. The symbols they contain can be used in research instruments, offering a way to ensure culturally meaningful data are collected and avoiding imposition of theory-laden concepts. They can be used to create hypothetical scenarios to which interviewees can respond in terms of their own likely reactions. They can be used to test the sub-cultural and spatial specificity of symbols and their interpretation. All this requires an understanding of the local culture of farming.

Farming culture is associated with local social structures. Stories may offer a mechanism for maintenance of hierarchies (Phillips, ongoing), raising notions of community leadership and power, and suggesting an important clue to the ability of farm people to respond to and cope with drought. Questions about stories emerge as potentially very important. How are stories created and transmitted? Who receives them? How are they interpreted? Where do they go? Are all stories made available to all community members? If not, why are some excluded? Is there a notion of community hierarchy implied in stories? Is the transmission of stories controlled in any way? Does the capacity to interpret and transmit stories place people in relationships of power?

The methodology we develop will allow us to explore larger sociological and philosophical issues about the way in which human beings obtain, create and utilise knowledge. A brief outline of the proposed methodology follows.

Methodology: towards a framework of social construction

Denzin and Lincoln (1994: 15) argue that there is 'no single interpretive truth': rather, there are 'multiple, interpretive communities, each having its own criteria for evaluating an interpretation'. Searching for a 'truth' - a single reality in the context of the drought experience - is not the purpose of this project. We will be using the stories that our families tell us to help us build a larger story. Denzin puts it this way:

> (There) is, in a sense, no final truth or final telling. There are only
> different tellings of different stories organized under the heading
> of the same tale ... (in) two different versions of the same story ...
> it becomes a different story in the new telling (Denzin, 1992
> cited in Erlandson *et al.,* 1993: 27).

The study will be undertaken using an approach variously defined as naturalistic (Lincoln and Guba, 1985; Erlandson *et al.*, 1993); hermeneutic (Froyland, 1991); interpretive (Reinharz, 1992); qualitative (Finch, 1986; Reinharz and Rowles, 1988) and constructivist (Guba and Lincoln, 1989; Denzin and Lincoln, 1994). The interpretive, naturalistic design allows for a 'continuing dialectic of iteration, analysis, critique, reiteration, reanalysis' (Guba and Lincoln, 1989: 84) - a potentially powerful and productive methodological approach. We believe that it is a research design that suits the nature of the topic to be studied and which, in turn, acknowledges the central role of those whose lives have been affected by the drought.

The study will be undertaken by comparing thirty farm families in two disparate regions affected by the drought - one in Central Queensland (beef) and one in the Riverina (sheep/wheat). The value of comparison enables the research to incorporate cross-regional issues. Farm families will initially be identified through discussion with the Queensland Department of Primary Industry in Central Queensland and NSW Agriculture in the Riverina and then will develop through a 'snowball' sampling, with families recommending other families.

The methodology, which is necessarily exploratory, consists of three components - interviews, (both semi-structured and structured); focus group discussions; and single case study design. The unit of analysis will therefore be at the farm (environmental), family (individual) and stakeholder (community) levels. Using the framework developed in the writings of Egon Guba (1978; 1981; and 1990), Egon Guba and Yvonna Lincoln (1981; 1985; and 1989) and David Erlandson (1993: 31) it is possible to identify a number of strategies which need to be adopted in order to begin to develop the 'comprehensive intensive interpretation of (various) realities' necessary for a constructivist enquiry of this nature. These key strategies, and the way we will be working within them are:

1 Prolonged engagement: The two areas under study are both within the geographic boundaries of the Research Centres, and both Universities have a history of involvement with communities and farm families in the regions concerned. We are fortunate that the project is being developed over a period of two years - a time period which enables comparison, discussion, reflection and comparative analysis. Focus groups will be developed to allow the issues of common concern to emerge and to allow differences between families to be identified. There will be four focus groups with an average of eight members, developed in each region. These focus groups will consist of stakeholders from various sectors of the agricultural community. Morgan (1988: 11) argues that the full potential of focus groups develop when both 'orienting oneself to a new field' (in this case, the social construction of drought) and 'generating hypotheses based on informants' insights'. In this way, the research explores the social context of drought, allowing a deeper understanding of the issues to emerge.

2 Persistent observation: 'A process of constant and tentative analysis' argues Erlandson (1993: 31) enables the depth of understanding of people's lived experiences to develop. The value of open-ended questions and the allocation of enough time to enable the participants to begin to explore their thoughts and feelings is essential. We plan to undertake the focus group discussions prior to the individual interviewing as a way of beginning to identify emerging 'patterns'. In this context too, learning, understanding, and appreciating and using the language of the participants will be important in establishing trust. This, in turn, will enable what Erlandson (1993: 30) calls a 'credible outcome' - one that 'adequately represents both the areas in which these realities converge and the points on which they diverge' to be produced during the research process.

Information about the families who have lived through the drought will be collected from taped, face-to-face interviews with members (usually the husband and wife) of 30 families in the Central Queensland region and 30 families in the Riverina. The semi-structured format will encourage attitudes and opinions associated with gender, age and other differences to emerge from the discussions (see Minichello, 1990). The interviews will provide a minimum of 120 detailed statements which will enable a cross-comparative quantitative analysis (including the frequency tabulation of findings) to be undertaken.

3 Triangulation: While the central focus of the study is the thirty families in both regions, we are also conscious of the need to gather different stories from other crucial sources. We have identified, for example, district agronomists from government agencies, farm financial counsellors, and rural support workers as those who might provide insights into the affects of drought in particular regions. We plan to consider these views in the context of the focus discussions held among the farmers, in order to begin to identify different constructions of reality (in this case, among farmers and 'experts'). Structured interviews will also be conducted with some rural support workers and farm financial counsellors. These will be conducted after the farm family interviews have been completed. Again, the number of interviews will be determined after discussion with the key stakeholders.

Single case study design will begin to explore the social construction of drought through the lived experience of four farm families within each region. Our rationale for this methodological approach rests with what Yin (1988) calls the 'revelatory case'. Here, the researcher has access to a situation or a phenomenon that has previously not been researched - the case study is 'worth conducting because the descriptive information alone will be revelatory' (Yin, 1988: 43).

4 Referential adequacy methods: We are aware that there is a great resource of visual material already available through the printed and television media. While not directly central to the project this information may, nevertheless, be helpful in undertaking a photographic study with a view (in the long term) to publishing our research in a way which foregrounds the voices and photographs to provide a more 'holistic view of the context' (Erlandson, 1993: 31).

5 Member checking: Within the ongoing nature of the project, we are planning to have a verification process - one which is underpinned by the Rural Social and Economic Research Centre's mission statement: that our work is 'guided by principles of social justice, reciprocity and ethics'. For those families involved in the case studies, we would anticipate having them read through our material (and verify that material) prior to publication. The interviews would be conducted by experienced researchers who understand the need for sensitivity, diplomacy and who would thus enable the respondents to be actively involved in the process (Reinharz, 1992). We believe that our interviews may be the first opportunity (outside the family) that the respondents will have to discuss these experiences. We are conscious of the responsibility we have in terms of moral, ethical and political consequences (Finch, 1984). To this end, all individuals interviewed will be asked to complete a consent form and the project will be submitted to ethics committees at both Universities. In addition, we plan to disseminate the findings of the study as widely as possible, including through the rural media, newsletters produced through government departments, as well as through rural organisations such as the Country Women's Association and Landcare. It may well be possible to develop a 'home page' on the electronic mail infrastructure and offer opportunities for discussion there.

6 *Peer debriefing:* We are fortunate to be working collegially on this project. Indeed, it would be difficult to imagine undertaking a study of this nature in any other way. We have already begun the process of reflecting upon existing information. We believe that this opportunity to begin to develop a theoretical framework in regard to the social construction of drought will add to the body of knowledge within rural sociology. Where the interviews will provide us with a broad range of responses, the case studies will enable a 'richness' of experience to be understood - enabling a comparative understanding of how some farm families have coped successfully while others have been less successful. The methodology is labour-intensive. We believe this might be an advantage in that these approaches have value in situations such as the current drought where there is a clear lack of sociological understanding of what is occurring on Australian farms.

Questions which may assist us to better conceptualise the social impact and thus develop the variety of constructions will include:

- How do farmers and their families come to perceive that a drought is threatening? How does this vary according to farm management style and values?
- In what way do communities identify the signs which indicate that a drought has commenced? How do people convey the signs to one another? Do the signs tell farmers that they might be undertaking unacceptable risks?
- How have the families who are determined to stay on the land made the strategic management decisions which allow them to do so?
- When did they realise that they would have to act strategically to prepare themselves for the effects of drought?
- What decisions did they make to balance risk taking and conservation? What relationship do these decisions have with farm management style?
- How does the family share the decision-making process?
- What role does intergenerational planning have in this?
- What impact do the attitudes and values of the farm woman have?
- What role does 'drought assistance' - in all its forms - play in decision making?
- Has there been a change in culture regarding responses to drought - from government, and from the farming community?

Contextualising the drought study

Current research being undertaken by the Rural Social and Economic Research Centre in Duaringa Shire, one hour's drive west of Rockhampton, is already indicating the ways in which rural communities are contracting as a result of the drought. This area has been drought declared for over four years. Since August 1995, during the time in which we have been undertaking our research, the Duaringa township (population 500) has lost its third police officer, the local store has closed down and the townspeople are fighting to maintain the Shire Administration in their township as well as keeping the railway station open. Service clubs in the area are also finding it hard to continue, as their members decrease. For example, the Lions Club has already closed down and, more recently, the Country Women's Association managed to survive only by a last minute recruitment of younger members.

It would appear that the drought crisis, together with the ongoing process of rural restructuring, is precipitating a move away from rural areas as these 'spaces' lose their production value. One of the primary impacts of the drought is a loss of population. As farming communities collapse and families move away, our research is showing that community development workers in rural areas face a serious problem if communities are going to survive - not only do they need to attempt to maintain existing levels of services but they also need to ensure that the outmigration from rural areas is reduced. Traditionally, community development work has tended to concentrate upon raising the level of human service provision. Thus, for example, while important, it would be relatively easy and in some ways counterproductive merely to criticise current governmental policy on the basis that services are being withdrawn precisely at the moment when they are needed most. While it might make economic sense - within a market framework - to provide services on the basis of numbers rather than looking at the broader picture of a community in crisis, nevertheless, our early findings are that the impact of the drought is having far-reaching consequences which are yet to be fully realised.

The primary purpose of the current work being done (within the RSERC) with Duaringa Shire is to identify the needs for social services. However, we are also concerned about providing some measure of reciprocity to a community which appears to have lost its sense of identity and its future. To this end, one member of our group spoke at the local CWA group in Duaringa about the possibility of starting a museum/tourist centre/craft shop in their town. The idea was taken up - enthusiastically - as something that 'could be done for Duaringa, for us.' It was decided that a public meeting would be called to discuss the proposal with all those who were interested in taking part. Andrea attended that meeting, together with thirty people from the town. There were representatives from the council, the CWA, Playgroup, Pensioners group, Lionesses, and the Pony Club. In the ensuing discussion it was very clear that although this proposal would make it possible to attract some tourists to Duaringa and to link in with the Council's tourist policy for the Shire, it would also give something 'positive' to the town. It was exciting to see the impact as people began talking about beautification projects, developing parks, utilising areas that were now unused, as well as the need to bring the local Aboriginal population into the project. There was, for the people involved, a need to link the suggested projects with other tourist projects for the Shire. One suggestion was to use the local shop (one of the original buildings in the town) for the museum, as its owner could no longer continue economically. As the owner lives in the house next door she could be paid to be the caretaker - a classic 'postmodern solution' to economic marginalisation (oblivion?). It was clear that the community regarded this as a community issue in which all should have a say and be invited to participate. To this end, a committee was formed which will seek incorporation so that it can apply for grants as well as form working parties to deal with various facets of research. The Shire Council has also made a commitment to back the project.

Further sociological study in this area could lead to some interesting work on the role of women in reshaping both the cultural and economic structure of rural towns. Traditionally, because of a patriarchal system of land tenure (see Poiner, 1990) women have 'disguised' the role they have played in the public affairs of country towns. Feminist (rural) sociological work has tended to study the role of women in decision making in the home. Yet evidence is starting to emerge that those decisions could affect not only the family but also what happens on the farm (Alston, 1995). The involvement with Duaringa Shire indicates another area in which women are heavily involved. As members of service clubs they are often the main gatekeepers of what are perceived to be 'welfare handouts' (see also Alston, 1995). Women are also the prime movers in making innovative suggestions and calling public meetings. Once again, it has been the impact of the drought which has highlighted the crucial role of women on the land. Gender issues will be highlighted in our future research.

Knowledge gained through farm families' lived experiences will be analysed and reinterpreted in order to assist farm families to understand the predicament of drought. It is anticipated that it will also enable an informed long-term management strategy to be developed to assist government, as well as rural adjustment and counselling agencies, in their activities. The identification of attitudes to structural readjustment and the incorporation of such government programs into decision making would enable policy development to proceed in a more informed manner. In addition, the knowledge of farmer perception could help to develop policies/programs which assist farmers to prepare and plan for drought. The intersection between family, women, community and networking will be of interest to both community developers and policy makers.

Acknowledgment

This research is being funded by the Rural Industries Research and Development Corporation and the Land and Water Resources Research and Development Corporation, whose assistance is gratefully acknowledged.

References

Alston, M. (1995) Women and Their Work on Australian Farms, *Rural Sociology, 60,* 3: 521-532.

Australian, 16 November 1994.

Australian, 9 December 1994.

Australian, 21 December 1994.

Bonanno, A., Busch, L., Friedland, W., Gouveia, L. and Mingione, E. (eds) *From Columbus to ConAgra: the Globalization of Agriculture and Food,* Kansas, University of Kansas Press.

Daly, D. (1994) *Wet as a Shag, Dry as a Bone,* Brisbane, Department of Primary Industries, Queensland.

Denzin, N. and Lincoln, Y. (eds) (1994) *Handbook of Qualitative Research,* London, Sage.

Erlandson, D., Harris, E., Skipper, B., and Allen, S. (1993) *Doing Naturalistic Inquiry. A Guide to Method,* Newbury Park, Sage.

Finch, J. (1986) *Research and Policy: The Uses of Qualitative Methods in Social and Educational Research,* London, The Falmer Press.

Finch, J. (1984) 'It's Great to Have Someone to Talk To': the Ethics and Politics of Interviewing Women, in Bell, C. and Roberts, H. (eds) *Social Researching: Politics, Problems and Practice* London, Routledge and Kegan Paul: 70-87.

Flora, C., Flora, J. Spears, J. and Swanson, L. (1992) *Rural Communities: Legacy and Change,* Boulder, Westview.

Froyland, I. (1991) *Police University Education: Expectations for a Changing World,* Unpublished PhD thesis, Simon Fraser University.

Gibbs, M. (1989) Decision-Making on Pastoral Properties, in James, K (ed.) *Women in Rural Australia,* Brisbane, University of Queensland Press: 30-43.

Gray, I., Lawrence, G. and Dunn, T. (1993) *Coping With Change: Australian Farmers in the 1990s,* Wagga Wagga, Centre for Rural Social Research, Charles Sturt University.

Guba, E. (1978) *Toward a Methodology of Naturalistic Inquiry in Education Evaluation,* Monograph 8, Los Angles, UCLA Centre for the Study of Evaluation.

Guba, E. (1981) Criteria for Assessing the Trustworthiness of Naturalistic Inquiries, *Educational Communication and Technology Journal,* 29: 75-92.

Guba, E. (ed.) (1990) *The Paradigm Dialog,* Newbury Park, Sage.

Guba, E. and Lincoln, Y. (1981) *Effective Evaluation,* San Francisco, Jossey-Baas.

Guba, E. and Lincoln, Y. (1989) *Fourth Generation Evaluation,* Newbury Park, Sage.

Industry Commission (1994) *Charitable Organisations in Australia: An Inquiry into Community Social Welfare Organisation,* Draft Report, Melbourne.

James, K. (ed.) (1989) *Women in Rural Australia,* Brisbane, University of Queensland Press.

Lawrence, G. (1990) Agricultural Restructuring and Rural Social Change in Australia, in Marsden, T., Lowe, P. and Whatmore, S. (eds) *Rural Restructuring: Global Processes and Their Responses*, London, David Fulton: 102-128.

Lawrence, G. and Killion, F. (1994) Beyond the Eastern Seaboard: What Future for Rural and Remote Australia? *Keynote Address, Annual Congress of the Australian Council of Social Services,*Brisbane, 26-28 October.

Lincoln, Y. and Guba, E. (1985) *Naturalistic Inquiry*, Beverly Hills, Sage.

Marsden, T., Lowe, P. and Whatmore, S. (1990) *Rural Restructuring: Global Processes and Their Responses*, London, David Fulton.

Marsden, T., Murdoch, J., Lowe, P., Munton, R. and Flynn, A. (1993) *Constructing the Countryside*, London, UCL Press.

Minichello, V. (1990) *In-Depth Interviewing: Researching People,* Melbourne, Longman Cheshire.

Morgan, D. (1988) *Focus Groups as Qualitative Research*, University Paper No.16, Newbury Park, Sage.

Mormont, M. (1990) Who is Rural? or How to be Rural: Towards a Sociology of the Rural, in Marsden, T., Lowe, P. and Whatmore, S. (eds) *Rural Restructuring: Global Processes and Their Responses*, London, David Fulton: 21-44.

Phillips, E. (ongoing) *To Be a Good Farmer: The Construction of Farm Practice in Two Riverina Localities,* PhD Research, Wagga Wagga, Charles Sturt University.

Poiner, G. (1990) *The Good Old Rule: Gender and Power Relationships in a Rural Community*, Sydney, Sydney University Press.

Queensland Department of Primary Industry (1994) *Drought Management in the Kunwarara Area: Beef Producers' Experiences and Perspectives*, Rockhampton, QDPI.

Redclift, M. and Whatmore, S. (1990) Household, Consumption and Livelihood: Ideologies and Issues in Rural Research, in Marsden, T. *et al.*, (eds) *Rural Restructuring: Global Processes and Their Responses*, London, David Fulton: 182-197.

Reinhartz, S. (1992) *Feminist Methods in Social Research*, New York, Oxford University Press.

Reinharz, S. and Rowles, G. (eds) (1988) *Qualitative Gerontology*, New York, Springer.

Shearing, C. and Ericson, R. (1991) Culture as Figurative Action, *British Journal of Sociology 42*, 2: 481-506.

Sydney Morning Herald, 31 December 1994.

The Country Web (1994) Special Drought Edition, NSW Agriculture.

Vanclay, F. and Lawrence, G. (1995) *The Environmental Imperative: Ecosocial Concerns for Australian Agriculture*, Rockhampton, CQU Press.

Yin, R. (1984) *Case Study Research: Design and Methods*, Beverly Hills, Sage.

Chapter 21

Sustainability and the restructuring of tradition: A comparative analysis of three rural localities

Ian Gray and Emily Phillips

Introduction

Locality research, as it explores the social and spatial features of rural restructuring, offers opportunities to examine change in cultural tradition and micro-level relationships in a context of global processes. While valuable work has been done at the local level on responses to global change, much of it has been driven by macro-level structural perspectives, leaving few opportunities to examine change in culture and related practices. This chapter explores changing aspects of farming cultural tradition through rural restructuring and the quest for agricultural sustainability. Rural society can be seen to be undergoing a process of 'detraditionalisation' within families and communities. This process can be seen to have direct and indirect implications for the social, economic and environmental sustainability of agriculture.

Farming tradition

Tradition can consist of any aspects of culture including the practices associated with culture. The only essential element is some notion of an historical process of transmission through generations. It can include objects, but beliefs rather than physical realities may constitute its most significant features. Shils (1981: 12) offers a broad definition: 'anything which is transmitted or handed down from the past to the present' through generations. It can encompass 'all accomplished patterns of the human mind, all patterns of belief or modes of thinking, all achieved patterns of social relationships, all technical practices, and all physical artefacts or natural objects' (*ibid*: 16). Shils adds the constraint, however, that an attribute of a culture must last at least three generations before obtaining the status of a tradition. This seems an arbitrary point; the more important qualification is that tradition can consist of beliefs about cultural institutions as well as the institutions themselves. Giddens (1994) asserts that what is thought to be tradition can be more important than what has long genuine historical roots. Shils and Giddens would agree, however, that tradition is important to the explanation of social practice and to the understanding of change. Both writers accept that traditions are intertwined with the identities and interests of people.

However regarded, tradition is an important prop to, and possibly the keystone of, the social organisation of agriculture. Agrarian identity and ideology, farm succession and inheritance practices and farm knowledge have been the principal features of the exploration of farm cultural tradition. The culture of family farming, as it has been transmitted across many generations among many societies, has been related to the persistence of the family farming system amid conditions which militate against it. Craig and Phillips (1983) discuss the ways in which agrarian ideology, a component of tradition, has legitimated the exploitation of family farms. Farm inheritance is central to the maintenance of tradition as it provides an instrument for transmission of beliefs, values and practices. With the family and community relations it implies, it also provides a conduit for the knowledge upon which farm practices are based.

While tradition has been found to be important in the maintenance of the family farm system, it varies in its nature and implications. Farmers have been found to operate their farms differentially according to different subcultural norms (Vanclay and Lawrence, 1995). Variation in tradition has been seen to effect different outcomes as farm families struggle to maintain their livelihoods (see for example, Salamon, 1985). This differentiation has a spatial dimension as tradition varies among local communities. This view offers a 'local diversity', as opposed to the 'globalisation', perspective (Buttel, 1994), the latter presenting an image of the social relations of agriculture being restructured uniformly across space under the global advance of agri-food capital. This chapter presents evidence that change in the social relations and conditions of agriculture is affected by cultural attributes which may vary across space.

Tradition and sustainability

Farm tradition, as far as it determines the practice of farming, has vast implications for the sustainability of agriculture and the family farm system. Unlike the extensive research which has theoretically and empirically connected culture with responses to farm economic and financial crises (including in Australia Gray *et al.*, 1993), examination of association between culture and farm practice related to conservation of farm land has barely begun. Locally derived and transmitted knowledge as a basis for farm operation, 'indigenous technical knowledge' (Kloppenburg, 1992) or 'craftship' (Mooney, 1988) can be seen as a significant aspect of farm tradition. The existence of variety in farm practice associated with subcultures among farmers has been noted (Vanclay and Lawrence, 1995). The significance in terms of land conservation practice of the other aspects of tradition, which are related to but distinct from knowledge, is little understood. Apart from some European research which has related intergenerational succession to farm conservation and development (Ward and Lowe, 1994), little is known about how traditions of succession might affect the sustainability of agricultural land in Australia. This gap in the literature persists as extension research continues to give it a low priority despite acknowledgment of succession as a probable significant factor in adoption of innovations in agriculture (Guerin and Guerin, 1994).

With Australia's agricultural land continuing to degrade while Australian farmers are being forced to yield to the demands of transnational capital (Lawrence and Vanclay, 1994) the relationship between farm tradition and sustainability obtains great significance. Sustainability can be defined in terms of the capacity of social and economic, as well as environmental systems, to support the continuation of agriculture in the long term. There is evidence that farmers in the New South Wales Riverina see it in such terms (Ampt and Phillips, 1994). Whether regarded from either the perspective of Shils or that of Giddens, tradition, as it provides motivation (Shils) or identity (Giddens), is an important determinant of farm people's responses to the challenge of sustainability.

The relationship between tradition and sustainability arises along environmental, social and economic dimensions. It can be seen as more or less direct, dependent on the conceptual admission of mediating factors. Tradition in the form of inherited land use habits directly impinges on the environmental dimension of sustainability. This is implicit in Vanclay and Lawrence's (1995) point about the prescriptions of subcultural norms: farmers suffer pressure to conform to the practices which are endorsed by fellow farmers. Non-conformity is logically predicated on conformity and as such it suggests processes of change. The existence of subcultures, their significance and change are open to examination, as suggested by Phillips and Gray (1995).

Association between culture and action may be apparent when tradition is seen to provide meaning to action through belief and identity construction. The work of Salamon (1985) has shown such connections empirically. Ideological aspects of tradition, beliefs about the value and meaning of farming, can be associated with different traditions. Specifically, farmers who are more entrepreneurial (seeking greater financial reward by risk-taking) have been found to be more prone to failure than those who adhere to a less materialist tradition and are able to call on support of family and community in times of stress. With regard to environmental aspects, Stone (1992) has proposed that those communities which have weaker social organisation are less able to take the necessary collective action against land degradation. This point is implicit in much of the debate surrounding the community-based, but arguably government-controlled, Australian Landcare 'movement', upon which much hope for the perpetuation of Australian agriculture rests.

Detraditionalisation

Traditions can disappear without tradition disappearing. Identities and motivation attached to attributes of culture can take different forms over time without a loss of tradition. In a sense, following Giddens rather than Shils, societies can be equally traditional when their traditions are recent inventions. Moreover, traditions may appear to be the possession of one interest group while serving another. The approach taken by Phillips and Gray (1995) recognises that tradition is continually reconstructed from within agricultural society, and is particularly visible at the local level. That process may occur under conditions created beyond agricultural society and farm-based interest groups.

The forces which bring pressure for detraditionalisation can have vertical or horizontal orientations, corresponding to Shils' (1981) concepts of endogenous and exogenous factors. Horizontal forces present a spatial dimension, arising commonly with population movement. Immigrants bring traditions which may threaten indigenous culture. Of potentially greater significance are the vertical forces upon farming: those of economic decline amid the global restructuring of agri-food industry.

Each of the approaches to the association between tradition and agricultural sustainability discussed above assumes that farm people have some degree of autonomy, even if only in their possession of a subculture. Each on its own focuses attention on the attributes of farm tradition. But farm tradition is not a construction of farm people alone; nor of course are the conditions in which sustainability is sought. The value placed on family farming and its attendant lifestyle is a social construction which has served the interests of urban-based capital as farm families have been moved to persevere through great adversity in conditions created largely by international capital. The significance of this aspect of tradition has been argued by Poiner (1990) in terms of local social relations and more generally by Craig and Phillips (1983). Phillips (forthcoming) uses ethnographic analysis to show how farm family members use locally specific traditions in their mediation of global economic forces with local cultural tradition and their own life trajectories. While some struggle to preserve their way of life, others are more susceptible to the forces of change.

The conditions in which farm people might seek sustainability are such as to raise questions about the possibility of them even attempting to do so. They must operate with the land resource available to them in the condition in which they receive or obtain it and under economic conditions determined by agencies operating at national and more significantly global levels. They are being forced to increase intensification of production, thereby continuing and accelerating long term processes of environmental degradation (Lawrence and Vanclay, 1994). Farmers find themselves placed on economic and technological 'treadmills'. The farm 'treadmills', on which farmers are forced continually to increase production at the same time as their returns decrease, were recognised in the United States as early as the 1950s (Buttel *et al.*, 1990).

279

The concept is equally applicable theoretically to Australia in the 1990s and it represents a situation which is recognisable to farmers (Gray *et al.*, 1995).

Australian farm tradition is under pressure to change. One can reasonably ask if it is sustainable. Australian farmers have persevered on a high-input treadmill, pursuing increased productivity with declining state support and knowing that doing so cannot be sustained socially (in terms of the strength of family and community relations) economically, or environmentally. Farmers are questioning this predicament (Gray *et al.*, 1995). Pile (1990) found that, somewhat ironically from an Australian perspective, pressure on British farmers to reduce production was making them question traditional values, seeking an escape from the production treadmill. However, a tension emerges when the meaning of farming as a multi-generation family enterprise becomes questionable. A 'motivation crisis' is avoided by changing the meaning of farming. Such reflection has also been revealed by Ward (1993).

Detraditionalisation may affect each type of association between tradition and sustainability discussed above. A cultural model of sustainability would suggest that those families who had stronger farm and community ties through longevity of farming and community membership would be more traditional and hence more likely to sustain their farm by handing it on to the next generation. Those who adhere to tradition may also be less materialistic in their ambitions, but if their adherence runs to farming practices, they may be more conservative, opting to retain traditional land management habits. Phillips (forthcoming) has indicated ethnographically that value placed on tradition, including succession, is related to the ways in which farm practices are changing amid globalisation. It remains to explore these relationships across a wider sample with a focus on sustainability.

Research design

The possible associations between detraditionalisation and approaches to sustainability are manifold. To explore this complexity of factors, specific associations will be considered between values pertaining to farming life, intergenerational transfer of farms and social networks and local demography as aspects of tradition and the economic, social and environmental dimensions of sustainability.

An interview survey of 153 farm people on 79 farms was conducted across three areas in the Riverina region of New South Wales. Forty-two percent of respondents were women. The age range of respondents was 18 to 79 years with a mean of 49 years. The three areas, each identified as a local community by respondents, have been given the fictitious names of Greater Redwood[1] (67 respondents), Milldale (37 respondents) and Grenbrook (49 respondents). Milldale and Greater Redwood are adjacent but have different soil type, the latter occupying an area of red loam, excellent for cropping. Milldale has more clay and granite land. Both are undulating to flat. Grenbrook is about 80 kilometres from Redwood and Milldale. It is less consistent in landform and soil type. It contains rich alluvial land with some swampy and sandy areas and a lot of heavy soil unsuited to cropping. The three localities provide a variety which illustrates many of the physical conditions for mixed farming in the NSW Riverina.

The sample was obtained by identifying a small number of farmers in each community and asking them for the names of other members of the community until all families recognised as community members had been identified. Some families who did not consider themselves, but were considered by others, to be members of the communities were included. Interviews were carried out in late 1994. Family members were interviewed together. Separate responses were recorded for each and discussion encouraged.

The bearing of cultural tradition was operationalised in terms of values and longevity and strength of community membership. Values were explored using 25 questions seeking indications of the level of importance (on a 5 point scale) given to features of farm life including family and community relations and lifestyle as well as material factors like building up a big farm and having a high income. An open-ended question also asked what features were felt to be important. Longevity of community membership was measured using questions about the number of generations in which respondents' families had lived in their communities, how long respondents had lived in those communities and for how many generations their farms had been in their families. Community network density was measured using questions about proportions of friends and relatives living locally. Social sustainability was operationalised in terms of desires and expectations about intergenerational succession, and for those who had children old enough to have taken a career, how many of their children had taken on their farm as a career. Economic sustainability was seen in terms of farm equity and perceptions of the 'high-input treadmill', as the latter would suggest an unsustainable situation developing.

Given that there is much technical debate about which techniques will in the long term give rise to sustainability (Barr and Cary, 1992) and given that not all techniques are likely to be appropriate on all farms, environmental sustainability was explored by asking about the types of farming techniques which respondents saw as most likely to conserve their land. They were then asked to what extent they used those techniques. This approach acknowledges the inherent subjectivity of sustainability. Although a large majority of Australian farmers is aware of land degradation and the measures which can be taken to combat it (Gray and Dunn, 1992; Vanclay and Lawrence, 1995), it was considered important that they be considered in this study.

Findings

Tradition

Features of farming life related to family, community and lifestyle were widely given great importance, suggesting that traditional values were being

281

maintained. For example, 90 percent of respondents felt that having social contact with other farmers was important, 91 percent felt that having the appearance of their crops and livestock compare well with those of others was important, 95 percent felt that giving children a chance to farm was important and 100 percent felt that being free to make their own decisions was important. However, rather fewer (77 percent) felt that having a high income was important and fewer still (62 percent) gave importance to building up a big farm operation. Responses to the open-ended question fell into four categories: those raising independence ('being your own boss') (offered by 60 percent of respondents), lifestyle and environment (65 percent), aspects of farm tradition like 'love of the land' and 'working with your family' (24 percent) and the satisfaction of confronting a challenge (27 percent). While some respondents lamented that farming was now 'just a living', none mentioned material prosperity as important.

Respondents stated that their families had lived in their communities for between one and five generations, with 39 percent stating one generation and 36 percent three generations. They had lived in their communities for between one and 79 years with the mean period being 31 years. Farms had been in their families for between one and four generations. About half of the respondents said that some of their relatives lived in their local community. More than half said that some and about one quarter said that more than half of their relatives live in their local community.

Having friends and relatives in the community is related to longevity (Table 1). Of those who had both friends and relatives locally, 77 percent said that all of their friends knew some or all of their relatives.

Table 1
Correlation coefficients among longevity and social network density variables

	Proportion of relatives living locally	Proportion of friends living locally
Generations farm in family	.53	.32
Years living locally	.41	.31
Generations living locally	.65	.34

All coefficients are significant at the .01 level.

Those who, in response to the open-ended question about what was important to them, mentioned independence, tradition and challenge had been living in their localities for longer in average terms than those who did not mention these features, although the difference between means for those who raised tradition is not statistically significant. Those who mentioned lifestyle and environment aspects had lived locally on average for a shorter period (Table 2).

Table 2
Mean years lived locally among those raising aspects of farming as important

	Mentioned	Not Mentioned	t-statistic	p
Independence	33.6	27.5	2.06	.05
Lifestyle/Environment	28.7	35.6	-2.28	.02
Tradition	34.1	30.2	1.12	.27
Challenge	37.0	29.0	2.46	.02

t-value calculated on unequal variance where Levene's test for equality of variances $p < .05$

Those mentioning traditional aspects as important tended to be less materialistic. This is suggested by comparison of the mean scores of those who mentioned and those who did not mention traditional aspects on a 'materialism' scale formed from 6 of the 25 questions about farm values. The six questions asked about importance given to having a high income, being seen to have a high income, building up a big farm operation, having a new car, having an annual holiday and having an attractive homestead. They offer an alpha reliability coefficient of .75. Those mentioning tradition at the open-ended question scored 3.2 on this scale while the others scored 3.6. While not large, the difference is statistically significant at the .01 level.

Social sustainability

A weak correlation is apparent between longevity of local residence and wanting children to continue in farming (including those children who were already farming) ($r = .19$, $p = .028$) when wanting children to continue is scored on a scale of 1 to 3: no - uncertain - yes). A stronger correlation ($r = .28$, $p = .001$) appears between period of residence on the farm and wanting children to continue farming.

Neither of these dependent variables refers either to the respondent's own farm or to what is actually happening. Those respondents who had sons or daughters old enough to have taken a career were asked how many of their children had chosen their farm as a career. When those whose sons/daughters had taken on their farm were compared with those whose sons/daughters had not, a stronger pattern emerged (Table 3). A similar pattern appears, with some limitations due to sample size, among those who had sons in their households in terms of longevity of residence and those who did not, across all three variables.

One might expect local longevity to be related to age and therefore to likelihood of having a child taking on the farm. However, no association is apparent between age and local longevity. One might also expect that level of equity in the farm might be related to the taking of the farm as a career, either positively as prospects for the farm are better, or negatively because additional labour was needed. Neither such association is apparent. The mean level of farm equity among those passing on the farm is the same (89.7 percent) for

Table 3

Mean scores on local longevity variables for those whose sons/daughters had and had not taken on the farm

	Son/daughter had taken on farm as career	Son/daughter had not taken on farm as career	t-statistic	p
Generations farm in family	1.8	1.4	1.76	.08
Years living locally	43.3	30.2	3.18	.01
Generations living locally	2.1	1.6	1.99	.05

t-value calculated on unequal variance where Levene's test for equality of variances p < .05

those whose sons/daughters had taken on the farm and for those whose sons/daughters had not. This does not eliminate the possibility of both effects occurring, however. (Stated levels of equity ranged from 30 to 100 percent.)

Economic sustainability

Three-quarters (75.8 percent) of the respondents perceived themselves as being on a treadmill. There is no association suggested between either farm equity or tradition in terms of local longevity/social network density and perception of being on a treadmill. There is some indication that those who place importance on tradition are likely to perceive themselves as being on a treadmill (80.6 percent). Mentioning challenge was less frequently associated with perception of the treadmill (63.4 percent).

Environmental sustainability

When asked what types of farming techniques respondents saw as most likely to conserve their land, a large variety of answers was offered. Most followed the prescriptions of conservation farming: reduced tillage, crop rotation, tree planting, lime application, perennial pastures etc. Some preferred lower inputs: lower production and in particular, less use of chemicals, reflecting the predicament which farmers face when deciding on means of conserving their

Table 4

Extent of use of techniques thought to conserve land

	Percent of Farms
Not at all	5
A little	14
Moderately	65
Extensively	16
Total	100

land. When asked how extensively they use those techniques, a range of answers was again offered against a four point scale (Table 4).

Respondents were also asked if they used them as much as they would like to and among those who said no, what was preventing them from using conservation practices as much as they would like to. Seventy-three percent of those who were not using conservation practices as much as they would like to attributed this to costs. Twenty-eight percent (43 respondents) mentioned other factors, about half of which related to either lack of knowledge or conservatism: 'sceptical, cautious, watching others, dad disagrees'. Seven respondents said that they had no choice but to over-crop their land. There is no evident association between attachment to tradition and citing conservatism or ignorance in explanation for lack of conservation activity.

There is, however, a relationship indicated, with some qualification due to sample size, between having a son/daughter return to the farm and extent of conservation activity. The mean score on the conservation activity scale for those with at least one son/daughter who had taken on the farm is 3.2, compare with 2.5 for those without (n = 33 farms, t = 2.88, significant at .01 level). When extent of conservation activity is dichotomised into those stating not at all and a little, and those stating moderately and extensively, the relationship is clear (Table 5).

Table 5
Having at least one son or daughter on the farm and extent of conservation activity

	son/daughter on farm (% of respondents)	No son/daughter on farm (% of respondents)
Conservation activity low	9	40
Conservation activity high	91	60
Total	100	100

Those who had at least one son or daughter working the farm were less likely to explain lack of conservation activity in terms of cost. Ninety percent of those who did not have a child working the farm attributed lack of conservation work to cost. There is no such association with conservatism/lack of knowledge.

Discussion

Tradition is important to farm people. Aspects of farm life often thought of as important parts of tradition were almost universally acknowledged as important and often raised spontaneously. Material aspects of farming were not considered to be so important and were not raised spontaneously. Some association is apparent between community, in terms of longevity of presence and strength of social networks, and tradition. Those with longer-term local associations raised independence, cultural traditions and challenges as important features of farm life, but were less inclined to mention environment and lifestyle aspects. Perhaps they offered no novelty, especially if people were confronted with isolation and a harsh living environment.

There is only weak evidence of a dichotomy between those of a materialistic orientation and those who adhere to family and community aspects of tradition. The relatively high frequency of apparent intergenerational succession, or at least potential succession, among those with stronger community ties is more significant. Possible explanations might include the greater stake which more intensively connected people have in their community, as it provides family and social contacts and associated security, perhaps some measure of the 'ontological security' proposed by Giddens. Cultural factors rather than economic ones appear to be significant to social sustainability. There is no association between them: those who would bear tradition, having greater community affiliation, may be in a similar financial situation to relative newcomers after the borrowing activity of the 1980s and the cost-price squeeze and drought of the early 1990s.

Perception of a treadmill situation is widespread across the three localities. There is only a weak suggestion of association with tradition, in that those who espouse the importance of tradition may be more likely to see themselves on a treadmill. Perception of a treadmill could be associated with tradition and a desire to maintain the strength of commitment to the farm and family in order to work towards a way to stop the treadmill and get off, but awareness of a treadmill would seem unlikely to be accompanied in the long term by faith in the values which helped to create a situation in which farm families' interests continue to be subjugated to those of larger capital. Farm people may lose faith in tradition as they have found it to have placed them on the treadmill, rendering them unable to exercise the freedom to determine their futures which farm families have long valued.

Some farmers acknowledge conservatism in farm practices, but there is no indication of an effect of adherence to tradition in a broad sense. There appears to be no association between valuing traditional aspects of farm life and reluctance to try new land conservation measures. The finding that those farms on which a member of the second generation has chosen to take up a career use conservation techniques more extensively is more important, even if necessarily tentative due to sample size limitations. Use of family labour is itself part of farming tradition. It is more likely to occur among the bearers of tradition: those with stronger community ties.

Ethnographic evidence collected in two of the communities (Phillips, forthcoming) suggests that there are groups of people among them which differ in terms of tradition and which relate to each other in a spatial dimension. Relationships between groups and communities may be very important, as may the ways in which those groups and communities are defined. Space and the social relations conducted across it provide the arena for the construction, reconstruction and transmission of tradition. Further understanding of those relations and processes is needed to complete this cultural perspective on sustainability.

Conclusion

The detraditionalisation of farming can be seen in both vertical and horizontal dimensions. As the restructuring of agri-food industry proceeds and farmers find themselves more firmly tied to the treadmill, those who adhere most strongly to traditional values may be those most likely to question their predicament. Those who see the challenge as important may be more willing to accept the treadmill and try to make the most of it. This point requires further empirical exploration. Nevertheless, perception of the problems associated with high-input, high-production, agriculture along with concern about specific inputs shows that at least some farmers are questioning their practices.

Horizontal detraditionalisation may also be occurring. The point that intergenerational transfer of farms may depend at least in part on the strength of community ties suggests that the social sustainability of agriculture will be under growing threat. As the populations of farming communities decline and, moreover, long term residents who succumb to financial pressure are replaced by newcomers, the stake which subsequent generations have in their farming communities will decline. Along with this process may come a spiralling decline in farm succession and maintenance. This process will be very difficult to stop. It implies that the supply of family labour upon which the family farming system, or perhaps rather urban and transnational capital's exploitation of it, has been based will be eliminated. Just as the family farm system has needed family labour to survive economic crises, so it now needs the input of family members in terms of labour and knowledge. They may be called upon to carry out the changes and the work necessary to climb off the treadmill and to take the steps necessary to avoid continuing environmental degradation. But the decline of local tradition, along with the attraction of alternative careers, may eliminate this historical support mechanism.

The relationship between farming cultures and sustainability is more complex than a theory which relates cultural norms directly to practices would suggest. This chapter has explored some of the less direct ways in which tradition, and changes in it, may affect the course of Australian agriculture in the long term.

Notes

1 'Greater Redwood' consists of 33 farms of which the 20 farms discussed in Phillips (forthcoming) are a subset clustered in an area near the centre of Greater Redwood.

Acknowledgments

The research upon which this paper is based was funded by the Land and Water Resources Research and Development Corporation, the Rural Industries Research and Development Corporation and the Grains Research and Development Corporation.

Our thanks go to Helen Swan and Alison Gelding for their help with interviewing and transcription, and especially to the people of the three areas studied for their invaluable time and patience.

References

Ampt, P. and Phillips, E. (1994) *Listening to Farmers: Sustainability, Research and Adoption*, A report on focus groups, Wagga Wagga, Centre for Rural Social Research, Charles Sturt University.

Barr, N. and Cary, J. (1992) The Dilemma of Conservation Farming: To Use of Not Use Chemicals, pp. 233-258 in Lawrence, G, Vanclay, F. and Furze, B. (eds) Agriculture, Environment and Society, Melbourne, Macmillan: 233-258.

Buttel , F., Larson O. and Gillespie, G. Jr. (1990) *The Sociology of Agriculture*, New York, Greenwood Press.

Buttel, F, H. (1994) Agricultural Change, Rural Society and the State in the Late Twentieth Century in Symes, D. and Jansen, A. (eds) *Agricultural Restructuring and Rural Change in Europe*, Wageningen Studies in Sociology 37: 13-31.

Cary, J. (1992) Lessons from Past and Present Attempts to Develop Sustainable Land-use Systems, *Review of Marketing and Agricultural Economics* 60 (2): 277-284.

Craig, R. and Phillips, K. (1983) Agrarian Ideology in Australia and the United States, *Rural Sociology* 48 (3): 409-420.

Dunn. A. (1995) What Farmers Know and do about Sustainability: A seminar paper, Wagga Wagga, Charles Sturt University.

Giddens, A. (1994) Living in a Post-Traditional Society, in Beck, U., Giddens, A. and Lash, S. *Reflexive Modernization: Politics, Tradition and Aesthetics in the Modern Social Order*, Oxford, Blackwell: 56-109.

Gray, I. and Dunn, A. (1992) Farmer Perceptions of Dryland Salinity in the Southern NSW Wheatbelt, *Australian Journal of Soil and Water Conservation* 5 (2): 44-49.

Gray, I., Lawrence, G. and Dunn, A. (1993) *Coping with Change: Australian Farmers in the 1990s*, Wagga Wagga, Centre for Rural Social Research, Charles Sturt University.

Gray, I., Phillips, E., Ampt, P. and Dunn, A. (1995) Awareness or Beguilement: Farmers' Perceptions of Change, in Share, P. (ed.) *Beyond Countrymindedness: Communications, Culture and Ideology in Rural Areas*,

Key Papers 4, Wagga Wagga, Centre for Rural Social Research, Charles Sturt University.

Guerin, L. and Guerin, T. (1994) Constraints to the Adoption of Innovations in Agricultural Research and Environmental Management: a Review, *Australian Journal of Experimental Agriculture* 34 (4): 549-571.

Kloppenburg, J. (1992) Science in Agriculture: A Reply to Molnar, Duffy, Cummins, and van Santen and to Flora, *Rural Sociology* 57 (1): 98-107.

Lawrence, G. and Vanclay, F. (1994) Agricultural Change in the Semi-Periphery: The Murray-Darling Basin, Australia in McMichael, P. (ed.) *The Global Restructuring of Agro-Food Systems,* Ithaca, Cornell University Press: 76-103.

Mooney, P. (1988) *My Own Boss: Class Rationality and The Family Farm,* Boulder, Westview Press.

Phillips, E. (forthcoming) Linking the Global to the Local: Ethnographic perspectives on farm practice and the globalisation of agriculture, in Burch, D., Rickson, R. and Lawrence, G. (eds) *Globalisation and Agri-Food Restructuring: Perspectives from the Australasia Region,* Aldershot, Avebury Press.

Phillips, E. and Gray, I. (1995) Farming Practice as Temporally and Spatially Situated Intersections of Biography, Culture and Social Structure, *Australian Geographer* 26 (2): 127-132.

Pile, S. (1990) *The Private Farmer: Transformation and Legitimation in Advanced Capitalist Agriculture,* Dartmouth, Aldershot.

Poiner, G. (1990) *The Good Old Rule: Gender and Other Power Relationships in a Rural Community,* Sydney, Sydney University Press.

Salamon, S. (1985) Ethnic Communities and the Structure of Agriculture, *Rural Sociology* 50 (3): 323-340.

Shils, E. (1981) *Tradition,* Chicago, University of Chicago Press.

Stone, S. (1992) Land Degradation and Rural Communities in Victoria: Experience and Response, in Lawrence, G., Vanclay, F. and Furze, B. (eds) *Agriculture, Environment and Society,* Melbourne, Macmillan: 173-183.

Vanclay, F. and Lawrence, G. (1995) *The Environmental Imperative: Eco-social Concerns for Australian Agriculture,* Rockhampton, Central Queensland University Press.

Ward, N. (1993) The Agricultural Treadmill and the Rural Environment in the Post-Productivist Era, *Sociologia Ruralis* 33 (3/4): 348-364.

Ward, N. and Lowe, P. (1994) Shifting Values in Agriculture: the Farm Family and Pollution Regulation, *Journal of Rural Studies* 10 (2): 173-184.

Chapter 22

Consumer attitudes to genetically-engineered food products: Focus group research in Rockhampton, Queensland

Janet Norton and Geoffrey Lawrence

Genetic engineering and agriculture

Genetic engineering can broadly be described as the alteration of the genetic information of an organism as a result of human action aimed either at adding new (foreign) genetic material or at deleting or rearranging existing genes within the organism (see House of Representatives Standing Committee, 1992). In agricultural research genetic engineering differs from traditional plant and animal breeding. In the latter, plants and animals with desirable qualities have been selected for breeding and cross breeding. The role of the scientist has been to employ largely conventional means of plant and animal reproduction and to continue to select plant and animal progeny construed to exhibit desirable qualities. In this manner - and as a result of over a century of experimentation in Australia - scientists have developed, *inter alia*, less fatty beef animals, those which are tick resistant, plants which are rust resistant and those which, through hybridisation, are capable of quite significant output increases.

With genetic engineering, desirable qualities of plants and animals can be identified within gene sequences and those gene sequences can be 'cut' and reassembled in an attempt to have the desirable trait expressed in future generations. It allows for more (scientific) certainty in genetic improvement, an increased rate of genetic change, and the ability to insert foreign genes into a host organism creating novel - transgenic - organisms (see Martin and Baumgardt, 1991). For example, it is possible now for scientists to take the gene sequence for a growth hormone from a cow or pig, place that within a microbial organism, breed that organism quickly and in large numbers, extract the hormone and then inject it into the target animal. It is a 'natural' hormone and the animal responds in the manner expected - by, for example, growing more quickly, or producing more milk. Scientists have also taken desirable gene sequences from animals and put them into bacteria, from bacteria and put them into plants, and from humans and put them into animals. Australian scientists believe that the improvements which are likely from the continued application of genetic engineering will include increased agricultural productivity, improved sustainability, a better environment, increased farm output and a reduction in the use of chemicals (see Lawrence and Norton, 1994; Vanclay and Lawrence, 1995). The Australian Government has given strong support for the continuation of genetic engineering in agricultural and food production, the major justification for which is that Australian farmers and food manufacturers will fall behind their overseas competitors if they do not adopt the new, productivity-enhancing, technology (see Bureau of Rural Resources, 1991; House of Representatives Standing Committee, 1992).

In relation to the food products resulting from genetically-engineered plants and animals, as well as those which are produced in the laboratory through genetic engineering, Australia's House of Representatives Standing Committee (1992) concluded that genetically modified products were unlikely to be harmful to human health. While noting that there were some food safety issues (such as hormone contamination of food) and recognising that a number of consumer groups had expressed concerns about genetically-engineered foods, the Standing Committee believed that any problems could be overcome if:

> new foods, new strains of existing foods, or new food additives which are developed using genetic manipulation techniques should be submitted to the (GMO) Release Authority as a pre-condition before release (House of Representatives Standing Committee, 1992: 208).

The GMO Release Authority would take advice from State and Federal Government Departments, call public hearings and to advertise the proposal (where this was deemed necessary) and make a determination on the desirability or otherwise of release.

Importantly, however, there would be no compulsory labelling of food products containing genetically modified organisms. The Standing Committee suggested there should be labelling of some products, but this would have to be decided on a 'case by case' basis under guidelines similar to those applying in the UK. The general rule applying in the UK is that foods derived from a transgenic organism, or from an organism which contains cells 'which differ from conventional products traditionally consumed in Western Europe' *should* be labelled (see House of Representatives Standing Committee, 1992: 252). In arguing against the submission of the Australian Consumers Association whose members had stated that all foods containing biotechnologically-derived substances should be labelled as such, the Standing Committee noted the growing difficulties of determining whether or not, at some stage in the production of foods, a recombinant organism had been utilised to assist production, and the possible consumer backlash against products labelled as containing genetically modified materials. It concluded:

> The labelling issue revolves around the moral right of the consumer to know, balanced against the practicability and value of providing information which is sought. The debate is all the more sensitive because genetically modified food may be seen as a marketing negative.
>
> If labelling was required for products produced by genetic modification, the industry would be singled out. It could suffer a financial penalty in trying to overcome possible consumer resistance and could be vulnerable to any emotional argument from those vehemently opposed to the technology.
>
> If there were no labelling, it could be argued that public concerns about the technology and the right of the consumer to make a choice in a fundamental area were being ignored. There might be a spate of 'GMO free' labels similar to those proclaiming 'cholesterol free' on products which have never contained cholesterol. Such an outcome is not desirable (House of Representatives Standing Committee, 1992: 253).

In other words, labelling may be sought in some circumstances, but concerns are raised that the industry would not prosper if consumers baulked at products simply because their labels were misunderstood. Consequently, conclusions reached by the Standing Committee state that labelling should not be mandatory, rather be done on a case by case basis. Submissions to the Standing Committee further suggest that consumers may not fully understand the implications of a food product being labelled as containing (or not containing) genetically modified materials. This may in turn result in consumer resistance to the new products, and advertisers may misconstrue the meaning of foreign genetic material to undermine new products, while seeking to enhance their own.

Consumer attitudes to genetic engineering: Evidence from Australia and overseas

Public concern over the use of genetic engineering for the production of agricultural commodities has occurred in Australia, just as it has in the US and European countries. Some of the main issues raised have been those relating to public health, the ethics of creating transgenic organisms, and environmental issues (see Lacy, Busch and Lacy, 1991: 139). The public health issues relate to the nature of foods eaten (unintended consequences of toxins in foods, or of resistance of new organisms to antibiotics). The creation of transgenic organisms raises issues of the 'unnaturalness' of placing foreign genes into a host organism, and of scientists 'playing god' by manipulating nature for their own purposes (Sparks, Shepherd and Frewer, 1994). The environmental issues concern the likely impacts of novel organisms - including their unintended consequences on soils, waterways and on other organisms. There has been concern in relation to the escape of pathogenic organisms, the effects on biodiversity, and the creation of species through gene transfer between transgenic and other organisms. The prospect of ecological disaster is considered by some groups to be one of the greatest concerns in relation to genetic engineering (see Hindmarsh, 1994; Phelps, 1994).

In Australia, Alexander (1992) reviewed public responses from the Will Pigs Fly? exhibition on genetic engineering mounted by the CSIRO. The majority of those who answered questions after seeing the (largely pro-biotechnology) show (see Hindmarsh, 1992) indicated they had major concerns in relation to scientists interfering with nature, the control which might be exerted by companies commercialising the new products, and in terms of risks to the environment (Alexander, 1992). Work undertaken by Halbrendt *et al.*, (as reported in Young and Roper, 1995) indicated that while some 58 percent of respondents had concerns about the use of bacteria to produce porcine somatotropin (for injection into pigs), some 75 percent said they would approve of the technique if it resulted in leaner pork.

More recent work by Kelley (see DIST, 1995) has produced some ambiguous results, the partial explanation for which is the limitations of the research instrument (see Hindmarsh, Lawrence and Norton, 1995; Norton, Lawrence and Hindmarsh, 1995). What Kelley found was that when respondents to a national survey were asked a series of questions about the products of genetic engineering, they were quite supportive. For example, some 77 percent would wear clothing made from genetically-engineered cotton, 56 percent would eat genetically-engineered pork, 61 percent would eat genetically-engineered tomatoes, and 60 percent would use cooking oil from genetically-engineered plants (see Kelley, 1995). However, it has been argued by critics (see Hindmarsh, Norton and Lawrence, 1995) that the high level of support he found for the products of genetic engineering might have been a consequence of his not indicating to respondents the origin of the genes in the transgenic organisms, not disclosing the possible risks associated with the new technologies, and in at least one case (mis)leading respondents to believe that all genetically-engineered products in Australia would be labelled as such (see Norton, Lawrence and Hindmarsh, 1995). In spite of this, and in another part of the survey, respondents revealed that they were concerned about the application of the new technology (only 5 percent of respondents said they were not worried) (see DIST, 1995).

Just as in Australia, studies of public attitudes and opinions in overseas nations have tended to be based on quantitative (survey) research methods. What tends to be found is that if questions are asked in the abstract - of the sort 'it is acceptable for scientists to manipulate genes' a majority of respondents tends to disagree - respondents tend to say that such research is inappropriate (Lacy, Busch and Lacy, 1991). However, when they have been told to assume that genetic experimentation will harm neither humans nor the environment, and when they are given particular applications as examples (production of disease resistant crops, more effective herbicides and better farm animals) respondents normally provide quite high levels (between 60 and 80 percent) of support for genetic engineering (Lacy, Busch and Lacy, 1991:148). A major European study indicated that a majority of respondents favoured genetic engineering of micro-organisms and of plants, but were not approving of the genetic engineering of farm animals (see Sparks, Shepherd and Frewer, 1994). There has also been found to be a difference of attitude between men and women. In one UK survey it was established that:

> compared to men, women indicated less need for the technology, gave lower ratings about improvements to the quality of life, reported lower benefits and greater risks ... expressed greater concern, and agreed more strongly that ethical issues were involved (Sparks, Shepherd and Frewer, 1994: 25).

In the British survey, more people expressed the views that biotechnology would produce low benefits rather than high benefits, high risks rather than low risks and low need rather than high need. The authors pointed out that there was a major dilemma for the proponents of new gene technologies. There is evidence of a lack of confidence by people in government and business organisations, yet it is those organisations which are involved in the production of most of the information about the new technologies. The public is seeing more information coming from groups in society which it does not trust, and so may become more sceptical as more information is produced! (see discussion in Sparks, Shepherd and Frewer, 1995). According to Rothenberg (1995: 2) the public puts its trust in 'environmental organisations, medical doctors, university professors, dietitians ... consumer organisations ... public health officials and farmers ...' while governmental regulators, biotechnology companies and industry sources had 'far less credibility'. What appears to be happening - perhaps as a consequence - is that public acceptance of biotechnology is beginning to decline, at least in Europe (see Jank, 1995).

Not a great deal of work has been done to assess the attitudes of consumers to genetically manipulated food products. Hoban's (1989) and Hoban, Woodrum and Czaja's (1992) work is the most extensive. Among populations in North Carolina, Hoban found that some 77 percent of respondents were very concerned or somewhat concerned about consuming genetically-engineered fruit and vegetable products. What has also been demonstrated in the US surveys is that respondents often reject as inappropriate or immoral, techniques which are currently in use but about which they understand little. About one quarter of Hoban's sample rejected plant hybridisation, for example. The lack of consumer knowledge about the science of modern food production, and of genetic engineering in particular (see Almas, 1994) is often construed by scientists to result in people's 'irrational' fears gaining the fore in discussions about the future of genetic engineering. It is not necessary to question the technology, but rather the capacity of people fully to appreciate its benefits (see Peacock, 1994). There is some confusion about the nature education provides.

According to Rothenberg (1995) the more that funding is provided for public education, the greater the acceptance of biotechnology. This is in direct contrast with the findings of Almas and Nygard (1993) whose research in Norway indicates the opposite.

One of the important findings of the previous surveys is that many respondents do not understand what is meant by the term genetic engineering. In one US study some two thirds of respondents said they understood what was meant, but in others little over 50 percent of people said they had little understanding, or no awareness, of the term (Lacy, Busch and Lacy, 1991). A problem for those quantitative researchers relying exclusively upon large scale surveys is that of knowing the 'knowledge base' of those responding. To what extent, it could be asked, should the attitudes and opinions of people who have very little idea about genetic engineering be included alongside those who do? The answer which can be given is that the public is going to help make decisions about genetic engineering, so that its present knowledge base will be that which determines what is likely to be approved or not approved. There is nothing wrong, then, with tapping into the biases and prejudices of respondents, when it is those biases and prejudices which may actually help to determine policy. It does raise the issue, however, of the extent to which alternative methodologies might be useful in seeking more informed views of respondents.

Focus Group Methodology

As suggested above, genetic engineering is a relatively new concept and there has been limited research into consumer attitudes to this new technology (see Zimmerman, Kendall, Stone and Hoban, 1994). When dealing with new concepts it is essential that researchers do not impose their views upon respondents. It is useful, in this situation, to use methods which provide data that closely mirror the attitudes of respondents. The use of focus groups allows the researcher to gather information that uses participants' own words and thought associations, with a minimum of intrusion by the researcher (Stewart and Shamdasani, 1990).

Four focus groups were conducted in the period July - August 1995. Each focus group consisted of from six to nine persons. Males and females were included in each of the groups, in approximately equal numbers. The groups were facilitated by the researchers and an assistant. The first group consisted of students of the Central Queensland University. Both postgraduate and undergraduate students were included and students from the faculties of engineering, arts and science participated. The three other groups were established at the three state high schools in Rockhampton. The schools recruited members of the school community to participate. Each group consisted of a mixture of parents and teachers. These selection methods resulted in relatively homogeneous groups who were familiar with each other. Kreuger (1988) argues that familiarity of participants does not affect the conduct of the group but rather the analysis of the results as the dynamics of the group may not be fully understood by the researcher. As the topic discussed was not directly related to the recruiting organisations, and the facilitator was not affiliated in any way with the organisations, it is argued that the familiarity of participants does not present any difficulties in data analysis. This was reinforced by the similarity of results from all groups.

This research study was designed to be different from large scale survey work. Not only did we wish to obtain group views (rather than individual views which are then usually aggregated for statistical purposes) but we also recognised the need to inform members of the group about aspects of the new technology. In other words, the focus groups became a venue for people to learn about, then comment upon, genetic engineering. This was seen to be an appropriate means of establishing the attitudes of members of the group to techniques and products with which they were anticipated to (and were found to) have little familiarity. We moved from a wide discussion about what it was, as consumers, they wanted from foods, and then the more specific issue of genetically-engineered agricultural and food products.

Each separate group was asked on three different occasions to summarise the discussion and to prioritise the group's findings. Thus, material explaining genetic engineering and detailing several genetically-engineered products was then introduced to the group. The facilitator explored the material with the group and clarified any questions that were asked. The group then had a short break. Participants then discussed each product in detail. The group then listed products according to the degree of support they had for each. Following this discussion, participants were asked to detail any concerns they had about genetic engineering. Concerns were then prioritised by the group. A number of questions relating to reasons for using genetic engineering were then asked of the group.

Results

The discussions showed that participants had definite ideas on the characteristics of food that they thought were important. A summary of the results of prioritisation of important characteristics of food is shown in Appendix A. Three of the first four characteristics, nutrition, taste and freshness are direct characteristics of food. The other characteristics, cost and convenience, and environmental issues, could be designated as social characteristics. Participants were concerned about nutrition and additives. In the words of one:

> I also want to know that the food is nutritious but it is also safe. Um, that you hear so much about chemicals these days that I'm very conscious when I buy food.

The concern about additives was reflected in the number of participants who spoke of reading labels of processed foods. They were very conscious of the various additives and whether or not such additives were harmful.

> Yeah, so I tend to read the labels. I read the labels to check that they're not something that I don't think I should eat.

Cost of food was not the most important characteristic for most respondents, However, it was an important consideration in purchasing. The cost of food was also bound up with other considerations:

> It's very hard with a financial strain. I try to by Australian made but ... it also depends on the price. I mean, everybody's got a budget so you've got to think of the price. You know, everybody's got so much for this week so, you know, you look around for the specials.

In general, participants showed that a great deal of thought went into the purchase of food and that there were many aspects that had to be considered before choosing a particular product. While some people bought according to 'labels' this was because of their previous knowledge of the contents and additives, and their approval of the foods' taste.

When asked to give a definition of genetic engineering, there was usually only one member of the group who had an idea of what was meant. Other participants were often vague and talked of 'cloning', 'manipulation' and 'artificial food'. Some participants were able to give a succinct definition:

> It's when they actually get into the DNA, the basic building blocks of each sort of life form and snip a bit off here and shove it in there.

Another stated:

> It's where you play around with the DNA genetics of a cell really, but the characteristics of a whole organism change as a result of changing the DNA.

Participants were interested in the exact nature of genetic engineering and of the practical examples provided to them. Discussion showed that they had reservations about the uses of some of the products derived from the new technology. The prioritised list of products can be seen in Appendix A. The blue rose had the most support - despite being considered by many to be 'artificial' and 'unnatural'. Its degree of support was based on the fact that it was a plant which would not enter the food cycle. Further support was forthcoming as it was seen as the transference of genetic material between 'plant and plant'. The second product on the list was cheese. As cheese was already being produced by this method, participants had few worries about eating it. There were, however, those who considered cheese manufactured in this way to be artificial. The two methods of enhancing wool production were placed next on the list. In both cases, participants did not consider that they would be eating the products, merely wearing the wool. The intention to protect sheep from blow fly strike was considered by most to be beneficial. Altering an animal to benefit the animal appeared to raise few ethical issues. Similarly the second application to sheep raised few concerns. With the exception of cheese, the products listed so far were not seen as being consumed by humans. The last four applications were all food products and the subject of much debate.

The genetically-engineered tomato provided in the example has been released in the United States but is not, as yet, available in Australia. The new tomato requires the insertion of a gene from a flounder in the tomato's DNA (this is one of several techniques available to scientists to prevent 'squashyness' in tomatoes). The insertion of an animal gene caused some concern, particularly to vegetarian members of the groups. Some participants expressed concern over social attitudes which could perhaps be seen as the reason for the development of such a product.

> I think there's a problem with social attitudes. We really should be able to look past the blemishes and things like that. If it improves the nutrition value of the tomato not just the appearance I would buy it.

With the example of wheat, participants mentioned two concerns. One was the effect of the wheat upon people who ate it and the other was consequences to the environment. The possible eradication of insects (as a result of the insertion of the *Bt* gene into the wheat plant) was viewed as potentially affecting bird and animal life, and questions were asked about the effect on the whole food chain. Doubt was placed on the statement that the toxins were 'not known to be harmful to humans'. The placing of the toxin within the plant caused concern:

> but I wash things and bacteria are hopefully not *in* things. So I don't know. I'm very mixed up and confused about that. If I didn't know it was happening I'd probably eat it without a worry, so once again if I knew it was happening I'd probably try and avoid it.

The last two products placed on the list were the pork products. Both of these products caused concern because of the introduction of hormones, although by two different methods, to the pig. The injection of hormones into the pig was viewed as less offensive than the introduction of a human growth promoter sequence into the pig's DNA.

Throughout the discussion, participants raised several concerns and they were then asked to consider these concerns more directly and to prioritise them (summaries of the focus group responses are found in Appendix A).

The long and short term effects on human health were of most concern to participants: they considered much more testing was required before these products were made available for human consumption:

> Are they sure of it, though? Are they going to tell us 20 years down the track that we've made a mistake?

Participants were also concerned over ethical and moral issues including who maintained control over the extent of experimentation that was being conducted. There were even those who linked it to supposed Hitlerian tendencies among scientists:

> I mean how far do we go? This genetic thing runs off from the Nazis.

The other aspect of control that caused concern was control by businesses who owned the patents of the new organism:

> Who owns the patents for the genetic engineering? Who therefore controls or owns our food supply? Who therefore controls basically our food chain? Are we being patented?

Labelling was also of concern. Participants felt that labelling of products should occur because it would provide them with a choice when it came to purchasing. The lack of labelling was seen as a means of hiding information from the consumer:

> Like trying to do it sneaky. Not out in the open. I mean if it's bad for us why not tell us about it? What, which products have changed?

The results of the focus groups showed that participants initially had little knowledge of genetic engineering and genetically-engineered products. After learning of genetic engineering, they seemed sceptical about what scientists were doing. Many reservations and concerns were raised. A series of questions were then asked in relation to specific products derived from genetic engineering and the reasons for purchasing products. If the product was safe, increase in nutrition was seen as a reason for purchase. However, making Australian farmers more competitive overseas, making agriculture more sustainable, and keeping farmers on the land were not seen as reasons to purchase these goods. Overwhelmingly, though, participants felt that there was a need for people to know more about these products. Despite their reservations, some participants felt the introduction of these products was inevitable:

> Well it's heading that way whether we like it or not. I mean, we, the buyer, are in a position to say yes or no but I mean the people of power basically what they say, it's already been decided regardless and whether we like it or not, you know, ... you like it or lump it, sort of thing. I think that's where it's wrong.

Summary of focus group sessions

The focus groups concentrated on two issues - current food preferences and habits, and genetically-engineered products. The initial discussion on food allowed the participants to speak with confidence about something with which they were already familiar. We learned what was important to them when choosing foodstuffs. This allowed the transition into the more unfamiliar territory of genetic engineering. As had been expected, knowledge of genetic engineering was very limited (Norton and Lawrence, 1995). For this reason a discussion aid containing details of genetic engineering and genetically-engineered products had been prepared. Discussion aids are a valid part of focus group research (Stewart and Shamdasani, 1990) and can be used to give participants information to stimulate discussion. Based on the material provided, participants were able to discuss concrete examples rather than hypothetical cases. This made the discussion process more relevant to all concerned.

The discussion on food demonstrated the minimal requirements that food required to be acceptable. These requirements were later applied to the genetically-engineered products that were discussed. Participants demonstrated a concern that some of these requirements may not necessarily be available within the new products as well as concerns for environmental and moral issues. These concerns parallel those found by overseas researchers. The lack of information available in regard to these products was also noted as a concern.

Health issues - both long and short term effects - were a major issue of concern. Participants consistently showed a distrust of information provided by scientists, again in keeping with findings from overseas studies. Past experience had made them wary of the promises being made by scientists. A typical statement in relation to this point was:

> Well as I said before, I don't, I honestly don't believe scientists when they say 'Trust us. We know what we are doing'. It's been proved so many times that certainly with the best available knowledge that it may be apparent that something doesn't seem to have any adverse effect but we all know that 10 - 20 years down the track, people have been proved totally wrong. So that's why I think, um, personally I like to be a bit on the cautious side rather than be, um, leap in and try these things without the information.

Busch (1991) argues that three issues are important when consumers consider genetically-engineered foods - consent, knowledge and fairness. All three of these issues were prominent in the discussions. The need for consent was clearly shown by the concerns that participants had over labelling issues. Labelling gives people the choice of whether or not to use the products. The lack of labelling was viewed as an attempt to hide information from the consumer:

> I think we're concerned that, you know, like things, that products are going to be on the shelf and they won't be labelled because manufacturers don't want to scare off consumers.

Others were concerned for consumers rights:

> They should all be labelled because people have a right to know what they're using; to know what they're putting into their bodies.

The need for knowledge was highlighted by the fact that participants felt an education programme on genetic engineering was necessary. This was seen as being a different issue to labelling. Labelling alone would not provide consumers with the necessary information to make a choice:

> the general public needs to be educated to what it is. What is genetic engineering and what does it actually mean, what are the consequences, what is an enzyme or something else that's in there, you know. Like otherwise people don't know ...

Busch (1991) considers fairness to be the 'overall balance of risks and benefits' and asks 'who bears the risks and who receives the benefits'? Similar sentiments were exhibited by the participants. There were those who thought that the only ones to benefit would be 'big business', a similar concern to that found by Alexander (1992). A typical comment was:

> you've got to have in mind that many of these things have probably got business behind them to a certain extent and that the dollar is no doubt one big factor in the development of these products. And again, I'm even less trusting of the multi-national corporations.

The risks were being taken by consumers and their children:

> See, you don't actually know until the next generation if that's going to create certain things.

> Well it's not going to be in our life it's going to be in our
> children's life and their children's life. What's going to happen to
> them if they're going to still be here?

Together with these issues of consent, knowledge and fairness were other issues
of concern such as environmental problems and nutrition. Mannion (1995)
gives three disadvantages of biotechnology in relation to environmental quality.
These are the potential to create invasive organisms, organisms that are toxic,
and organisms that may profoundly alter the global biogeochemical cycles.
While respondents did not use these terms explicitly, they did talk in terms of
the loss of the wild gene pool and of the danger to food chains that could be
caused by the release of genetically-engineered organisms. Unlike other
Australian and overseas research findings, environmental issues rated fairly low
in the scale of concerns of the Rockhampton groups.

Throughout the discussion, participants assumed that resultant genetically-
engineered foods would have at least the same nutritional value as the 'natural'
products. Indeed, an increase in nutrition was seen to be a reason for purchasing
such products. Some critics of the genetic engineering of foods have indicated,
however, that improved nutrition is not the primary objective of genetic
engineering. According to Young and Lewis (1995):

> These advances have been based on relatively little knowledge of
> basic human nutritional needs. More importantly, these advances
> have been predicated with no understanding of dietary nutrient
> interactions. Changing nutrient composition of foods through
> biotechnology may alter nutrient interactions, nutrient-gene
> interactions, nutrient availability, nutrient potency, and nutrient
> metabolism. Biotechnology has the potential to produce changes
> in our foods and in our diet at a pace far greater than our ability
> to predict the significance of those changes on ... nutrition.

Increased nutrition is the one area that produced support and yet is the one area
where research appears to be lacking. Further research in this area may improve
the public's perception of genetic engineering.

While the results from the research conducted are not able to be
generalised, it is important to see how they compare with other research on the
topic. Zimmerman *et al.*, (1994) report a more favourable response to
biotechnology following focus group discussions. This was not the case in this
study - with participants expressing concerns over genetic engineering at the
end of each of the four focus group discussions. This study would, rather, tend
to support the view that approval of genetic engineering decreases as people
obtain more information about it (see Almas and Nygard, 1993) and so
contrasts to the findings of Rothenberg (1995) who claims that the opposite
occurs. However, Zimmerman's study does report that consumers 'clearly
indicated they wanted information about foods produced through
biotechnology', as has been similarly shown by this study.

The US Congress Office of Technology Assessment (1987) concluded that:

> In summary, most Americans appear to be pragmatists on the issue of genetic engineering. They are concerned about both the morality and the risks of the technology. The survey finds that while the public express concern about genetic engineering in the abstract, it approves nearly every specific environmental or therapeutic application ...

The results from Kelley's Australian study indicate something similar:

> The community takes a balanced view about the benefits and risks of the technology: people appreciate its potential benefits in improving health and medicine, developing better crops and foods and in improving the environment but at the same time recognising there may be risks (*Australasian Biotechnology*, 1995: 246).

While we would accept that our qualitative study is quite limited in scope, and while we recognise that focus group research has no statistical validity, the findings of our research do not support the statements by OTA or from Kelley's study. Participants showed concern over the abstract ideas of genetic engineering. The introduction, by the group facilitator, of specific examples of current research demonstrated that participants had significant concerns over the uses of genetic engineering. When faced with the prospect of consuming these products participants were reluctant to do so in the absence of further information.

Discussion and conclusion

It would seem, from the above analysis, that at least five issues have become apparent:

- consumers of foods appear to be quite concerned about genetic alteration of foods they might ingest. This relates to consumer interest in purchasing nutritious/wholesome and unprocessed/fresh products over those which are 'manufactured' or are in some other way seen to be manipulated
- consumers demand more information about genetically-engineered foods. They are suspicious about the 'refashioning of nature' which is occurring in Australian laboratories and want more information about what is happening and what it means in relation to the foods they eat
- consumers want any genetically-modified foods to be labelled as such. Again, they want to ensure that, as consumers, they have as much knowledge as possible upon which to make their decision to purchase or not purchase. They show, here, a desire to control the food agenda, not be

'victims' of science. Consumers are likely to resist those products which are not properly labelled

- genetically-engineered products which promise to improve the welfare of animals, or may lead to fewer chemicals in the environment, receive approval *so long as those products are not ingested*. Here, the issue of the meaning and importance of 'natural' foods is again raised as is that of the limits to scientific experimentation. It would seem that research with plants and bacteria is much preferred over animal research
- the ultimate concern about the application of genetic engineering to agriculture and food products was that of the effects on human health. In a society becoming increasingly preoccupied with body image, and health-conscious eating, genetically-engineered foods stand in stark contrast to those which are less manipulated, or are produced organically. Unless consumers can be convinced, on health grounds, that the new products are superior to those which they are used to purchasing, it is unlikely that they will endorse a genetically-engineered future for agriculture or food production in Australia.

At its broadest level, genetic engineering applied to farming and food should be considered both in relation to the political economy of agriculture (see Buttel, Larson and Gillespie, 1990; Goodman and Redclift, 1991; Almas, 1992; Vanclay and Lawrence, 1995) and the tendencies in advanced societies towards 'postmodernisation' (see Crook, Pakulski and Waters, 1992; Waters, 1995). Feminist perspectives can provide insights into the power structures of science and a critique of male dominance in knowledge production (see Kollek, 1990).

The literature within the political economy of agriculture tends to highlight the dependence of farmers on productivist agriculture and their apparent inability to move beyond 'high tech' solutions to their problems (see Lawrence, 1995; Gray, Phillips, Ampt, and Dunn, 1995). Producing in a competitive export market, Australian farmers are seeking to overcome problems of long term decline in their terms of trade by enhancing the productivity of their operations (Lawrence, 1987). They have done this in the past by utilising the latest products of agribusiness - fertilisers, pesticides, new seed varieties, and so on. Agricultural industries are constantly seeking new inputs which will boost output and improve efficiency. New, genetically-engineered products promise these benefits. Some also promise to overcome the environmental problems which have been a direct result of the application of scientific inputs in past rounds of production. In terms of the existing trajectory of productivist agriculture, the new products would become direct replacements for some environmentally harmful combinations. Farmers are told that without the new techniques their ability to survive in farming will be in jeopardy. Their main representative body, the National Farmers' Federation (1993: 84) provides overwhelming endorsement for the development and application of biotechnologies in agriculture and the food industry, even if the farmers themselves remain somewhat unconvinced (see Norton and Lawrence, 1995).

The role of the corporate sector in developing and selling the new inputs to farmers and firms in the food sector is another aspect of analysis for political economists. Companies have spent billions of dollars developing such products as bovine somatotropin, herbicide-resistant crops and new seed varieties. They want returns on investments. They also recognise the profits which might be made: it is estimated that by the year 2000 a market for biotechnological products of between US$40 and $60 billion will have been developed (see Kleinman and Kloppenberg, 1991). Companies are seen as attempting to maintain an hegemonic position in product R&D by 'promulgating a vision of biotechnology that will further its interests' by convincing consumers that it is essential to support a genetically-engineered future (see Kleinman and Kloppenberg, 1991: 430). There has been an attempt by the large corporations and the state to 'sell' the benefits of science and do so on the basis that if *only* people understood the long term advantages of research, community support would naturally follow.

Some critics of genetic engineering remain convinced of the potential benefits of some of the techniques, but want to remind us that those techniques are not objectively 'neutral', but are part of a wider system of capitalist profit-making and agenda setting. As Kloppenberg (1991:488-489) states:

> Let me say that I would like to think that - properly used - biotechnology can provide us with important tools to move towards a truly sustainable agriculture. But can we trust Monsanto to get us there?

The problem for the corporate and other firms involved in R&D activities is, as was detailed above, that the products are meeting with mixed reaction from an increasingly cynical public. Why, in a technically advanced society, should there be scepticism about the likely benefits of science? It is here that postmodern concerns need to be considered. Postmodern theorists have identified the rejection of Big Science as one of the features of late capitalism. The public appears to recognise that science and technology have created many problems and that 'progress' is not automatically linked to technological developments (Crook, Pakulski and Waters, 1992). The attitudes of focus group members certainly paralleled this. Scientists were sometimes viewed as being out of touch with public sentiment and of attempting, somewhat arrogantly, to dictate the future. Postmodern writers believe the rejection of modernity and the questioning of its scientific base is a symptom of social disorganisation which can be understood as 'an incompatibility between continuing centralisation and continuing differentiation' within society (see Crook, Pakulski and Waters, 1992). Respondents appeared to oppose the domination of nature by humankind, while recognising that specific benefits could be obtained from particular applications of genetic engineering.

The main point which struck us was the (generally) clear division in approval of those genetically-engineered products which were designed to be ingested by consumers, versus those which were for other purposes. With the exception of cheeses - which respondents recognised were already being produced by genetically-modified organisms - people did not want to eat the products of genetic engineering. One of the main findings of the focus group research is that consumers are much more likely to approve of genetic engineering where it will improve animal health or resistance of plants to disease, but generally to disapprove of it where the products of such research appear in foods.

Again, in this context, we come back to postmodern concerns. It has been suggested that there has been a movement toward 'clean and green' foods in the advanced nations. Consumers are rejecting 'artificial' foods, purchasing instead, less chemically-laden and supposedly more healthy foods. Concerns for the body and for health has lead to a rejection of the blind application of chemicals and of food manipulation and has been accompanied by a move toward organic production. Those supporting organic production are often the most vehemently opposed to biotechnology and genetic engineering (see Lawrence, *et al.,* 1992; IFOAM, 1994). There would seem to have been, among our focus group respondents, a view that the foods derived from genetic engineering were somehow unnatural. As such, its products would be less likely to be accepted than those which, for example, were produced by organic (or more natural) means. The question might be asked: are scientists developing novel, genetically-modified foods at the very time society is moving to reject such foods as unacceptable to modern living?

Feminist (and feminist-influenced) writers, in particular, ask questions relating to which groups in society determine the agenda for food production and consumption. For Kloppenberg (1991: 499) genetic engineering derives from a reductionist paradigm and promotes methods which are 'exceedingly powerful, but ... fundamentally anti-systemic'.

Genetic engineering allows those companies which already have control over existing agricultural inputs and food manufacture to continue to control the agenda leading to the treatment of symptoms, rather than to the causes of problems. According to Kollek (1990) much of today's biological experimentation has to do with increasing the influence and power of science. Problems are defined by scientists in a manner which leads to a conclusion that more science needs to be applied. Such science is viewed as patriarchal, allowing the privileging of certain conceptualisations and understanding people and the environment as things to be studied, controlled and regulated. The control exerted by science and concerns about what was occurring in the laboratories were certainly important themes in the focus group discussions.

Applying the feminist critique to the genetic manipulation of farming and food products, it might be suggested that the new technology will help to obfuscate what is happening on the farm and in the laboratories of food companies, reducing the ability of consumers to understand how their foods are derived, and leading to increasing control by those companies who are using the new techniques. Two other issues might also be raised here - the increasing likelihood of corporate control as new products are patented, and the potential resistance of consumers to that control (as perhaps we are seeing in the move by consumers increasingly to purchase 'clean and green' foods).

As Brandth and Bolso (1994: 137) have argued:

> feminist scholarship has criticised science and its institutions for being shaped by the interests and concerns of Euro-American middle-class males. In so doing, feminism raises fundamental questions about the nature of truth, objectivity and rationality ... Nature (for men) is seen as something to be controlled and conquered.

As these authors have shown in their review of literature, women believe that genetic engineering is much less acceptable than do men. They continue:

> women more than men want to prohibit the release of genetically-engineered organisms into the environment. Women more than men will not buy meat or dairy products processed by means of (genetically-engineered) hormones. Women more than men are against the right to patent engineered plants or animals. This sex difference in value orientation is confirmed in similar studies done in the United States and in the European Community (Brandth and Bolso, 1994: 142).

The extent to which a 'degendered' science and technology might serve better the interests of humanity is brought into question by the authors who indicate that socialisation has been an extremely powerful force in inculcating scientific values in both men and women who choose a scientific career. Women have been 'fitted into science' and women are, as consumers, the recipients of information about the benefits of science. So, despite women's heightened concerns about the application of genetic engineering, there is no necessary reason why women might be the key to rejection of a reductionist scientific paradigm. As feminist theorists, Brandth and Bolso (1994) are doubtful that the hegemony of biotechnology and genetic engineering can be easily overcome even if, through the application of feminist theory, its limitations are easily exposed.

Some of the 'large picture' issues raised above may appear somewhat tangential to what was, after all, a small scale, temporally specific and spatially limited qualitative study. An attempt has been made, however, to establish the place of some of the findings of this early research within a wider framework of sociological concerns. In conclusion, it would appear that just as consumers appear to be becoming increasingly interested in purchasing more wholesome, 'clean and green' foodstuffs, they are tending to question the right of scientists to tamper with foods, and are cynical about the motives of corporations involved in genetic engineering, it is apparent that governments, scientists and commercial firms are spending increasing amounts of public and private money in the pursuit of biotechnological solutions to the problems of agriculture and of the food industry. Focus group research has indicated that consumer resistance to such developments is quite high and that the more people know about genetically-engineered products the more they are likely to feel uncomfortable about those products. This is very much the case with biotechnologically-derived foods over other genetically-engineered plant and animal products. They certainly would not want to purchase genetically modified foodstuffs without clear labelling and a good deal more information about likely health implications relating to the ingestion of those foods.

Acknowledgments

This research was supported by a University Research Grant from Central Queensland University, whose assistance is gratefully acknowledged. Our thanks go, as well, to the participants in the Rockhampton focus groups study.

References

Alexander, N. (1992) Will Pigs Fly? Taking Genetic Engineering to the People, *Search* 23, 7: 210-211.

Almas, R. (1992) Social Consequences of the New Biotechnologies in Norway, *Paper delivered at the Fifth Annual Meeting of the Rural Sociology Society*, Pennsylvania State University, Pennsylvania, 16-19 August.

Almas, R. (1994) New Biotechnology and the Greening of Politics: Value Cleavages and Public Opinion in Risk Society, *Sosiologisk Tidsskrift*, Norway, Skandinavian University Press: 23-40.

Almas, R. and Nygard, B. (1993) European Values and the New Biotechnologies: Post-Materialism or a New Arena for Rural-Urban Conflict? *Paper presented to the XVth European Congress of Rural Sociology*, Wageningen University, The Netherlands, 2-6 August.

Australasian Biotechnology 5, 4, August 1995.

Brandth, B. and Bolso, A. (1994) Men, Women and Biotechnology: a Feminist 'Care' Ethic in Agricultural Science? in Whatmore, S., Marsden, T. and Lowe, P. (eds) *Gender and Rurality*, Critical Perspectives on Rural Change Series VI, London, David Fulton: 136-149.

Bureau of Rural Resources (1991) *Biotechnology in Australia: Perspectives and Issues for Animal Production*, Working Paper WP/16/91, Canberra, Bureau of Rural Resources.

Busch, L., (1991) Biotechnology: Consumer Concerns about Risks and Values, *Food Technology*, April: 96-101.

Buttel, F., Larson, O. and Gillespie, G. (1990) *The Sociology of Agriculture*, Westport, Greenwood.

Crook, S., Pakulski, J. and Waters, M. (1992) *Postmodernization: Change in Advanced Society*, London, Sage.

Department of Industry, Science and Technology (DIST) (1995) *Attitudes to Biotechnology in Relation to Food and Health: Results of the 1994 CSIRO Consumer Survey*, Canberra, DIST.

Goodman, D. and Redclift, M. (1991) *Refashioning Nature: Food, Ecology and Culture*, London, Routledge.

Gray, I. and Phillips, E., Ampt, P. and Dunn, A. (1995) Awareness or Beguilement? Farmers' Perceptions of Change, *Unpublished paper*, Centre for Rural Social Research, Wagga Wagga, Charles Sturt University.

Hindmarsh, R. (1992) CSIRO's Genetic Engineering Exhibition: Public Acceptance or Public Awareness? *Search* 23, 7:212-213.

Hindmarsh, R., Lawrence, G. and Norton, J. (1995) Manipulating Genes or Public Opinion? *Search* 26, 4: 117-121.

Hoban, T. (1989) Anticipating Public Response to Biotechnology, *The Rural Sociologist* 9, 3: 20-24.

Hoban, T., Woodrum, E. and Czaja, R. (1992) Public Opposition to Genetic Engineering, *Rural Sociology* 57, 4: 476-493.

House of Representatives Standing Committee on Industry, Science and Technology (1992) *Genetic Manipulation: the Threat or the Glory?* Canberra, Australian Government Publishing Service.

International Federation of Organic Agriculture Movements (IFOAM) (1994) *Ecology and Farming*, IFOAM 8, November: 21-26.

Kelley, J. (1995) Australian Support for Genetic Engineering, *Search* 26, 5: 141-144.

Kleinman, D. and Kloppenberg, J. (1991) Aiming for the Discursive High Ground: Monsanto and the Biotechnology Controversy, *Sociological Forum* 6, 3: 427-447.

Kloppenberg, J. (1991) Alternative Agriculture and the New Biotechnologies, *Science as Culture* 13: 482-506.

Kollek, R. (1990) The Limits of Experimental Knowledge: A Feminist Perspective on the Ecological Risks of Genetic Engineering, *Issues in Reproductive and Genetic Engineering* 3, 2: 125-135.

Kreuger, R. (1988) *Focus Groups: A Practical Guide for Applied Research*, Beverley Hills, Sage.

Lacy, W., Busch, L. and Lacy, L. (1991) Public Perceptions of Agricultural Biotechnology, in Baumgardt, B. and Martin, M. (eds) *Agricultural Biotechnology: Issues and Choices*, Indiana, Purdue University Agricultural Experiment Station.

Lawrence, G. (1987) *Capitalism and the Countryside: the Rural Crisis in Australia*, Sydney, Pluto.

Lawrence, G. (1995) *Futures for Rural Australia: From Agricultural Productivism to Community Sustainability*, Rockhampton, Rural Social and Economic Research Centre, Central Queensland University.

Lawrence, G. and Norton, J. (1994) Industry Involvement in Australian Biotechnology: the Views of Scientists, *Australasian Biotechnology* 4, 6: 362-368.

Lawrence, G., McKenzie, H. and Vanclay, F. (1993) Biotechnology in Australian Agriculture: the Views of Farmer Representatives, *Prometheus* 11, 2: 234-251.

Mannion, A. (1995) Biotechnology and Environmental Quality, *Progress in Physical Geography* 19, 2: 192 - 215.

Martin, M. and Baumgardt, B. (1991) The Origins of Biotechnology and Its Potential for Agriculture, in Baumgardt, B. and Martin, M. (eds) *Agricultural Biotechnology: Issues and Choices*, Indiana, Purdue University Agricultural Experiment Station: 3-21.

National Farmers' Federation (1993) *New Horizons: A Strategy for Australia's Agrifood Industries*, Canberra, National Farmers' Federation.

Norton, J. and Lawrence, G. (1995) Farmers and Scientists: Views on Agrobiotechnologies, *Agricultural Science* 8, 5: 39-42.

Norton, J., Lawrence, G. and Hindmarsh, R. (1995) Genetic Engineering: Public Approval or Public Concern? (Letter to the Editor) *Search* 26, 6: 186-187.

Peacock, J. (1994) Genetic Engineering of Crop Plants Will Enhance the Quality and Diversity of Foods, *Food Australia* 46, 8: 379-381.

Phelps, B. (1994) Genetic Engineering: Fast Track for False Promises, *Habitat Australia*, February: 38-43.

Rothenberg, L. (1995) What the Public Thinks of Biotechnology and What the Industry Needs to Consider by Way of Response to Those Perceptions, *Paper delivered at the Fourth Pacific Rim Biotechnology Conference*, Melbourne, February.

Sparks, P., Shepherd, R. and Frewer, L. (1994) Gene Technology, Food Production and Public Opinion: A UK Study, *Agriculture and Human Values* Winter: 19-28.

Stewart, D. and Shamdasani, P. (1990) *Focus Groups*, Newbury Park, Sage.

US Congress Office of Technology Assessment (1987) *New Developments in Biotechnology*, Washington, Government Printing Office.

Vanclay, F. and Lawrence, G. (1995) *The Environmental Imperative: Ecosocial Concerns for Australian Agriculture*, Rockhampton, CQU Press.

Waters, M. (1995) *Globalization*, London, Routledge.

Young, A. and Lewis, G. (1995) Biotechnology and Potential Nutritional Implications for Children, *Pediatric Nutrition* 42, 4: 917 - 930.

Young, D. and Roper, H. (1995) Pay-offs to Agricultural Genetic Engineering Research, *Outlook 95*, Canberra, ABARE: 51-58.

Zimmerman, L., Kendall, P., Stone, M., and Hoban, T. (1994) Consumer Knowledge and Concern about Biotechnology and Food Safety, *Food Technology* 48, 11: 71-77.

Appendix A

Important characteristics of food

1 Nutrition
2 Taste
3 Cost
4 Freshness
5 Convenience /Ease of Preparation
6 Environmentally Friendly/Australian Made
7 Other - (social value/unprocessed/variety/shelf life)

Support for genetically modified products (in order of acceptance)

1 *Blue Rose* - Genes for blueness from petunias and cornflower are inserted into a rose, and expressed as blue petals.
2 *Cheese* - A bacterium has a gene sequence inserted so that it can act, as rennet does, in turning milk into cheese.
3 *Sheep - Blowfly* - A tobacco gene inserted into the sheep's genetic material can make it resistant to blowfly strike.
4 *Sheep - Amino Acid* - Sheep can be genetically modified so that they produce an amino acid which boosts wool production by as much as 30 percent.
5 *Tomato* - The tomato is modified by the insertion of a flounder gene which prevents the tomato from softening, and enhances taste.
6 *Wheat* - Wheat plants have a gene from a bacterium inserted which acts as a toxic agent for pests. If they attack the plant they die.
7 *Pork - PST* - A hormone from the pig is inserted into bacteria which produce large volumes of the hormone in a fermentation vat. It is extracted, and then injected into the pig to increase rate of growth.
8 *Pork - Human gene* - A human gene sequence is inserted into the pig. When triggered, it increases the hormone level in pigs, thereby promoting growth.

Concerns about GMOs

1 Health - long term and short term effects
2 Testing
3 Ethical and Moral Issues
   (a) Control
   (b) Animal Suffering
   (c) Use of Human Genes
4 Labelling
5 Environment / Biodiversity
6 Nutritional Value
7 Other - Ownership
   Distribution of benefits

Chapter 23

Bio-policy translation in the public terrain

Richard Hindmarsh

'The time has come' the Walrus said , 'to talk of many things: ... of why the sea is boiling hot - and whether pigs have wings'. The difficulty with CSIRO's travelling exhibition 'Genetic Engineering: Will Pigs Fly?', is to know how to react - whether to be enchanted like the Carpenter by the potential of thermophilic bacteria and pinnate pork, or be distracted like the poor oysters he and the Walrus are about to consume. Critics, more knowingly, feel it is simply throwing sand into our eyes and that it will abet the aims of corporate sharks who are after more than mere oysters.[1]

'Yes, we'll eat those tomatoes'

'Yes, we'll eat those tomatoes' barracked a *Canberra Times* headline on 18 October, 1994. A preliminary survey on public attitudes to genetic engineering (GE) - or recombinant-DNA (rDNA) technology - had claimed that 'Most Canberrans would like to try eating genetically engineered tomatoes, and many would willingly grow them in their home gardens' (Mussared, 1994a: 12).

The survey was conducted by the Department of Industry, Science and Technology (DIST) - the federal government agency specifically empowered to support bio/technological change. The results had, according to DIST's Biotechnology Section Director Dr Alan Laird, 'shown consumers to be overwhelmingly positive about the new technology' and had '"provide[d] a measure of confidence for the agri-food industry to proceed with biotechnology"' (Mussared, 1994a: 12). Yet, perhaps reflecting the 'true' measure of DIST's confidence in the results, the Department declined to release the full findings to the *Canberra Times* (Mussared, 1994a), or to the bio-critical campaign group the Australian Gen-Ethics Network (1995).

So, why had DIST declined to release the full findings? Why were partial results released at that time? Why were 300 respondents generalised to be 'Most Canberrans' and in turn 'consumers' *per se*? Why did the Department break with conventional survey methodological practice in releasing preliminary (or pilot) survey findings when the survey was the precursor to a national survey? and, Why were respondents of the preliminary survey told that Australian regulatory authorities had cleared the gene-spliced tomatoes as being safe, that most scientists agreed with that assessment, and that some national green groups wanted the tomatoes banned (Mussared, 1994a: 12)? In reality, only one regulatory authority - the national Genetic Manipulation Advisory Committee (GMAC) (the virtual in-house peer review committee for rDNA experimentation) - had considered the fruit, but only for a small scale field trial, and no Green group had called for a ban.

Because of the growing controversy over genetic engineering, particularly about splicing DNA across species barriers, as well as public acceptability, safety, and appropriate labelling of gene-altered foods, and because some bio-products are already commercially available, the questions posed above deserve to be answered in some depth.

From just the brief introduction above, the exercises of conducting the preliminary survey and the release of its results appear designed to elicit support for genetic engineering. A certain positive image of the bio-engineered tomato was conveyed to a 'representative' sample of the public who, misled like the 'poor oysters', judged it to be acceptable. This result was then promoted as the 'truth' to the broader community with no qualification about the questionnaire's hypothetical information. In addition, not discussed was why Green groups might want the tomato banned. Their concerns about genetic engineering *per se* were thus placed outside the discourse and marginalised.

The pro-biotechnology article was not alone; a 'package' of pro-GE articles was published. Unusual both in the number of articles presented and calibre of proponents speaking out at any one time in any one media space, one comprehensive article entitled 'Benefits of genetic engineering are already with us' was by CSIRO's Dr Jim Peacock (1994: 12) - one of Australia's foremost supporters of genetic engineering. Another (Grose, 1994: 12) was a 'sympathetic' interview with GMAC regulatory head Professor Nancy Millis - an outspoken advocate of 'minimalist' regulation and of biotechnology. That this 'media-event' occurred suggested more was in the offing than just 'non-squashy tomatoes'.

In the week before, two bio-critical items had appeared in the *Canberra Times*. The first, a letter to the editor by Hindmarsh (1994a) was in response to another provocative article by Mussared (1994b), and the second, by UK commentator Colin Spencer (1994: 6) projected a problematic depiction of novel foods that included criticism of the non-squashy tomato.

In analysing all the articles, by subject and publication order, and because Mussared (1994a) identified Peacock's article as a response to Hindmarsh's 'strongly critical assessment of genetic engineering practice and policy', it appears all three pro-articles formed a complementary package. The Peacock article and the Millis interview were there to counteract Hindmarsh's and Spencer's criticisms, and the tomato/survey story served to both counteract Spencer's article and promote GE foods.

Essentially, the *Canberra Times* represented a *translation* channel for actors in the biotechnology/GE debate to enrol public interest to their versions of the natural and social world (see Callon, 1986). The translation process, in the context of social power relations, is where actors 'articulate conceptions of the world and the roles of the actors that are in it, and impose these conceptions on one another: in short they ... *translate*' (Law, 1986: 32). The sociology of translation is part of actor-network theory (Callon, 1986) which addresses the ways in which the use of (agency) power is constructed to secure outcomes, and does so by demonstrating how networks of power are constituted and reproduced through conscious strategies and unwitting practices constructed by the actors themselves (Clegg, 1989: 204).

In the *Canberra Times* exchange, proponents articulated an inevitable and responsibly-regulated genetic engineering world where the public's role is one of ('well-informed') acceptance. In this biotopia, any concern about the technology amounted to 'misunderstanding' (a long and tired rhetorical strategy of bio-proponents to counter adversity). Conversely, critics articulated a questioning of radical technological change where the public's role is direct participation. The outcome, influenced by *how* information was presented by the *Canberra Times*, was that proponents were given the 'upper hand' to both articulate public acceptability and downplay concerns.

That the *Canberra Times* acted in this way is, however, not surprising given (1) the historical use of translation as a central tool of power in the global biotechnology/GE (bio-) policy terrain, and (2) the enrolment of the mass media as a translation channel to align society to biotechnology. These two themes, especially with regard to the Australian debate, are the focus here. Actor-network theory is however not endorsed as all encompassing theory of the nature of power, but instead is placed within a contextual frame of power - within an existing and overriding terrain of structural power whether that be ideological, hegemonic, institutional, economic or political. [2]

This is an appropriate conceptualisation of power relations for analysing modern biotechnology because when we explore its emergence we find it already embedded within pre-established technocratic systems of domination, where entrenched power is produced and reproduced systemically through episodic power (power to structure), dispositional power (power as capacity or control) and through facilitative power (power as ability to achieve) (see Clegg, 1989). When and where entrenched power is contested, actors of dominant power use both dispositional and facilitative power to fix and refix relations of meaning and membership in the policy terrain; also interpreted as strategic or operational power, this involves the ability to *act* or *manoeuvre* to secure favourable outcomes. By the same token, those who contest the terrain also manoeuvre but do so to resist or challenge dominant actors, and ideally to reconfigure the terrain.

Translation theory provides a useful concept with which to deconstruct strategic processes, and to describe a central way in which the technological agenda of change is shaped by technocratic systems of knowledge-power (see also Foucault, 1977). Power relations is an area neglected by environmental interests, but as Arne Naess (1990: 131) expounds, 'In environmental conflicts, it is ... important to *map out the power structures* relevant in pushing the decisions and determining the different stages in the conflict'. Only by doing so can we really gain insights into how environmental and social progressive concerns are disempowered, and improve the climate for their expression.

A brief account follows of the global bio-policy terrain. This provides the necessary backdrop for situating an Australian example of translation which involves a discourse exchange of proponents and critics relevant to the subject of public acceptability, the final legitimising platform for corporate control of agriculture through biotechnology.

Let us look now, in turn, at the nature of the bio-policy terrain, the translation process, the *bio-policy* translation process, the role of the media, and finally, at public acceptance routines especially the Australian 1994 survey.

The bio-policy terrain

The bio-policy terrain represents a strategic political landscape of intersecting forces that compete over the ownership and configuration of deoxyribonucleic acid (DNA). Organisational power used structurally and strategically decides policy formation, which, in turn, determines the contours of the terrain, or configuration of the DNA-commons of biodiversity. At the sectoral level of agriculture, this means no less than the social and ecological organisation of agriculture, and by extension, the future sustainability of that organisation.

Economic-rationalist and mechanistic-cybernetic views currently prevail in the terrain, whereby the DNA-commons is now subject to corporate/state enclosure through patenting for eventual and widescale genetically altered monoculture forms. In that process, not only is naturally-occurring genetic diversity being eroded, but so are eco-social/ethical-organicist held-views that believe the DNA-commons should be retained in an emancipated state for the common good, and for community-based approaches like eco-agriculture.

Since the inception of rDNA technology in 1973, the bio-policy terrain has been marked by intense struggle between propagonists representing the above views. As implied, rDNA- or bio- proponents have dominated policy formation and largely outmanoeuvred those who contest them. This is borne out where in only some 15 years of commercial investment, rDNA technology looks set to have a major impact on the 21st century; where despite many unresolved issues about its ethical and scientific basis, political alliances, and social and environmental impact, international bio-development continues unabated; and where corporate imperatives shape and propel the technology (in order to realise predicted sales worth some US$70 billion annually by the year 2000).

315

The translation process represents a central avenue to secure such favourable outcomes for global capital.

The translation process

The translation process involves four sequential and interwoven movements:

1 the attempt by actors to enrol others to their viewpoint or preferred policy/action position. To do this, the indispensability of their 'solutions' is projected for the others' 'problems'. **Problematisation** is achieved when the others are channelled or negotiated through the terms of reference that the enrolling actors define or fix.
2 **Intéressement** is where others are enrolled into roles proposed or defined by the enrolling actor/s. Devices are constructed between the 'interested' actors and all other entities who define their identities otherwise.
3 **Enrolment** is where after the problem has been translated, and alternatives blocked, a diversity of allies are enrolled to the preferred solution. Coalitions are constructed among the members and meanings which they have sought.
4 **Mobilisation** is where methods are used to ensure that enrolled agencies are fixed in representing the translated 'vision'. Essential for success is a process of progressive mobilisation of agents who render propositions credible and indisputable by acting as a unit of force.

The bio-policy translation process

Articulation of the beneficial visions of agricultural biotechnology/GE began with problematising the science of genetics as a solution to the problems that nature poses for the industrialisation of agriculture. To enrol industrial-agricultural interests to support genetic-determinist approaches, agri-genetics was projected - first through plant hybridisation, then through molecular biology (the underpinning science of genetic engineering), and finally through biotechnology/GE - as a unique R&D approach to plant breeding that would overcome natural reproductive barriers to the industrialisation of food and fibre production. The implicit vision was the further appropriation, substitution and commodification of nature (see Goodman *et al.*, 1987; Kloppenburg, 1988) resulting in increased capital accumulation.

Industrial-genetics translation began in earnest during the 1930s. The catalytic actor was the Rockefeller Foundation (the 'philanthropic' component of the Standard Oil/Exxon petrochemical empire), which has a primary organisational goal of promoting capitalist society (Yoxen, 1981). In its turn, the Foundation was enrolled to the belief that biology was the 'science of the future' by popular statements of leading scientists and scientific journals (Abir-Am, 1982; Bud 1994). These linked biology and science-based technology

316

(bio-technology) to the control of human destiny and productive agriculture. Timely events also proved convincing. Between 1934 and 1944, US agribusiness sales of hybrid-seed corn went from virtually nothing to over $70 million (Kloppenburg, 1988: 93).

Parallel to its Green Revolution programme of diffusing industrial-agriculture into third world countries - 'an integral part of the (US) post-war effort to contain social revolution and make the world safe for profits' (Cleaver, 1972: 82) - the Rockefeller Foundation, between 1932 and 1957, initiated and supported bio-scientific management and funding programmes in the US and Europe. From the late 1930s, universities - particularly private ones in the US - and later, scientific foundations and state health and medical research agencies also became enrolled to fund molecular biology research. A powerful bio-research coalition coalesced to shape future agricultural and medical production systems.

At the same time, the state, particularly the US, also became enrolled through the prophesies of bio-industrial revolution. A legal conduit to private ownership of genetics research and its product was instituted. Patenting, a device of interest constructed between entrepreneurial scientists and their patrons (industry and the state) vis-a-vis those in opposition, further defined the terms of reference for the development of molecular biology to be commercial.

This entire infrastructure frame - of law, government, corporate sponsorship and allied research institutions - seeded the fundamental scientific discoveries, such as the double-helical structure of DNA in 1953, the deciphering of the genetic code by 1966, and the techniques for deleting and recombining genes in 1973. Simultaneously, the worldview of molecular biology was translated amongst biologists as the central dogma of biological thought.

Yet, also in 1973, a setback to the bio-translation process occurred in the form of significant dissent. A number of molecular biologists, as well as environmental groups, raised serious concerns about the potential biohazards of splicing together different life-forms. To absorb this protest, the political elite of the bioscientific community (the bio-elite) convened a series of political manoeuvres through the 1970s (see Wright, 1986; Krimsky, 1991) which problematised the issues of biohazards or safety as low risk, and later, as commercial opportunity. A cohesive coalition mobilised internationally to translate these visions, internally at the level of the bio-scientific community and externally at the level of the public. In doing so, internal control of the regulatory agenda was retained vis-a-vis external control. A central relay in this successful bio-translation strategy at the external level has been the media.

The role of the media

Kawar (1989: 723) argues that:

> The mass media relies on the scientific community for information subsidies. Science and technology news are

> transferred to science reporters through a variety of channels;
> direct contact with prominent members of the scientific
> community, attending scientific meetings, and following the
> science news media ... The key actors in the DNA research
> community and biotechnology industry ... then control the
> information given to the media, precisely those interests likely to
> be threatened by the expansion of the issue to the general public.

The media thus serve as a primary channel for bio-scientists to recruit the
public to 'believe' (Loge, 1991). In this vein, Yoxen (1983: 28) relates that
ever since the 1950s, a time that saw the discovery of the double-helix, the
media have popularised an image of bio-science as a techno-revolution of
enormous potential.

During the 1970s, the mass media defended that image by playing an
important role in absorbing the protest mentioned above. Relaying information
that the (bio-) scientific community made available (Goodell, 1986: 173), the
media steadfastly cast the bio-industry as a beneficial 'safe blue-chip industry'.
For example, headlines such as *Newsweek*'s 'The Miracles of Spliced Genes'
(Clark, 1980) and *The New York Times* 'Industry of Life' (Parisi, 1980)
followed closely in the wake of scientific popularisation articles like
'Recombinant DNA: Warming Up for the Big Payoff' (Wade 1979), published
in *Science*.

Moreover, little initiative was taken by the media to broaden the discussion
about safety issues beyond that of technicalised bio-safety 'black boxes',
designed by the bio-elite to discourage the public from seeking bio-regulatory
control (see Loge, 1991: 15). Encouraging such censure was the mobilisation in
force of proponents who both translated bio-visions and discredited critics (see
Goodell, 1986: 175).

Subsequently, protest was absorbed, public confidence and investment in
the technology was boosted, and bio-scientists reinforced their role as central
makers of regulatory policy (Krimsky, 1991: 38; Bud, 1994). Expanded
economic opportunities, international competitiveness and scientific leadership
replaced bio-safety as the driving agenda of biotechnology (Goodell, 1986;
Kawar, 1989).

Such translation has continued to date despite novel hazards now posed by
widescale environmental release of genetically engineered organisms. It has
been instrumental in securing the necessary platform for commercialisation of
biotechnology/GE - a plethora of weak or minimalist regulations implemented
by agencies supportive of bio-business. Now that bio-commercialisation is
emerging, a key strategy of the bio-elite is to shift public perception of
biotechnology/GE from attitudes ranging from ambivalence, distaste or outright
hostility to acceptance.

Having set the contextual international backdrop, we now turn from that
generalised context to the specific bio-translation process of securing public
acceptability in Australia.

Australian public acceptance routines

To articulate public acceptance, proponents construct translatory conduits at two main levels (1) the internal level of institutional power (including the bio-scientific community), and (2) the external level of the wider community.

The internal level

From the late 1980s onwards, institutional bio-proponents have constructed several devices to both launch strategic routines to gain public acceptance and to translate the necessity of gaining public acceptance.

An example of the former is where, in 1990, top executives from the Commonwealth Scientific and Industrial Research Organisation (CSIRO), in projecting an organisational dependency 'upon the future release and widespread usage of genetically engineered plants, animals and other organisms', decided a task force was needed to develop,

> a major, well developed strategy ... to facilitate the future release and *acceptance* of this new genetic material ... to educate politicians, bureaucrats, lobby groups and the general public on the benefits which will arise from this elite material. In addition, people will need to be *re-assured* on the possibility of harmful side-effects (my emphasis) (see Hindmarsh, 1994b: 264).

Addressing the latter is where, in 1991, a federal Bureau of Rural Resources report argued that public acceptance of recombinant DNA technology was essential to the survival and competitiveness of agriculture (White, 1991: 61). Similarly in 1993, the media release of an Australian Science and Technology Council (ASTEC) report (ASTEC, 1993a) read (in part): 'Public understanding and support of gene technology will be essential if it is to achieve widespread acceptance and commercial success ... ' (ASTEC, 1993b).

Yet, although the ASTEC report referred to consensus building between proponents and opponents of gene technology as the way forward to achieve public acceptance, an earlier and more internal report (Office of the Chief Scientist, 1993), where authorship significantly was considerably interlocked to that of the ASTEC report, stated:

> The Working Group believes that scientists and industry involved in gene technology must take the lead in promoting community discussion of the technology. Not to do so will appear as though those involved in the technology are indifferent, or even hostile, to public debate. It will also leave the field open to those who oppose the technology and its applications.

Two levels of translation are thus apparent, the 'explicit' one of projecting a *reassuring* image of 'building mutual confidence and consensus', and the 'implicit' one of proponents shaping the 'education of the public' at the external level.

The external level

Two outstanding public acceptance devices have so far been constructed in Australia to translate the benefits of biotechnology/GE to the public. The first, a strategic 'educative' programme by CSIRO and the second, which we focus on here, a national survey by DIST. Other devices have since been constructed, most notably the Gene Technology Information Unit which is discussed below. The CSIRO device - a travelling exhibition called 'Genetic Engineering: Will Pigs Fly?' has been deconstructed adequately elsewhere (see Hindmarsh, 1992; Love, 1993).

The 1994 Australian survey

For our analysis here, we follow in the steps of the 'route of translation' that the actors constructed (or the ones we know about) in a discourse saga involving the national survey. This will further elaborate on how the Australian bio-policy network is constituted especially through conscious strategies and unwitting practices constructed by the proponents themselves, and how that network manoeuvres to align Australian society to genetic engineering/biotechnology production systems.

Step 1: The route of translation arbitrarily begins with the DIST preliminary survey. The first contextual theme - *the discourse of persuasion* - is introduced, exemplified by the statement 'Yes, we'll eat those tomatoes'.

Step 2: DIST *declines* to release the **preliminary** survey's full findings to the media and public interest groups. The second contextual theme - *information censure* - is introduced.

Step 3: Senator Chris Schacht - the then DIST Minister for gene technology - opens the 4th Pacific Rim Biotechnology Conference (5-9 February 1995, Melbourne). Themes of the conference include biotechnology education and commercialisation. Schacht, obviously enrolled to participate in discussion about gene technology, announces the 'preliminary' results of the **national** survey on public perceptions of gene technology (funded by DIST, constructed by the International Social Science Survey [ISSS] [Australian National University] with feedback from DIST [1994], and undertaken by the ISSS). Schacht highlights: 'Those surveyed were overwhelmingly supportive of the use of gene technology ... '. Given this window of opportunity, Schacht challenges industry to increase its public awareness activities in gene technology.

Simultaneously in Canberra, at the commodities *Outlook 95 Conference* (7-9 February), convened by (pro-biotech government agency) the Australian Bureau of Agricultural Resource Economics (ABARE), bio-translators project the vision of genetic engineering for sustainable productivity of agriculture, for competitiveness, and the dependency of GE research payoffs on public acceptance. Proponent articulation of commercialisation and public acceptance thus emerges on a number of fronts.

Step 4: On 8 February 1995, the first DIST press release (from Schacht's office) on the survey claims, 'A majority of the Australian public supports using genetic engineering to develop new medical treatments, healthier and improved foods, and improved pest-resistant crops ...'. It cites **some** of the survey findings, but only ones that are related to benefits vis-a-vis risks.

Step 5: On 9 February the Australian Gen-Ethics Network (AGE-Net) releases a press statement arguing that the results, biased by the framing of the questions, misrepresent public attitudes toward GE; as well, the risks of GE are not addressed. AGE-Net, a project of the Australian Conservation Foundation, is a network of groups and individuals that promotes critical discussion and debate on the environmental, social and ethical impacts of genetic engineering.

Step 6: Three newspapers report the DIST release. The *Financial Review* (Quiddington, 1995) notes, significantly, that the positive results come as the first GE food products are being approved. This article reports AGE-Net's reservations. Conversely, *The Australian* (1995) and *The Weekend Australian* (1995) simply repeat the thrust of the DIST press release. Overall, a positive view of the survey is translated to the public.

Step 7: Sceptics of the survey results contact either Dr Jonathan Kelley (Director of ISSS) and/or DIST's Alan Laird and ask variously for complete survey results, methodology, survey design and so on. The positive results contradict international opinion poll trends. Social scientists and others want to conduct independent evaluations.

Step 8: DIST *declines* to disclose data for the second time. Instead, DIST states that the data and analyses will be published by Kelley in the appropriate academic literature, that the full results will be presented as a report once analysis has been completed, and that the report 'is *likely* to be publicly available in early May 1995' (my emphasis) (Laird, 1995). If this indeed occurs, it will be three months after the 'positive' press release. No qualification is made as to what subject/s the remainder of the survey focussed upon.

Step 9: Given such uninformative and vague replies to academic inquiry, and given the background context of the survey as one of intense debate, and because (i) survey results have already been published in the public domain,

321

and in a questionable manner, and (ii) the proposition of respondent 'majority support' for genetic engineering is highly questionable, Hindmarsh and colleagues decide to critique the 'bio-truth' being vigorously translated.

Step 10: Their critique (Hindmarsh *et al.*, 1995) published in the May edition of *Search* concludes that the Australian study both misinformed respondents before eliciting their opinions, and respondents' answers were further skewed towards the 'positive' by *how* the questions were framed.

The misinformation given to respondents is a re-run of the preliminary survey exercise, as is the misrepresentation of extrapolating the 'respondents' to be 'A majority of the Australian public'.

Step 11: A rejoinder by Kelley (1995a) defends the survey's methodology, displays some statistical 'black boxes', introduces new material about respondents' 'worries' about GE, and concludes, 'These results suggest that the Australian public will become more supportive of genetic engineering in the future if levels of knowledge increase ...'. This suggestion is highly questionable, given various overseas polling trends (see INRA, 1993), and is, of course, dependent on *what and how information is given to increase the public's levels of knowledge.*

Step 12: Hindmarsh sends Senator Schacht, the then-responsible Minister, a letter that (i) encloses the critique of the survey in order to question its positive claims; and (ii) complains that DIST and Kelley hampered external scrutiny of the survey by not releasing relevant data.

Schacht (in June 1995) replies and repeats Laird's line about publishing the survey at some (vague) time in the future. He also asserts '*As you know*, the first press release was based on a small section of the survey ...' (my emphasis). On the contrary, Hindmarsh *did not know* this because Schacht's department would not provide any data or indicate anything indicating this (see Step 8). Schacht does not address any criticisms of Hindmarsh *et al.*, (1995) and finishes off his letter by stating, 'It is unfortunate that you felt compelled to release your critique without being in possession of the full report'.

Step 13: A second press release from Schacht's office concerning the survey suddenly materialises (22 May). Similar to the first, it reads 'Australians Positive about Gene Technology', with the central message being that 'the majority of respondents feel that the benefits (of GE) will outweigh the risks'.

Step 14: The media respond. *The Age* (Grattan, 1995) echoes the (inappropriate, arbitrary and confusing statistical) depiction of the public's 'worries' about genetic engineering. The *Herald Sun* (Livingstone, 1995) is more balanced, but relays verbatim DIST's message that the findings complement those released in February (see Step 4). The most critical article - *The Australian's* 'Genetics technology anxiety grips nation' (Cribb, 1995) -

interprets the 'worries' greater than the press release states. Overall, a positive picture of the survey is conveyed in the scientific literature and mass media.

Step 15: In June, DIST release the final report of the survey (Kelley, 1995b).

Step 16: Norton *et al.,* (1995) (including Hindmarsh) respond to Kelley's rejoinder (see Step 11). It points out that Kelley did not address the issues raised in the critique of Hindmarsh *et al.,* (1995), nor did it reveal Kelley's own findings that some 95 per cent of respondents had some level of concern regarding aspects of genetic engineering.

Step 17: Another bio-translator enters the debate. In a letter to *Search* that attacks Hindmarsh *et al.,* David Leyonhjelm (1995a) identifies himself as Director of the PST Information Service (an organisation funded by transnational corporations Cyanamid and Bunge to promote the rDNA pig growth hormone, porcine somatotropin [PST]). For some time, PST and the PST Information Service have attracted intense criticism from environmentalist and consumer groups (see Australian Gen-Ethics Network, 1994; Eco-Consumer, 1995).

Leyonhjelm depicts Hindmarsh and colleagues as being 'longstanding opponents' rather than 'critics' of GE. (Critics are those who find fault with certain aspects of the technology and its social agenda while opponents undeniably reject all elements of the new biology.) A central strategy of tactical proponents of genetic engineering is to undermine critics' concerns as legitimate - the depiction of Hindmarsh and colleagues as 'opponents' appears synonymous with that trend. Leyonhjelm also misleadingly accuses Hindmarsh and colleagues' criticism as being out of step with both environmentalists and consumers.

Step 18: Hindmarsh (1995) responds to Leyonhjelm's letter. The response's publication is also accompanied by a rejoinder from Leyonhjelm (1995b). Because of Leyonhjelm's arguably 'unwitting' entry into the debate, Hindmarsh is able to both reveal and question Leyonhjelm's apparent conflict of interests - Leyonhjelm is not only Director of the PST Information Service but also Director of Baron Strategic Services, the organisation appointed by DIST (with a two-year $500,000 grant attached) to be the central component of its Gene Technology Information Unit (GTIU). In turn, Leyonhjelm manoeuvres to defend his position and attempt further to discredit Hindmarsh. Leyonhjelm's unwitting entry also allows us to locate and identify the GTIU's role in the bio-translation network, which 'is to foster a more favourable environment for the products of gene technology' (GTIU, 1995a: 1). A DIST directive for the GTIU is 'swiftly to respond to any inaccurate and alarmist reports (about gene technology) occurring in the media, and provide balanced, informed input to debates, meetings or other forums' (DIST, nd: 2). But the critique of Hindmarsh *et al.,* is hardly alarmist and the question of accuracy is one of interpretation and academic rigour. Perhaps Leyonhjelm in signing his

323

letters as Director of the PST Information Service rather than as Director of the GTIU sought to distance himself from the DIST directive?

Indeed, Leyonhjelm's own problems of 'accuracy' would have been highlighted if he had signed his letters as Director of the GTIU. For example, the GTIU press release (1995b) states:

> The GTIU is part of the government's response to the need for providing high quality public information on the emerging field of gene technology. It is widely believed that society does not have sufficient understanding of gene technology to understand its impact or debate its benefits ... The approach taken by the GTIU is based on the recognition that most Australians welcome the use of gene technology to help develop better foods and medicines, confirmed by the ISSS survey early this year.

This statement reveals the logical paradox with proponents' promotion of the ISSS survey: if respondents do not have sufficient understanding of gene technology then how can results of the ISSS survey be used to conclude that most Australians support the use of gene technology? To make matters worse, Leyonhjelm (1995b) elsewhere seems unclear about the necessary rigour that questionnaire construction demands, 'It would not matter how you asked the questions' he states with regard to the ISSS survey, 'provided the information contained in the question was accurate ...'

Many GE commentators I have spoken to refer to the GTIU as a propaganda outfit, even one of its own representatives recently told me (at the 1995 National Conference of the Australian Science Teachers' Association) that its brochure - 'Today's Technology: Gene Technology at Work' (GTIU, 1995c) - would be considered as propaganda if it had not mentioned critics' views. Examination of the brochure, however, finds that it undermines and trivialises the views of critics and comes close to glorifying those of proponents. According to Lasswell (1965, cited in Gusfield, 1980), propaganda is the making of deliberately one-sided statements to a mass audience, which blocks out alternatives and other worldviews. More generally, Gerbner (1972, cited in Thomson, 1977: 4) refers to the 'cultivation of dominant image patterns as the major function of the dominant communication agency'.

This brochure and other material - specifically teachers' aids pamphlets that project dominant bio-proponent image patterns (GTIU, nd) - are disseminated widely to high-school science teachers (see Bittisnich and Smith, 1995: 17). This represents a key Australian bio-translation relay in a broader network of more powerful relays like the OECD (1992: 5) which has stated 'the most crucial, and in the long-run, most effective programmes (of public education in biotechnology) are those addressed to the education system, particularly teachers, then to the general public (through the media) and to decision-makers'.

From this brief deconstruction of the GTIU, there is good credence for the notion of it being a propaganda conduit, certainly for it being a frontline bio-translator that presents a 'laundered' version of the technology to the public. The switching of personnel between 'front' organisations in order to increase one's manoeuvrability in order to attack critics would seem part of the process.

Step 19:   The August issue of the journal of the Australian Biotechnology Association (ABA) - *Australasian Biotechnology* - then picks up the strategic attack on the survey's critics. Hindmarsh *et al.*, (1995) are accused of being premature in their critique; and of being 'way off the mark' in their analysis (Tribe, 1995). Similar to Leyonhjelm, David Tribe suggests Kelley's rejoinder 'neutralises several of the criticisms'. Finally, but ironically, Tribe states that 'Kelley's articles are really worth the effort for anyone interested in *marketing* biotechnology, or in the *general acceptance* of gene technology' (my emphasis).

Step 20: Hindmarsh and Norton (1995) respond to Tribe's attack. They point out that DIST's first press release relating to the benefits (Step 4) was 'premature' and that this then set the context for subsequent critique (see Step 9). Also that Kelley's rejoinder was inadequate (see Step 17), and that Tribe's remarks about the survey marketing biotechnology appears to be a true reflection of the type of research conducted.

Tribe's 'unwitting' entry into the discourse in turn allows us to locate and identify the ABA's role in the bio-translation process, and by association, some other translators (both pro and critical). The ABA is the trade association of Australia's bio-industrial complex and unites interests from business, government and the bio-scientific community. *Australasian Biotechnology* is its translation conduit at the internal level of biotechnologists. In no less than four of the last six issues of the ABA's journal, DIST has translated a positive image of the survey results.

Like the GTIU, the ABA also disseminates free to secondary schools a series of pamphlets promoting biotechnology. Part of its lobbying to government involves translating discreditation of critical groups, who, variously, are depicted as 'unrepresentative and often uninformed', or 'embellish their outpourings with half-truths'.

Another disseminator of free bio-translatory material to secondary schools is the Genetic Manipulation Advisory Committee. On the whole, the material projects bio-proponent dominant image patterns, including that of responsible regulation for GE.

By way of contrast, the Gen-Ethics Network is the only organisation providing critical information to schools. Its education kit raises substantial environmental, social and ethical concerns about biotechnology/GE, but its small administrative grant from the federal government is inadequate for it to disseminate the material freely or widely.

Step 21:   This is the last step to date in the national survey translation saga. Still dissatisfied with Senator Schacht's reply to his letter (Step 8), Hindmarsh writes again (15 December 1995) to the Senator but this time seeks explanation

325

as to why DIST prematurely released the positive results in the context of Schacht's reply and Norton and Hindmarsh's defence in *Australasian Biotechnology*. Hindmarsh also asks why the department is still promoting the results (it is now on the Internet as well) when the survey remains controversial, and points out that his and colleagues' criticism has not been refuted contrary to claims by Tribe and others.

Finally, Hindmarsh suggests to Schacht that circulation of the survey should be suspended until further independent assessment of it has occurred, and an internal review undertaken. Some five months later, following the Coalition victory at the March 1996 federal election, the new DIST Minister, John Moore, replies with a simplistic endorsement of the findings of the survey.

Conclusions

This account demonstrates clearly how actors representing existing structures of domination in the Australian bio-policy terrain (including CSIRO, ASTEC, DIST, ABARE, GMAC, the ABA and the GTIU) constitute a strategic (albeit informal) interorganisational network of power that acts to align Australian society to bio-development. Other linkages such as those of research, funding and organisation reinforce this view (see Hindmarsh 1994b).

Network elements both construct and mobilise entirely different translation messages at the internal level of institutional power and at the external level of the public. In shaping the policy agenda this way, 'conscious strategies and unwitting practices' have revealed the device of 'disinformation' - manifested as misinformation, censured information flows, closed debate, discreditation of critics, and elements of propaganda - as a central strategy of the bio-policy network.

Some of those tactics emerged in the proponents' response to the various criticisms of Hindmarsh and colleagues. Despite those criticisms being well-argued and 'non-alarmist', and regardless of whether or not they occurred in the context of normal academic inquiry and practice, they were confronted (rather than intellectually debated) by bio- political elements exercising agency power from dominant positions of structural power.

That critics were subject to such an attack from key representatives of the Australian bio-elite indicates at least three things, (1) that tactical proponents, regardless of institutional background, act to block any perceived setbacks to the bio-translation process, (2) the survey criticism of Hindmarsh *et al.,* (1995) had much weight; a finding that converges with, (3) the bio-elite acting true to the earlier assessment of Hindmarsh (1994a) that argued: 'So far, the scientists, bureaucrats and industrialists who control the research and development of GE have shaped the agenda to resist public knowledge and participation'. It was this assessment and its articulated role of the public as being one of direct participation in the bio-policy process, that arguably triggered off proponent mobilisation with regard to the media-event that included the 'Yes, we'll eat those tomatoes' article, and which then over-flowed into the defence of the national survey.

In the broader context, proponents can be seen to be constructors and/or relays of bio-translatory strategy. The commonality and sequence of international and Australian bio-network strategies and translation visions, indicates that the Australian bio-elite (perhaps both consciously and unwittingly) is a relay in systems of global power that exist *behind* the construction of bio-development. The expression of the OECD's vision of the education system as the most 'crucial' conduit for bio-translation saw, in turn, the construction of an international relay chain where Australian relays include the CSIRO, ASTEC, the ABA, GMAC, and finally the GTIU. In turn, four of these agencies act to expand the translation chain by attempting to enrol science teachers as further relays. The ultimate goal, obviously, is to enmesh society to biotechnology/genetic engineering at, what Burris (1989: 327) refers to as, 'the micropolitics of everyday life and thoughts'.

In supporting this process, the Australian media can also be seen predominantly as a bio-translatory relay, barring limited critical reportage. In general, the media have translated the dominant-image patterns of bio-proponents (see also Love, 1992).

These findings also highlight the success of the proponent network continually to construct and reconstruct its centrality in the bio-policy terrain, and thus to control the agenda. This reinforces the view that scientific and technological endeavour does not exist in a political vacuum but instead is predominantly and socially shaped by the structural and strategic power of technocratic enterprise. Clearly, biotechnological change is not irresistible nor inevitable but is the result of a concentrated effort by corporate powers and their allies in government and the bio-scientific community to align society to the technology, and to dismiss or undermine any opposition in the process.

The outcome sought, and which is now emerging, is increasing corporate-state enclosure of the DNA-commons and the bio-industrialisation of agriculture. This does not auger at all well for long-term ecological sustainability, which is now recognised widely as a prescription for economic development (WCED, 1987). Empowerment of eco-social interests and the realistic consideration of their concerns is necessary and urgent. A focus on deconstructing bio-translation processes is one important step in that direction.

Notes

1 Ian Anderson, the editor of *Search* in 1992, who was the originator of much of this passage (part of which is cited from the C.S. Lewis tale of 'Tweedledee and Tweedledum'), suggested it for the introductory abstract to my article that critiqued the exhibition. However, according to Anderson, it was not then used because of CSIRO's strong objection.

2 Concerning agency/structure conceptions of power see Giddens, 1984; Clegg 1989.

References

Abir-Am, P. (1982) The Discourse of Physical Power and Biological Knowledge in the 1930s: A Reappraisal of the Rockefeller Foundation's 'Policy' in Molecular Biology, *Social Studies of Science* 12: 341-382.

Australian (1995) Fears of Genetic Engineering Fall, 9 February.

Australian Gen-ethics Network (1994) Get Pork off Your Fork, *The Gene File,* November.

Australian Gen-ethics Network (1995a) Survey Results Misrepresent Public Attitudes toward Genetic Engineering, Press Release, 9 February.

ASTEC (1993a) *Gene Technology: Issues for Australia*, Occasional Paper No 27, Canberra, Australian Government Publishing Service.

ASTEC (1993b) Media Release: Release of ASTEC Study on Gene Technology, 7 December.

Bittisnich, D. and Smith, G. (1995) Teaching and Learning Gene Technology in Australian Schools, *Australasian Biotechnology* 5, 1: 16-17.

Bud, R. (1993) *The Uses of Life: A History of Biotechnology*, New York, Cambridge University Press.

Burris, B. (1989) Technocracy and the Transformation of Organizational Control, *The Social Science Journal* 26, 3: 313-333.

Callon, M. (1986) Some Elements of a Sociology of Translation: Domestification of the Scallops and the Fishermen of St Brieuc Bay, in Law, J. (ed.) *Power, Action and Belief: A New Sociology of Knowledge?* London, Routledge and Kegan Paul.

Clark, M. (1980) The Miracles of Spliced Genes, *Newsweek*, 17 March: 62-62 (cited in Goddell, 1986).

Cleaver, H. (1972) The Contradiction of the Green Revolution', *Monthly Review* 24: 80-111, p. 82.

Clegg, S. (1989) *Frameworks of Power*, London, Sage Publications.

Cribb, J. (1992) Pigs Won't Fly but Genetics Promises a Brave New World, *Weekend Australian* 8 February: 6.

DIST (1994) Gene Technology Survey, Minute - Biotechnology Section, 9 March.

DIST Biotechnology Section (nd) Gene Technology Information Unit: Guidelines and Selection Criteria.

Eco-Consumer (1995) Pig Growth Hormone: Time to Target the Smallgoods Industry and Retailers, *Eco-Consumer Newsletter* March.

Foucault, M. (1977) *Power/Knowledge*, New York, Pantheon.

Gerbner, G. (1972) Mass Media and Human Communication Theory, in McQuail, D. (ed.) *Sociology of Mass Communications*, Penguin, cited in Thomson, O. (1977) *Mass Persuasion in History*, Edinburgh, Paul Harris.

Giddens, A. (1984) *The Constitution of Society: Outline of the Theory of Structuration*, Berkeley and Los Angeles, University of California Press.

Goodman, D., Sorj, B., and Wilkinson, J. (1987) *From Farming to Biotechnology: A Theory of Agro-Industrial Development*, New York, Basil Blackwell.

Goodell, R. (1986) How to Kill a Controversy: The Case of Recombinant DNA, in Friedman, S., Dunwoody, S., and Rogers, C. (eds) *Scientists and Journalists: Reporting Science as News*, New York, The Free Press.

Grattan, M. (1995) Most back Benefits of Genetic Science, *The Age* 22 May: 7.

Grose, S. (1994) Knowledge Lacking, *Canberra Times* 18 October: 12.

GTIU (Gene Technology Information Unit) (1995a) *GTIU Forum* 1: 1.

GTIU (1995b) Introducing the Gene Technology Information Unit, Press Release, GTIU.

GTIU (1995c) Gene Technology at Work, *Today's Technology* 3.

GTIU (nd) Teaching Notes: Todays Technology: Gene Technology at Work.

Hindmarsh, R. (1992) CSIRO's Genetic Engineering Exhibition: Public Acceptance or Public Awareness? *Search* 23, 7: 212-213.

Hindmarsh, R. (1994a) Genetic Engineering Policy, Letter to the Editor, *Canberra Times* 11 October: 10.

Hindmarsh, R. (1994b) Power Relations, Social-Ecocentrism and Genetic Engineering: Agro-Biotechnology in the Australian Context (unpublished PhD Thesis, Faculty of Science and Technology, Griffith University).

Hindmarsh, R. (1995) Conflicting Interests Within the Gene Technology Information Unit, *Search* 26, 8: 251, Letters.

Hindmarsh, R., Lawrence, G., and Norton, J. (1995) Manipulating Genes or Public Opinion?, *Search* 26, 4: 117-121.

Hindmarsh, R. and Norton, J. (1995) Letter to the Editor, *Australasian Biotechnology* 5, 6: 366.

INRA (Europe) (1993) *Biotechnology and Genetic Engineering: What Europeans Think about It in 1993*, Report written for the European Commission, INRA (Europe) European Coordination Office.

Kawar, A. (1989) Issue Definition, Democratic Participation, and Genetic Engineering', *Policy Studies Journal* 17, 4: 719-744.

Kelley, J. (1995a) Australian Support for Genetic Engineering', *Search*, 26(5): 141-144.

Kelley, J. (1995b) *Public Perceptions of Genetic Engineering: Australia, 1994*, Final Report to the Department of Industry, Science and Technology, International Social Science Survey, Institute of Advanced Studies, Australian National University.

Kloppenburg, J. (1988) *First the Seed: The Political Economy of Plant Biotechnology, 1492-2000*, Cambridge, Cambridge University Press.

Krimsky, S. (1991) *Biotechnics and Society: The Rise of Industrial Genetics*, New York, Praeger.

Laird, A. (1995a) Correspondence to Hindmarsh, 5 April.

Lasswell, H. (1965) Propaganda, *Encyclopedia Britannica* 18: 580; cited in Gusfield, J. (1980) Introduction, in Altheide, D. and Johnson, J. *Bureaucratic Propaganda*, Boston, Allyn and Bacon.

Law, J. (ed.) (1986b) *Power, Action and Belief: A New Sociology of Knowledge?* London, Routledge and Kegan Paul.

Leyonhjelm, D. (1995a) Voting for Biotechnology at the Check-out, *Search* 26, 6: 186, Letters.

Leyonhjelm, D. (1995b) Scary Monster Stories Derail Biotechnology Debate, *Search* 26, 8: 251, Letters.

Leyonhjelm, D. (1995c) The Gene Technology Information Unit, *Australasian Biotechnology* 5,3: 136.

Livingstone, I. (1995) Genetic Food Worry, *Herald Sun (Melb)* 22 May: 3.

Loge, P. (1991) Language is a Virus: Discourse and the Politics and Public Policy of Biotechnology, Paper prepared for the 12th International Meeting of the Society of Environmental Toxicology and Chemistry, Seattle, WA, 6 November.

Love, R. (1992) The Public Perception of Risk, *Prometheus* 10, 1: 17-29.

Love, R. (1993) The Public Relations of Science, the Flying Pig and the Jet-propelled Cane Toad, *Chain Reaction* 68: 21-23.

Mussared, D. (1994a) Yes, We'll Eat those Tomatoes, *Canberra Times* 18 October: 12.

Mussared, D. (1994b) Time for Politicians to Engineer a Debate, *Canberra Times* 20 September: 11.

Naess, A. (1990) *Ecology, Lifestyle and Community: Outline of an Ecosophy*, (Translated and edited by D. Rothenberg), Cambridge University Press.

Norton, J., Lawrence, G., and Hindmarsh, R. (1995) Genetic Engineering: Public Approval or Public Concern?, *Search* 26, 6: 186-197, Letters.

Office of the Chief Scientist (1993) *Gene Technology*, Prime Minister's Science and Engineering Council, Canberra, Australian Government Publishing Service.

OECD, Group of National Experts on Safety in Biotechnology (1992) *Public Information/Public Education in Biotechnology: Results of an OECD Survey*, Paris, OECD.

Parisi, A. (1979) Industry of Life: The Birth of the Gene Machine, *The New York Times*, 29 June: F1 (cited In Goodell, 1986).

Peacock, J. (1994) Benefits of Genetic Engineering are Already with Us, *Canberra Times* 18 October: 12.

Quiddington, P. (1995) Public Seems to Accept Genetic Engineering, *Financial Review* 10 February: 23.

Spencer, C. (1994) Can Altered Food be Stomached? *Canberra Times* 15 October: 6.

Tribe, D. (1995) Conspiracy by Biobiz to Marginalise Critics, *Australasian Biotechnology* 5, 4: 209.

University of Melbourne Assembly Report (1979) *Report on Genetic Engineering*, Assembly Reports.

Wade, N. (1979) Recombinant DNA: Warming Up for the Big Payoff, *Science* 206, 9 November: 663-665.

WCED (World Commission for Environment and Development) (1987) *Our Common Future*, Oxford University Press.

Weekend Australian (1995) Gene Technology Wins Over Majority, 18 February: 47.

White, W. (1991) *Biotechnology in Australia: Perspectives and Issues for Animal Production*, Bureau of Rural Resources, Working Paper WP/16/91, Canberra, Department of Primary Industries and Energy.

Wright, S. (1986) Molecular Biology or Molecular Politics? The Production of Scientific Consensus on the Hazards of Recombinant DNA Technology, *Social Studies of Science* 16: 593-620.

Yoxen, E. (1981) Life as a Productive Force: Capitalising upon Research in Molecular Biology, in Levidow, L. and Young, R. (eds) *Science, Technology and the Labour Process,* Vol. 1, London, CSE Books.

Yoxen, E. (1983) *The Gene Business: Who Should Control Biotechnology?*, New York, Harper and Row.

Chapter 24

Rural Australia: insights and issues from contemporary political economy

Geoffrey Lawrence

What do we know about rural Australia?

The following Table attempts to outline, as briefly as possible, the problems and issues facing rural Australia. This categorisation is based on Canadian experience (see Prairie Farm Rehabilitation Administration, 1992) which seems to suggest that the 'rural' is undergoing the same processes of change in at least several of the advanced nations. It is not possible to elaborate upon all of the problems/issues raised in Table 1. Summaries relating to these points can be found in a number of recent analyses (see sources such as Lawrence, 1987; Cullen *et al.*, 1990; Lawrence *et al.*, 1992; Gray *et al.*, 1993; Humphreys, 1993; Lawrence and Share, 1993; Sorensen and Epps, 1993; Cheers, 1994; Lawrence and Vanclay, 1994; Sher and Sher, 1994; Vanclay and Lawrence, 1995; Burch *et al.*, 1996), including chapters of this book.

The Table is an attempt to synthesise the various concerns raised by the authors above so as to provide a general picture of the life choices and experiences of citizens in rural Australia. Given the importance attributed to agriculture - and the impact of agricultural pursuits upon the environment - it is appropriate to begin with farming.

Agriculture is experiencing terms of trade decline. Despite suggestions that wheat producers may be doing well or that prices for wool are improving, or that there is increasing demand for fresh vegetables in the Asia-Pacific, there are serious and unrelenting pressures upon Australia's agricultural industries: the prices paid by farmers for the inputs to agriculture are increasing at a faster rate than the prices which overseas and domestic consumers are prepared to pay for the products of agriculture.

Farmers are required to seek ways to address this problem. They are forced to become more efficient, to increase their productivity, to abandon products which continually fail to provide returns to capital, to produce new foods or fibres (or adopt new ways to value add to existing products), to shed labour (and substitute it for machines and other capital items), to reduce expenditure

Table 1
Basic problems and issues facing rural Australia

TYPE OF PROBLEM OR ISSUE	ON FARM	RURAL COMMUNITY

ECONOMIC	Farm profitability
	  commodity mix
	  high cost of inputs
	  deteriorating prices
	  cost - price squeeze
	Off farm employment
	Value adding - pluriactivity
	Intergenerational mobility
		Community viability
		  keeping businesses
		  attracting new businesses
		  rundown of infrastructure
		  relocation of govt activity
		Provision of new employment
		Unemployment and
		  underemployment

SOCIAL	Decline in farm numbers
	Inequalities - gender and race
	Farmer stress
	Farmer education
	Deterioration in farm family life
	  domestic violence
	  suicide
	  less integrated community
	Farm poverty
		Population loss (growth)
		Accessibility to services
		Ageing populations
		Social problems for rural youth
		Social isolation
		Development of appropriate
		  service delivery models
		Community decline - leadership
		Rural poverty

ENVIRONMENTAL	Soil degradation
	Water pollution
	Species decline
	New developments - feedlots
	Animal welfare
	Farm chemicals
	Sustainable agriculture (green
	  and clean) versus a
	  productionist' trajectory
	Application of biotechnologies
		Waste disposal
		Town water supply
		Assessing impact of population
		Farmlands for residential use
		Encouraging citizen participation
		  in decisions about environment

POLITICAL	Loss of political power
	Farm subsidisation vs free
	  markets
	Drought policy
	Catchment management and
	  Landcare
	Nature of agriculture's
	  integration with Asia
		Loss of political power
		Regionalisation as a form of
		  (re)centralisation
		Conservative local government
		No integrated regional/rural
		planning
		Critical mass in funding formulae

Source: Derived from Prairie Farm Rehabilitation Administration (1992: 8 -9)

on 'household' items and to look, where possible, for other combinations of labour and capital which increase profit levels (Lawrence, 1987). In the latter case it may be desirable for farmers or farm family members to work off the farm to improve income. In Australia, today, about one third of farms are at least partly sustained through off farm income: this figure rises dramatically when commodity price slumps insure that income from agriculture will remain low for lengthy periods. In one recent survey some seventy percent of Australian farms had members working off the farm (see Gray *et al.*, 1993).

The environmental problems associated with the chemically-based 'high tech' approach to Australian agriculture are now well documented (see, for example, Lawrence *et al.*, 1992; Vanclay and Lawrence, 1995) and include soil degradation, salinisation, waterlogging, pollution of river systems, eutrophication, the spread of blue-green algae, threats to wildlife and species decline. Most of these problems are a result of the practices which farmers have adopted to remain competitive in the international trade arena.

Yet the problem for Australian farmers is that they produce, by and large, for an export market which is corrupted by protection and subsidisation from abroad. The European Economic Community (EC) is very interested in sustaining a rural population and it does this by artificially supporting, through subsidisation from taxpayers, the cost of foods (National Farmers' Federation, 1993). The US wants its farmers to sell more in the world marketplace - as well as to conserve some of its most valuable farmland - and so finds ways to provide its international customers with bonuses and its producers with incentives. The outcome of EC and US agricultural policies is that Australian producers lose about $2 billion per year in sales that they might otherwise secure (see NFF, 1993). The World Trade Organisation - formed in 1994 as a global free-trade regulating body (see McMichael, 1996) - may help to roll back the advantages currently enjoyed by Australia's competitors - but that is not to say that Australian farmers will be able to overcome the terms of trade decline they currently experience. After all, efficiency and productivity increases are being forced upon all commercial producers throughout the world. And virtually all producers have access to the products which will help to make them more efficient (and which increase the volume of food and fibre in the marketplace).

It is unlikely that Australian farmers will be greatly advantaged by a return to relative prosperity in agriculture. In fact, with improved farm viability and better prices for farmlands will come a rush by many to sell their properties. According to the Director of the Australian Bureau of Agriculture and Resource Economics (ABARE), up to 20 percent of producers are expected to leave agriculture over the next few years as prices *improve* (see *Australian*, 2 February 1994: 36). An earlier prediction - based on price movements in agriculture - was that Australia's current 135,000 farmers will fall to 70,000 by the year 2,000 (see Summons, 1984). It should be remembered that at present about four fifths of the value of Australia's agricultural output is produced by about one fifth of Australia's producers (see *Australian Farm Journal*, February 1992: 16). The smaller producers are largely irrelevant to Australian farming. Orthodox, 'free market' economists expect primary producers to realise the pressures to 'adjust' out and capitulate (see Gow, 1994; 1996). For reasons of lifestyle, lack of work opportunities elsewhere, age, or education, many refuse to leave.

Agricultural economists tend to view such behaviour as irrational and as a barrier to best use of resources in farming. Yet, it is based on quite rational calculations: many farmers are unable or unwilling to be retrained and will struggle to have their definition of farming - as a small, family-based enterprise providing a living for those who are willing to work physically hard - accepted as legitimate. (They were certainly successful in doing so in previous periods of Country - later National - Party rule.) They may not be able to conceive of any other form of work and many will have their status, identity and family history tied up in land ownership in the district (see Gray *et al.*, 1996). To suggest these people are a 'low income problem' (Gow, 1994) and must leave agriculture for their own good and the good of the nation is to deny their desire and ability to resist those economic forces which have undermined their viability.

Conditions for Australians living in the rural hinterlands (that is, those communities located within regions dominated by agriculture) mirror those of the farming community. Of the 37 economically poorest electorates in Australia, some 33 are located in rural regions (Commonwealth Electoral Division, 1988). Rural regions have fewer job opportunities for workers: often towns will be dominated by a single industry or company and will not have the diversity of work options to attract a diverse and skilled workforce (see Powell, 1987). Unemployment is often higher in rural regions and there is usually considerable hidden unemployment and underemployment - especially for women (see Powell, 1987). The jobs available to women are often unskilled, casual or part-time and are invariably poorly paid. It has been found that, as a group, rural women are overqualified for the work they do: something which disadvantages professionally-trained women such as nurses and teachers (see Alston, 1990; Gibson *et al.*, 1990).

While urban images of rural Australia often focus on the benefits of the uncomplicated and 'healthy' lifestyle available to rural people, research suggests that the general health of rural people is, by urban standards, very poor (see Humphreys, 1993). Rural populations have above-average rates of premature mortality and death through heart disease, cancer, suicide and tuberculosis (see Humphreys, 1990 and 1993; Cullen *et al.*, 1990). Poverty, and the associated family problems which arise from income deprivation, is higher in rural than urban areas (see discussion in Lawrence, 1987). The health status of Aborigines is disgraceful: Aborigines have a mortality rate over four times that for whites and life expectancy is about 20 years lower (reported in Share *et al.*, 1993).

Government reports have shown that, in relation to access to social services, people living in communities of between 5,000 and 10,000 face what they describe as 'considerable' disadvantage, while those living in communities of below 5,000 people face 'extreme' disadvantage (see discussion in Lawrence, 1987). According to Cheers (1994: 3) those living in isolated areas are especially affected. They face a 'lack of information about what is available; the absence or inaccessibility of many services; poorer quality services; higher costs associated with accessing specialist services; inappropriate urban service and funding models; and poorly-motivated staff'.

What is concerning a number of rural welfare practitioners (see for example, Cheers [1994]) is that the population changes being experienced in (particularly inland) rural regions will leave the aged population increasingly vulnerable. Salt (1992) found that of those communities which lost population in 1990-91 approximately 88 percent were rural. Most of these were in inland areas, with coastal rural regions showing quite good growth associated with the movement of urban retirees and those wanting a rural lifestyle (see Sorensen and Epps, 1993). There seems to be a pattern emerging in the inland regions - with a decline in population being matched by a decline in services. Yet the people remaining are often the very groups in need of social services and other welfare and health support. The elderly are often not able to move. They cannot sell their houses for prices which prevail in the cities (and which they might be expected to pay if they move). There are few people interested in purchasing property in declining communities, leaving the aged semi-'trapped' in locations which are experiencing withdrawal of programs as governments rationalise their services (see Lawrence and Williams, 1990; Humphreys, 1993; Cheers, 1994; Lawrence and Stehlik, 1996).

How might we explain some of these developments? Is the economic demise of much of rural Australia 'inevitable'? The so-called 'rural restructuring thesis' is an attempt to link local changes to those which are occurring at the global level.

The theoretical underpinnings of rural restructuring

Marsden *et al.*, (1993) have identified three approaches which have been employed to understand recent changes in rural society. The first, and arguably the most important, is that of the regulationists of whom the best known are Aglietta (1979) and Lipietz (1987, 1992). In their analysis, a regime of accumulation (a particular economic arrangement with corresponding social norms and values) provides for economic and social reproduction. Each regime of accumulation is associated with a mode of regulation - a politico-institutional means of fostering capital accumulation (profit-making). The mode of regulation comprises fiscal and monetary policy, taxation laws, a framework for wage negotiations, and policies directing capital flow - both domestic and foreign. In any particular period, a mode of accumulation will correspond with a mode of regulation to ensure continued economic activity and social reproduction. This is not unproblematic: the extent of class and other political activity determines the contours of any regime of accumulation/mode of regulation including, importantly, its longevity.

There have been, to date, two identifiable regimes of accumulation within advanced capitalism. The first was an 'extensive' regime which lasted to the end of the First World War and was associated with the opening of new frontiers for capitalism. The second has existed since the end of the Second World War (see Kenney *et al.*, 1991; McMichael, 1994) and has been 'intensive' in form - requiring the further application of technology rather than labour to increase the rate at which surplus value has been generated.

Some authors (Kenney *et al.*, 1991) have argued that the intensive regime can be labelled as Fordism - a system in which mass production from factories was 'matched' by mass consumption from consumers whose wages and social conditions were regulated via Keynesian economic policies. Under the Fordist regime, capital accumulation was guarded by the nation state. Profits were 'shared' by the various classes in a manner which gave stability to the system of production and yet stimulated further the use of intensive technologies.

Fordism was considered to have entered a crisis period beginning in the early 1970s. Kenney *et al.,* (1991: 182) have outlined the problem as experienced by the US:

> A combination of the overheated and lagging US-Viet Nam war economy and the 1974 OPEC oil crisis radically undermined US fordism...within the larger economy, real per capita income decreased, rates of productivity declined and overproduction became endemic. Additionally, during the 1970s, unemployment and inflation rose, and measures of economic activity oscillated significantly and unpredictably. The post-war economic growth model entered into crisis.

It is further suggested that production within the US might be beginning to be characterised as 'post Fordist' - associated with new ways of organising (and new ways of controlling) surplus generation.

In terms of agriculture it is suggested that while Fordism guaranteed the farmer a politically stable environment in which to operate - and helped to ensure that the profits from farming were invested in the industrial products which would be employed to generate further profits, the crisis of agriculture after the early to mid 1970s represented a turning point in the mass production/mass consumption relationship. Consumers were beginning to demand more healthy ('green' and largely chemical free) products, the nation state could no longer guarantee profitability in a world of increasing competition in the production of foods and fibres, and the Keynesian policies which had placed a welfare net under rural people was being removed (see Kenney *et al.,* 1991; and Buttel, 1993). The economic conditions of farm production and wider consumption, together with the reductions in state support for rural regions, became a catalyst for the restructuring of rural society.

A second perspective - one which introduces the concept of 'flexible specialisation' - has emerged alongside that of the regulationists. The basic insight is that older forms of production are outmoded and that the capitalist world is entering a new (if not disorganised) era in which consumer requirements for new and varied products, together with the inherent sluggishness of large-scale producers properly to address issues of style and taste, and the ability of new electronic and other technologies to allow small scale production to be profitable, have combined to make mass markets and mass production obsolete (see Piore and Sabel, 1984; Lash and Urry, 1987 and 1994). The emphasis now is on decentralised production units which allow small(er) scale capital to profit from more responsive production arrangements and from niche marketing. In agriculture, the move to 'flexible specialisation' might be represented by the collapse of any 'factory farming' as well as the demise of statutory marketing authorities and their replacement with agribusiness-linked, specialised, marketing firms.

The third account, according to Marsden *et al.,* (1993) is that which emphasises the spatial aspects of change within the global economy. It, too, sees the demise of Fordist forms of production but emphasises, in particular, how economic change has spatial consequences for the social division of labour. In Britain, for example, Massey has suggested that capitalist development in association with neo conservative policies has created spatially uneven patterns of industrial growth - significantly disadvantaging the more economically marginal areas and populations. In the US, Buttel (1993) has suggested that the withdrawal of state support is likely to result in further polarisation between regions. This point was raised in relation to Australia by Lawrence (1987) and more recently by Lawrence and Share (1993), Rolley and Humphreys (1993), Stilwell (1992, 1993), Cheers (1994), and Dixon and Hoatson (1996).

In other words, while the parameters and dynamics of change within the modern capitalist world remain somewhat indeterminate it is certain that there is restructuring occurring and that the impact of such restructuring is no longer exclusively about whether the family farm will survive or not (this assumes the rest of rural society would somehow expand or contract as a direct consequence of movements in agriculture) but about the place of the rural region within the context of a changing capitalism. Rather than focus on the problems of farming and the role of the farm lobby in securing benefits from the state as a means of retaining their position within the economy, it is necessary to ask broader questions: questions including those about rural policy in an era of 'green' consumerism, the application of new technologies in non metropolitan areas, the place of the rural in regional development, and finally, the way in which rural regions are inserted into the global economy.

Changes predicted as rural restructuring continues in Australia

While it is not possible to provide, here, a thorough account of all the processes associated with change in rural Australia, the following is a summary of the likely impacts of the changes predicted by the rural restructuring literature:

The emergence of green consumerism

'Green' consumers are those who eschew mass produced foods (those which may have chemical additives, be packed in environmentally unfriendly wrappers, and be made in ecologically unsound ways) and who demand, instead, 'clean' foods - those construed, by virtue of the way they have been grown and delivered, to be wholesome, nutritious and produced in a manner which protects the environment.

The Europeans and Japanese, particularly in the last decade, have been increasingly concerned about food safety and food quality. At the same time that the cheaper, mass produced, foods have become accepted among consumers whose incomes prevent wider choice, a large group of reportedly middle-class consumers in those countries has demanded 'quality' foods. The same is occurring today as consumers in the newly industrialising countries - with ever higher real levels of income - are demanding better foods.

It is presently thought that through the implementation of ecologically sustainable development options Australia will improve its environment and produce the sorts of foods which consumers are increasingly demanding. The development of Landcare, Federally-funded initiatives to grow more trees, integrated catchment management and whole farm planning are seen to provide the basis for a more sustainable agriculture in Australia (see Lawrence, *et al.*, 1992; Vanclay and Lawrence, 1995; and Lockie, this volume). It is sometimes contended that a more sustainable agriculture would, in being family-farm based and presumably less productionist in character, lead to a more sustainable structure for rural communities. But, at the moment, there is no evidence to suggest this will be the case. The very notion of what might be sustainable and how sustainability might be achieved is also being questioned (see Lawrence, 1993; Beder, 1994). And, for example, given that family-farm agriculture has caused the problems of environmental degradation in the past we should be wary in anticipating it will be the vehicle for environmental renewal. Just as importantly, while there might be evidence from the US that farmers may be adopting post-Fordist options which link farmers to niche markets for environmentally-friendly foods, this may not be the case in Australia. In fact, there is evidence to suggest that Australian farmers are obeying Fordist signals which demand the continued production of bulk commodities for undifferentiated markets (see Lawrence and Vanclay, 1994; Burch, *et al.*, 1996; and Lyons, this volume).

While there is some doubt that a post-Fordist agriculture is emerging in Australia (and, consequently, that it may be providing community benefits to rural regions) three other developments may be viewed positively. The first is the emergence in rural regions of new options for farmers (describe in the literature as 'pluriactivity') which may help them to survive in spite of any deterioration over time in the terms of trade for agriculture; the second is the movement to some rural regions of retirees, tourists and those spending money in recreational and leisure pursuits; the third is the ways in which the meaning of 'rural' is changing to reflect the first two developments. Rural is not a fixed entity but a social construct which undergoes alteration as specific sets of actors compete to give meaning to social space (see Mormont, 1990). If, through pluriactivity, farmers can pursue new directions which assist them to improve their livelihood, they may be better able to stay in the district and contribute to economic growth. Similarly, if rural space is inhabited by those who are no longer prepared to tolerate the chemicals from sprays or the noise of farm machinery or the lack of foresight of local government, this group may mobilise to ensure that *its* definition of rural and *its* interpretations of the best use of resources is that which prevails.

The form and direction of technological change

The adoption of new productivity-boosting technologies by farmers has meant, in the context of poor markets for agricultural goods, that farm numbers can contract: some farmers will become less efficient and less productive than their counterparts and 'read' from market signals that they must leave agriculture. Of course, some do leave while others use whatever is available to provide them with a living in farming (see Lawrence, 1987; Gray *et al.*, 1993). According to Cribb (1994:13) from the mid 1960s until today the number of farms has fallen from 200,000 to 120,000 and the rural workforce has declined by over 100,000. Since, in communities which are agriculturally-dependent, every farm job generates between two and three service/manufacturing sector jobs, the loss has had quite a profound 'negative multiplier' effect on those communities.

Increased efficiency in farming, brought about by new technologies, has enabled ever larger volumes of food and fibre to be produced with a reduced agricultural workforce. If efficiency increases are going to continue - and there is no reason to suspect that they will not - then it might be reasoned that population decline will continue. That people will use cars and other easily accessible forms of transport to shop and buy services in regional centres is suggested as another factor in the demise of the small town (see Henshall Hansen Associates, 1988; Smailes, this volume).

While it is more or less certain, if the present trajectory in agriculture is taken as given, that there will be fewer farmers and - quite possibly - fewer people in traditional farming regions, does this mean fewer people in rural Australia? Some have argued (see contributors to Share, 1995) that, with new satellite and telecommunication technologies, it is entirely possible for businesses to expand in regional areas. With communication costs being reduced over time and the cost of an inner-city location costly for business, some components of city-based business - as well as some businesses themselves - might expand to regions which provide a least cost option. (For example the case for the decentralisation of legal practices in Australia has been well argued by Williamson, 1990.) Were Australia to become more like the US which has non-uniform wage rates for various job classifications, the regional wage rates might be expected to fall - providing yet another incentive for businesses to locate in non metropolitan areas. This is certainly something which the NFF would see as appropriate for rural regions. This peak farmer organisation - consistent with its neo-liberalist economic agenda - would have little difficulty accepting that lower wage rates is a means of increasing regional competitiveness (NFF, 1993) even if, as would seem likely, lower standards of living would prevail.

Instantaneous communication - brought about by various 'electronic byways' (see Parker, *et al.*, 1992) - might, in conjunction with cheaper air fares, better service provision and an improved quality of life in regional centres, act as a catalyst for population growth in those centres. In the US a new sort of individual entrepreneur has been identified - the so-called 'lone eagle'. The label is given to a highly trained professional who uses communications networks to link to world markets from what might be viewed as a quite isolated location - a mountain cabin in Colorado, or a small farm in Vermont. Their particular 'skill' is to combine their work activities with an aesthetically pleasing or otherwise enjoyable geographical location. Virtually no work has been done in Australia on this new 'postmodern' worker.

New prospects for regional development

Since the perceived excesses of the Whitlam Labor Government's Department of Urban and Regional Development (DURD), decentralisation policy has been largely out of favour with Canberra policy makers. Where its influence continued at the State level - as in Bjelke-Petersen's Queensland of the 1970s and 1980s - it had a strong 'development' bias ensuring State monies would fund the building of dams, roads and bridges to help stimulate private (often overseas) investment in tourism, mining and agriculture. At the Federal level, the pursuit of economic rationalist policies from Fraser-to-Hawke-to-Keating-to-Howard has not assisted in encouraging 'balanced' regional development. While the regions continue to be injected with dollars for social security, policing, education, these are based on per capita calculations. In an era of increasing fiscal restraint, the result has been the 'rationalisation' and centralisation of services, not the provision of services on grounds of equity and access (see Rolley and Humphries, 1993; Lawrence and Stehlik, 1996; and Tonts and Jones, this volume).

While there remain very important distributional (social justice) and environmental (containment of urban pollution) reasons for initiating decentralisation (see Cheers, 1994), writers such as Stilwell (1993) and Fagan and Webber (1994) question whether there will ever be any possibility of government-directed economic growth in periods where neo-conservative economics is in ascension. Stilwell (1993) argues that as the 'externalities' of city living (congestion, pollution, environmental destruction and lifestyle limitations) become more unbearable, decentralisation should emerge as a possible 'solution'. But, he notes:

> decentralisation policy is simultaneously less likely to be implemented in these circumstances because of the fundamental conflict between such an 'interventionist' approach to regional policy and the 'economic rationalist' doctrines. This is the paradox - that the case for decentralisation becomes stronger as the result of a policy orientation which undermines the possibility of official support for a vigorous decentralisation programme.

In this sense it is no wonder that criticism has been drawn by the publication of the report of the Task Force on Regional Development (1993) (see Guille,

1994). The Task Force was established to examine economic and industry development issues from a regional perspective, to examine factors affecting the investment of private sector capital in regional areas, and to see if 'adjustments' might need to be made in government service delivery to help facilitate regional development. The then Prime Minister, Paul Keating, had identified regional development as a high priority for Australia at a time when it was entering new relations with a more trade-liberal Asia-Pacific region.

The two volume report showed, as expected, that there were major disparities between regions. It recommended the establishment of Regional Economic Development Organisations which would, through a network of local businesses, produce integrated regional development plans and help to 'promote', for the eyes of business, regional Australia. The regions were to be 'empowered' so that local people could find local solutions to local problems, and not to be reliant on government funding support for economic development.

The approach here was one in which the Labor government sought to ensure that changes occurring in, and economic opportunities being identified for, Australia, would be spread geographically and not be concentrated in the cities or other more privileged economic zones. The problem with this sort of thinking is encapsulated by Guille (1994: 25):

> The Taskforce Report is based on three principles: all regions should have equal access - as far as possible - to basic infrastructure; the regions should have the opportunity to develop their local economies; and those regions suffering some specific disadvantage, for example, remoteness, should have equal access to special assistance. (However) these principles are in direct conflict with the principles of market liberalisation (which stresses) marginal return and user pays principle (and) 'trickle down' development.

Needless to say, since the election of the Howard government in 1996, interventionist options have been viewed as inappropriate and the REDOs have lost their funding. Like Stilwell, Guille recognised the difficulties surrounding the endorsement of state policies which *may* help to 'direct' business investment into regional Australia - in the face of economic forces which appear to lead to the centralisation of economic activity in the major cities. Epps and Sorensen (1993) suggest that smaller rural settlements will most probably have to rely upon the 'wits and the wiles' of politicians, rather than to any regional policy, for their existence.

The above seems to be an (albeit brief) summary of what we already know about regional development in Australia. So, what might the restructuring literature lead us to consider in this context? There are three issues of direct importance: flexible specialisation (the possibility that the regions hold the key to extended reproduction for capitalist enterprises which wish to 'escape' the more unionised and potentially less conducive profit making, conditions of the cities); the political pressure which may be placed on governments simultaneously by urban dwellers for a less crowded and less polluted environment, and by rural dwellers for new economic activity as a catalyst for unemployment relief and social development; and finally, the growth of an environmental consciousness which places the consumer of food closer to the source of that food and leads to the demise of intensive food production systems.

It is not possible to discuss these ideas at length here: it *is* possible to indicate that some form of decentralisation will, of necessity, be a crucial element in the social development of rural communities in Australia during the remainder of this decade (see Lawrence and Share, 1993; Cheers, 1994). The extent to which decentralisation and regional planning may be efficacious in relieving significant parts of rural Australia of their decline will be based on the political struggles waged over the meaning and purpose of the 'rural' in contemporary Australian society and the extent to which neo-conservative economic policies, and the impacts of those policies, can be reversed.

Global influences

It is not yet known what form the rural region will take within an integrated global system of capitalism (see Bonanno *et al.*, 1994). Is it to be a location which competes internationally with other regions of the same country - and other countries - for corporate-based investment dollars? And, what degree of autonomy will particular regions within the nation state be allowed in their economic dealings with transnational capital? We know, already, that agribusiness is 'playing off' regions within Australia with regions in Thailand and New Zealand in regard to the sourcing of inputs for processed foods (see Burch, *et al.*, 1996). Will regions become evermore vulnerable to the profit-making decisions of transnational capital in an era of reduced financial commitment by the nation state?

It has been suggested that suprastate bodies are emerging to regulate the global economy (see McMichael, 1994; McMichael, 1996). If this is so - and the result were to be the extension, world wide, of a more liberal trade regime - are rural Australians likely to be advantaged? Some say 'yes'; after all, if our agriculture is as efficient as economists suggest will we not benefit from the sale of more agricultural goods in the international marketplace? (see NFF, 1993). In contradistinction, a world in which the World Trade Organisation's rulings were to override those of the nation-state might leave rural regions relatively unprotected and their future uncertain (McMichael, 1994). One cannot dismiss notions of agency here. Perhaps the rural region would become a more politically important unit than it is at present under a complex system of federal/state/local decision-making. Perhaps regional self-help and self-determination would be more meaningful if the decisions made by regionally-based citizens had direct global outcomes. Political movements based on regional problems, issues, and potential developments, might arise if power were genuinely devolved and people felt they had a basis for effecting change at the local/regional level.

Conclusion

It is argued in this chapter that while there has been considerable interest by rural sociologists and human geographers in establishing the place of the family farm within the structure of capitalism, we must now recognise that the place of the farmer is of diminishing importance in determining the fate of rural regions. It is clear to many contemporary analysts that as global forces become more important in determining the political, economic and cultural shape of Australia in the late 1990s it is necessary to develop new ways of examining change.

Just as new trends and developments - such as the growth of tourism and the service sector in general, the rise of environmentalism, the move to 'flexible specialisation' in manufacturing, and the advent of 'global sourcing' - have become features of international capitalism, so too, we are required to develop and apply new concepts to understand the significance of those changes. As Marsden *et al.*, (1993) and Le Heron (1993) suggest, the application of a more spatially-informed regulation theory may be the best way to understand the changes occurring in rural regions of the advanced economies. It ensures that the focus of analysis will be the way in which the 'local' is being incorporated by the 'transnational' - including the significance of the emergence of 'green' policies, the potential demise of the influence and power of the nation state, the importance of global capital, the differences occurring spatially as capital penetrates particular areas, new forms of struggle and resistance, and the implications of applying new technologies.

Important questions are raised (and others, quite obviously, are ignored) in a regulationist/structuralist approach to agrarian change (see Buttel, 1996; Gray, 1996; Lawrence, 1996). It is suggested that in looking to the future impacts of restructuring in rural areas of Australia, it is necessary to recognise that some levels of government may become increasingly irrelevant to economic development of the regions. The task is to establish which development paths are possible within a global economy and to inform political action aimed at improving social development, equity and justice within rural Australia.

Acknowledgments

This paper was presented in a different form at the *Political Economy Anniversary Conference*, University of Sydney, 22 October 1994. It draws upon and updates material from one section of 'Rural Restructuring: Sociological Meaning, Social Impacts and Policy Implications', Presented to the *International Conference on Issues Affecting Rural Communities*, James Cook University of Northern Australia, Townsville, 10 - 15 July 1994 and from sections of 'Beyond the Eastern Seaboard: What Future for Rural and Remote Australia?' Brisbane, 26 - 28 October 1994. Linda Hungerford, Frances Killion and Dani Stehlik of CQU are thanked for their helpful comments.

References

Aglietta, M. (1979) *A Theory of Capitalist Regulation*, London, New Left Books.

Alston, M. (ed.)(1990) *Rural Women*, Key Papers Series, Number 1, Wagga Wagga, Centre for Rural Social Research.

Australian, 2 February 1994.

Australian Farm Journal, February 1992.

Bonanno, A. (1987) *Small Farms*, Boulder, Westview.

Bonanno, A., Busch, L., Friedland, W., Gouveia, L. and Mingione, E. (eds)(1994) *From Columbus to ConAgra: the Globalization of Agriculture and Food*, Kansas, University Press of Kansas.

Beder, S. (1994) 'Revoltin' Developments: the Politics of Sustainable Development', *Arena Magazine* 11, June/July.

Burch, D., Rickson, R. and Lawrence, G. (eds)(1996) *Globalisation and Agri-food Restructuring: Perspectives from the Australasia Region*, London, Avebury.

Buttel, F. (1993) Environmentalization and Greening: Origins, Processes and Implications, in Harper, S. (ed.) *The Greening of Rural Policy*, London, Belhaven Press.

Buttel, F. (1996) Theoretical Issues in Global Agri-food Restructuring, in Burch, D., Rickson, R. and Lawrence, G. (eds) *Globalisation and Agri-food Restructuring: Perspectives from the Australasia Region*, London, Avebury.

Buttel, F. and Gertler, M. (1982) Agricultural Structure, Agricultural Policy, and Environmental Quality: Some Observations on the Context of Agricultural Research in North America, *Agriculture and Environment* 7.

Buttel, F., Larson, O. and Gillespie, G. (1990) *The Sociology of Agriculture*, New York, Greenwood Press.

Cheers, B. (1994) Social Development as a Facet of Regional Development, paper to be presented at the *First National Regional Australia Conference*, Whyalla, South Australia.

Commonwealth Electoral Division (1988) *Comparison of 1986 Census Characteristics*, Current Issues Paper Number 11, Legislation Research Services, Canberra, Commonwealth Electoral Division.

Cribb, J. (1994) The Unsettling of Australia: Disturbing Trends on the Way to 2001, *The Australian Magazine* February: 12 - 13.

Cullen, T., Dunn, P. and Lawrence, G. (eds)(1990) *Rural Health and Welfare in Australia*, Wagga Wagga, Centre for Rural Social Research.

de Janvry, A. (1980) Social Differentiation in Agriculture and the Ideology of Neopopulism, in Buttel, F. and Newby, H. (eds) *The Rural Sociology of the Advanced Societies*, Montclair, Allenheld.

Dixon, J. and Hoatson, L. (1996) Strategies for Communities Under Economic Rationalism, Paper presented at the *International Conference of the Community Development Society*, Melbourne, 21-24 July.

Dunn, P. (1989) Rural Australia: Are You Standing in It? *Rural Welfare Research Bulletin* 2, July.

Epps, R. and Sorensen, T. (1993) Prospects for Rural Australia, in Sorensen, T. and Epps, R. (eds) *Prospects and Policies for Rural Australia*, Melbourne, Longman.

Fagan, R. and Webber, M. (1994) *Global Restructuring: the Australian Experience*, Melbourne, Oxford University Press.

Fairweather, J. (1992) *Agrarian Restructuring in New Zealand*, Research Report No 213, Agribusiness and Economics Research Unit, Canterbury, New Zealand, Lincoln University, April.

Friedland, W. (1991) Introduction: Shaping the New Political Economy of Advanced Agriculture, in Friedland, W., Busch, L., Buttel, F. and Rudy, A. *Toward a New Political Economy of Agriculture*, Boulder, Westview.

Friedland, W., Barton, A. and Thomas, R. (1981) *Manufacturing Green Gold*, New York, Cambridge University Press.

Gibson, D., Baxter, J. and Kingston, C. (1990) Beyond the Dichotomy: The Paid and Unpaid Work of Rural Women, in Alston, M (ed.) *Rural Women*, Key Papers Number 1, Wagga Wagga, Centre for Rural Social Research.

Gow, J. (1994) Farm Structural Adjustment - an Everyday Imperative, *Rural Society* 4, 2: 9-13.

Gow, J. (1996) Structural Adjustment in Australian Agriculture Revisited, *Rural Society* 6, 1: 24-30.

Gray, I. (1996) The De-Traditionalization of Farming in Burch, D., Rickson, R. and Lawrence, G. (eds) *Globalisation and Agri-food Restructuring: Perspectives from the Australasia Region*, London, Avebury.

Gray, I., Lawrence, G. and Dunn, T. (1993) *Coping with Change: Australian Farmers in the 1990s*, Wagga Wagga, Centre for Rural Social Research.

Gray, I., Stehlik, D., Lawrence, G. and Bulis, H. (1996) Impacts of Drought on Australian Rural Communities: Is it Socially Binding or Socially Divisive? Paper presented at the *International Conference of the Community Development Society*, Melbourne, 21-24 July.

Guille, H. (1994) Regional Development: a Critique of the Kelty Report, *WISER* 1,2.

Henshall Hansen Associates (1988) *Study of Small Towns in Victoria*, Melbourne, Henshall Hansen Associates.

Humphreys, J. (1993) Planning for Services in Rural Australia, *Regional Journal of Social Issues* 27.

Lash, S. and Urry, J. (1987) *The End of Organised Capitalism*, United Kingdom, Polity Press.

Lash, S. and Urry, J. (1994) *Economies of Signs and Space*, London, Sage.

Lawrence, G. (1987) *Capitalism and the Countryside: the Rural Crisis in Australia*, Sydney, Pluto.

Lawrence, G. (1993) Biotechnology and Globalisation: Prospects for Sustainability, *Paper Presented at the Ecopolitics VII Conference*, Griffith University, Brisbane, 2 - 4 July.

Lawrence, G. (1996) Contemporary Agri-food Restructuring: Australia and New Zealand, in Burch, D., Rickson, R. and Lawrence, G. (eds) *Globalisation and Agri-food Restructuring: Perspectives from the Australasia Region*, London, Avebury.

Lawrence, G. and Share, P. (1993) Rural Australia: Current Problems and Policy Directions, *Regional Journal of Social Issues* 27.

Lawrence, G. and Stehlik, D. (1996) A Direction Toward Sustainability? Australian Regional Communities and Care for the Aged, *Journal of the Community Development Society* (forthcoming).

Lawrence, G. and Vanclay, F. (1994) Agricultural Change in the Semi-Periphery: the Murray-Darling Basin, Australia, in McMichael, P. (ed.) *The Global Restructuring of Agro-food Systems*, Ithaca, Cornell University Press.

Lawrence, G. and Williams, C. (1990) The Dynamics of Decline: Implications for Social Welfare Delivery in Rural Australia, in Cullen, T., Dunn, P. and Lawrence, G. (eds) *Rural Health and Welfare in Australia*, Wagga Wagga, Centre for Rural Social Research.

Lawrence, G., Vanclay, F. and Furze, B. (eds)(1992) *Agriculture, Environment and Society: Contemporary Issues for Australia*, Melbourne, Macmillan.

Le Heron, R. (1993) *Globalized Agriculture: Political Choice*, Oxford, Pergamon.

Le Heron, R., Roche, M., Johnston, T. and Bowler, S. (1991) Pluriactivity in New Zealand's Agro-commodity Chains, in Fairweather, J. (ed.) *Proceedings of the Rural Economy and Society Section of the Sociological Association of Aotearoa (NZ)*, Canterbury, Agribusiness and Economics Research Unit, Lincoln University.

Ling, J. (1994) Queensland Rural Communities: Future Challenges, Paper presented to the *International Conference on Issues Affecting Rural Communities*, Townsville, 10 - 15 July.

Lipietz, A. (1987) *Mirages and Miracles: The Crisis of Global Fordism*, London, Verso.

Lipietz, A. (1992) *Towards a New Economic Order: Postfordism, Ecology and Democracy*, New York, Oxford University Press.

Macklin, R. (1990) The Symbolic Construction of Rural Australia, *Rural Welfare Research Bulletin* 5.

Marsden, T., Lowe, P. and Whatmore, S. (eds)(1990) *Rural Restructuring: Global Processes and their Responses*, London, David Fulton.

Marsden, T., Murdoch, J., Lowe, P., Munton, R. and Flynn, A. (1993) *Constructing the Countryside*, London, UCL Press.

Massey, D. (1984) *Spatial Divisions of Labour: Social Structures and the Geography of Production*, London, Macmillan.

McMichael, P. (ed.)(1994) *The Global Restructuring of Agro-food Systems*, Ithaca, Cornell University Press.

McMichael, P. (1996) *Development and Social Change: A Global Perspective,* California, Pine Forge.

Mooney, P. (1988) *My Own Boss?* Boulder, Westview.

Mormont, M. (1990) Who is Rural? or, How To Be Rural: Towards a Sociology of the Rural, in Marsden, T., Lowe, P. and Whatmore, S. (eds) *Rural Restructuring: Global Processes and Their Responses,* London, Fulton.

National Farmers' Federation (1993) *New Horizons: A Strategy for Australia's Agrifood Industries,* Canberra, National Farmers' Federation.

National Farmers' Federation (1994) *Annual Report 1993,* Canberra, National Farmers' Federation.

Nichol, B. (1990) What is Rural? *Rural Welfare Research Bulletin* 4, April 4-6.

O'Toole, K. (1993) Changing the Focus From 'Rural' to 'Local' State, *Regional Journal of Social Issues* 27.

Parker, E., Hudson, H., Dillman, D., Strover, S. and Williams, F. (1992) *Electronic Byways: State Policies for Rural Development Through Telecommunications,* Boulder, Westview.

Piore, M. and Sabel, C. (1984) *The Second Industrial Divide,* New York, Basic Books.

Powell, R. (1987) quoted in Share, P., Lawrence, G., and Gray, I. Rural Australia, in Najman, J. and Western, J. (eds) *A Sociology of Australian Society,* Melbourne, Macmillan.

Prairie Farm Rehabilitation Administration (1992) *Rural Prairie Sustainability: A Background Paper,* Regina, Saskatchewan, PFRA.

Rolley, F. and Humphreys, J. (1993) Rural Welfare - the Human Face of Australia's Countryside, in Sorensen, T. and Epps, R. (eds) *Prospects and Policies for Rural Australia,* Melbourne, Longman Cheshire.

Roobeek, A. (1987) The Crisis in Fordism and the Rise of a New Technological Paradigm, *Futures* 19.

Salt, B. (1992) *Population Movements in Non Metropolitan Australia,* Canberra, Australian Government Publishing Service.

Share, P. (1995) Communication and Culture in Rural Areas, Wagga Wagga, Centre for Rural Social Research.

Share, P., Lawrence, G. and Gray, I. (1993) Rural Australia, in Najman, J. and Western, J. (eds) *A Sociology of Australian Society,* Melbourne, Macmillan.

Sher, J. and Sher, K. (1994) Beyond the Conventional Wisdom: Rural Development as if Australia's Rural People and Communities Really Mattered, *Journal of Research in Rural Education* 10, 1.

Sorensen, T. and Epps, R. (1993) *Prospects and Policies for Rural Australia,* Melbourne, Macmillan.

Stilwell, F. (1992) *Understanding Cities and Regions: Landscapes of Capital and Class,* Australia, Pluto.

Stilwell, F. (1993) *Reshaping Australia: Urban Problems and Policies,* Australia, Pluto.

Summons, M. (1984) The Big Battalions Take Over, Rural Review, *Australian* 6 February.

Taskforce on Regional Development (1993) *Developing Australia: a Regional Perspective*, Canberra, National Capital Printing.

Vanclay, F. and Lawrence, G. (1995) *The Environmental Imperative: Eco-social Concerns for Australian Agriculture*, Rockhampton, CQU Press.

Whatmore, S., Munton, R., Marsden, R. and Little, J. (1987) Interpreting a Relational Typology of Farm Businesses in Southern England, *Sociologia Ruralis* 27, 2/3.

Williamson, B. (1990) Decentralisation of Legal Practices, in *Rural Welfare Research Bulletin* 4, April.

Index

A

Aboriginal Australians 102-103,
145, 247-248, 253, 273, 335
agrarianism 9-23, 277
agribusiness 2, 32, 64-75, 168,
304, 338
agrichemicals 190, 304
agricultural environment 28, 62,
81, 107, 218-234, 238-248,
280, 291, 315, 339
agricultural extension 34, 42, 278
agriculture (see farm)
agro-industrialisation 167-176
Asia 73-74, 342
attitudes
consumer (see consumer
attitudes)
farmer attitudes 56
student 201-214
Australian Bureau of Agricultural
and Resource Economics
(ABARE) 253, 258
Australian Conservation
Foundation (ACF) 25, 223
Australian Gen-Ethics Network
319-327

B

biotechnology
environmental concerns 302
genetic engineering 7-8, 290-
308, 312-327
policy 312-327

C

Central Queensland 201-214, 270-
273
Central Queensland University
201-214, 264, 290-308
Charles Sturt University 257, 264
chemicals (see agrichemicals)
climate (see drought)
commodity systems approach 5,
178-186
communication 3, 106-117, 154,
202, 212-214, 230, 250, 259,
340
community
general 119, 159-165, 218-234,
238-248, 263, 265, 281-282
rural 77, 140-151, 188-199,
238-248, 332-344
sustainable development 233-
235, 238-248, 253-254, 281,
283-284, 287
computers 38-52
Conservation Farming 33
consumer attitudes 290-308
contract farming 64-75, 173-174
Cooperative Research Centre for
Viticulture 38-52, 55-62
core/periphery 137
counter urbanisation 135
country towns 119-138, 154-165,
201-214
CSIRO 312-327
cultural capital 191

D

Darling Downs 246
deregulation 9